G C S

A-Z

C000053860

DOUBLE
SCIENCE

h a n d b o o k

GCSE

A-Z

DOUBLE SCIENCE

handbook

Keith Hirst

Hodder & Stoughton

A MEMBER OF THE HODDER HEADLINE GROUP

British Library Cataloguing in Publication Data
A catalogue entry for this title is available from the British Library

ISBN 0–340–73060–9

First published 1998
Impression number   10 9 8 7 6 5 4 3 2 1
Year   2002 2001 2000 1999 1998

Typeset by GreenGate Publishing Services, Tonbridge, Kent.
Printed and bound in Great Britain for Hodder and Stoughton Educational,
a division of Hodder Headline plc, 338 Euston Road, London NW1 3BH,
by Redwood Books, Trowbridge, Wilts

HOW TO USE THIS BOOK

This book explains the main ideas in any GCSE Science course – both Co-ordinated and Modular. It includes a range of basic terms which will meet the needs of most students taking a GCSE Science course. The entries also cover the more popular extension topics in GCSE Biology, Chemistry and Physics topics.

Each item starts with a simple, one-line definition and goes on to explain the term in a little more detail, showing how it relates to other areas of science.

An effort has been made to form a balance between providing a simple explanation that might be understood by someone meeting the term for the first time and producing an entry which is sufficiently detailed to meet the requirements of an examiner who asks the question 'What is meant by the term...?'.

There is an extensive system of cross-referencing; italics have been used to identify terms which have separate entries.

The best methods of presenting all the chemistry and physics calculations you are likely to need are provided.

During your course, the *GCSE A–Z Double Science Handbook* is essentially a book to pick up and put down; a book to browse through and use to add to your understanding of basic ideas. It is also a book which will enable you to clarify your understanding when meeting new ideas. In addition, it should prove useful for revision at the end of the course; to help you use it effectively for this purpose, two appendices have been added:

- Revision lists: these identify the main ideas which you will need to understand for a GCSE examination. For each concept, there is a list of key words which should act as starting points for your revision. Cross-references will then allow you to build on this understanding.
- Examiners' terms: many candidates fail to do themselves justice in examinations, not because they have failed to learn the subject material thoroughly, but because they have not followed the instructions on the paper. For this reason, a glossary of instructions that examiners use is provided. You should use this for reference throughout the course. If you become familiar with these terms from the beginning, you should be successful in turning your hard-earned knowledge into examination marks.

Keith Hirst

ACKNOWLEDGEMENTS

I am grateful to Bill Indge, author of the *Complete A–Z Biology Handbook*, for suggesting my name as author to the publishers; Ian Marcousé and Tim Gregson-Williams for their helpful suggestions as the style of the book evolved; the editorial team who worked wonders with the rough drafts they received; and my wife Pat for her support during the months when she became an 'author's widow'.

Keith Hirst

abdomen: the lower of the two body cavities, separated from the upper body cavity, the *thorax* (chest), by the *diaphragm*. You need to know which organs are in the abdomen and which are in the thorax.

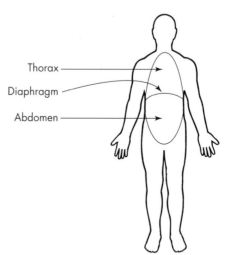

The main contents of the abdomen are:
- most of the organs of the *digestive system*
- the organs of the *reproductive system*
- the organs of the *urinary system*.

absolute zero: the coldest possible temperature.
- The temperature at which molecules are coldest, i.e. have their lowest possible energy
- and therefore their minimum possible amount of movement.
- This temperature is –273° on the Celsius scale
- which is zero on the Kelvin scale.

absorber: a surface which is a poor reflector of radiation. It is important when designing objects to know whether they will absorb most of the radiation they receive, or reflect most of it.
- The main source of radiation is the Sun.
- Dark, matt surfaces are good absorbers of radiation.
- Light, shiny surfaces are poor absorbers of radiation.

absorption: the process by which materials are taken into cells. You need to know the different ways in which essential materials are taken in by living organisms. There are three main methods of absorption:
- *diffusion*, e.g. the absorption of oxygen in the lungs
- *osmosis*, e.g. the absorption of water by root hair cells
- *active transport*, e.g. the absorption of mineral ions by root hair cells.

acceleration: the rate at which the speed (*velocity*) of an object changes. An advert for a car might say '0–60 in 4 seconds'. This means that it takes 4 seconds for the car to accelerate from rest to a speed of 60 km per hour.
● The change in velocity is (final velocity – starting velocity).

FORMULA

For an object moving in a straight line with steady acceleration:

$$\text{acceleration} = \frac{\text{change in velocity}}{\text{time taken for change}}$$

UNITS

acceleration: metre/second squared (m/s²)
velocity: metre/second (m/s)
time: second (s)

EXAMPLE OF CALCULATION USING NUMERIC DATA
A car accelerates steadily from 5 m/s to 30 m/s in 10 s.
Calculate the acceleration of the car.

$$\text{acceleration} = \frac{\text{change in velocity}}{\text{time taken for change}}$$

$$= \frac{(30 \text{ m/s} - 5 \text{ m/s})}{10 \text{ s}}$$

$$= 2.5 \text{ m/s}^2$$

EXAMPLE OF CALCULATION FROM A GRAPH
The graph shows the change in velocity of a car travelling in a straight line. Calculate the acceleration of the car.

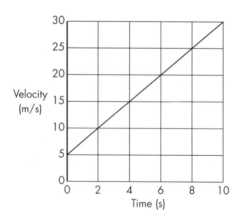

In this type of question you use the same equation, but read the values from the graph. Again, the initial velocity = 5 m/s and the velocity after 10 s = 30 m/s.

$$\text{acceleration} = \frac{\text{change in velocity}}{\text{time taken for change}}$$

$$= \frac{(30 \text{ m/s} - 5 \text{ m/s})}{10 \text{ s}} = 2.5 \text{ m/s}^2$$

acceleration due to gravity (g): the amount of acceleration that the force of gravity gives to an object on Earth. This enables you to calculate, for example, how quickly a sky-diver will fall through the atmosphere.
- The approximate value of g is 980 cm/s^2 (9.8 m/s^2).
- Neglecting air resistance, any object falling freely will increase its speed at the approximate rate of 980 cm/s during each second of its fall.

acid rain: produced when acid gases such as sulphur dioxide dissolve in rain water. Its effects on forests and lakes can be devastating.

CAUSES

Natural
- from sulphur dioxide released during volcanic eruptions
- from nitrogen oxides formed during lightning storms

Effects of human activities
- combustion of *fossil fuels*, releasing sulphur dioxide and nitrogen oxides into the atmosphere

EFFECTS

- damage to trees including loss of leaves
- heavy metal ions are leached into freshwater habitats – these ions are poisonous to aquatic organisms

acidic oxides: oxides that dissolve in water to form *acids*, e.g.

$$\text{carbon dioxide} + \text{water} \longrightarrow \text{carbonic acid}$$
$$CO_2(g) + H_2O(l) \longrightarrow H_2CO_3(aq)$$

- Most acidic oxides are oxides of non-metals (whereas oxides of metals are mainly *basic oxides*).

acids and alkalis: when a substance dissolves in water it forms a solution which may be acid, alkaline or neutral. You need to know what makes *solutions* acid or alkaline.
- *Indicators* can be used to show whether a solution is acid, alkaline or neutral; the pH scale is used to describe <u>how</u> acidic or alkaline.

$$0 \longleftarrow \qquad 7 \qquad \longrightarrow 14$$

Increasing acidity   Increasing alkalinity

3

- An acid reacts with an alkali to form a salt and water.
- Acids release $H^+(aq)$ ions when dissolved in water.
- Alkaline solutions contain OH^- (aq) ions.
- In *neutralisation*, the H^+ and OH^- ions combine with each other:
  $$H^+(aq) + OH^-(aq) \longrightarrow H_2O(l)$$
- Strong acids dissociate (split up) almost completely when dissolved, e.g. when hydrogen chloride dissolves in water it dissociates completely to produce a strong acid, hydrochloric acid:
  $$HCl(g) \longrightarrow H^+(aq) + Cl^-(aq)$$
- Weak acids only partly dissociate in water; the ions are in equilibrium with the undissociated acid molecules, e.g. ethanoic acid dissociates only partly in water:
  $$CH_3COOH(aq) \rightleftharpoons CH_3COO^-(aq) + H^+(aq)$$
- Alkalis are soluble metal oxides or hydroxides.

activation energy: the minimum amount of energy particles must have in order to react. It is like lighting a gas ring with a match; the thermal energy from the match is sufficient to start the gas molecules reacting with oxygen molecules.

- *Catalysts*, including *enzymes*, lower the activation energy of a reaction. The graph shows changes in energy during a reaction.

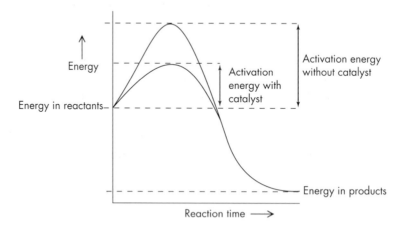

active site: the part of an *enzyme* molecule into which the reacting molecule(s) fit during a reaction. It is rather like a 'keyhole' – the reacting molecules correspond to the 'key'.

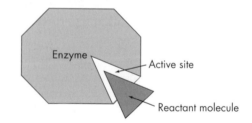

- Enzymes are specific (only catalyse one reaction) because only molecules of the correct shape 'fit' the active site.
- This is why we need different enzymes to digest different food materials.

active transport: moving molecules from a region of low concentration to a region of high concentration, i.e. moving them <u>against</u> a *concentration gradient*. Without active transport we would not be able to absorb most of the soluble food from the gut into our blood.

- Substances have a tendency to move from a region of high concentration to a region of low concentration.
- Moving substances in the opposite direction requires energy.
- The energy is usually supplied by *respiration*.

EXAMPLES OF ACTIVE TRANSPORT INCLUDE:

- absorption of mineral ions from soil solution by root hair cells
- reabsorption of glucose in the kidney tubules
- movement of sugars into phloem cells in plant leaves.

adaptation: a feature that makes a structure more suitable for its job (function), e.g. the long neck of the giraffe is an adaptation to feeding from high leaves on trees.

- Adaptations usually evolve by natural selection over numerous generations to solve problems of survival.

addiction: the craving for a drug – the feeling that you need to take a drug regularly and to experience its effects – and being unable to give it up.

- Addiction is usually the result of chemical changes in the body produced by the drug.
- Hard drugs such as heroin are difficult to give up because they produce severe withdrawal symptoms such as sickness and pain.

addition polymer: a compound formed when *unsaturated* molecules join together to form a long molecule (*polymer*) with no other substance being formed in the reaction.

- The formation of this kind of addition polymer is represented by:

$$n\begin{bmatrix} H \\ \diagdown \\ H \diagup \end{bmatrix}C = C\begin{matrix} H \\ \diagup \\ \diagdown H \end{matrix} \longrightarrow \begin{bmatrix} H & H \\ | & | \\ C - C \\ | & | \\ H & H \end{bmatrix}_n$$

- Many of the plastics we use every day are addition polymers, e.g. poly(ethene), commonly known as polythene, is an addition polymer made from ethene.

addition reaction: a reaction where two substances react to form a single product, e.g. margarine is made by combining hydrogen and vegetable oil.
- Most addition reactions involve the conversion of an *unsaturated hydro-carbon* into a saturated hydrocarbon, e.g.

    ethene + hydrogen $\longrightarrow$ ethane

ADH: a *hormone* involved in controlling the water balance of the body. Without ADH the body would very quickly become dehydrated.
- ADH is released from the *pituitary gland* at the base of the brain when *receptors* in the brain detect a lowering of the concentration of water in the blood.
- ADH is transported to the kidney where it causes the kidney to reabsorb more water.
- This results in a smaller volume of more concentrated urine.

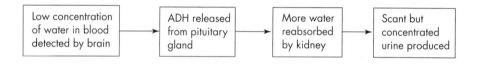

Low concentration of water in blood detected by brain	ADH released from pituitary gland	More water reabsorbed by kidney	Scant but concentrated urine produced

adolescence: period in life when your sex organs become active and you begin to change from a child into an adult.
- It usually happens between the ages of 10 and 14.
- It is brought about by hormones secreted by the ovaries in females and the testes in males
- which cause bodily changes such as the growth of breasts in females and facial hair in males.

adrenal glands: a pair of glands, one above each kidney, that are important when we are in danger or under stress.
- They produce the hormone *adrenaline*.
- They are ductless/endocrine glands – the hormone they produce passes directly into the bloodstream.

adrenaline: a chemical messenger (*hormone*) produced by the *adrenal glands* that helps us when we are in danger.
- Adrenaline is often referred to as 'fight or flight' hormone.

This hormone helps the body to respond to emergencies by:

- increasing both heart rate and the volume of blood pumped out of the heart at each beat
- dilating the blood vessels that supply the muscles and thus increasing their blood supply
- constricting the blood supply to organ systems such as the digestive system
- stimulating the conversion of glycogen to glucose and thus making more glucose available for *respiration*.

aerobic respiration: respiration which needs the presence of oxygen. Most of the energy needed for your body processes comes from this type of respiration. During this reaction:

- glucose (a sugar) is *oxidised*
- energy is released
- carbon dioxide and water are formed.

WORD EQUATION

glucose + oxygen $\longrightarrow$ energy + carbon dioxide + water

BALANCED EQUATION

$C_6H_{12}O_6 + 6O_2 \longrightarrow$ energy + $6CO_2 + 6H_2O$

The energy released during aerobic respiration may be used:

- to build up larger molecules from smaller ones
- to enable muscles to contract
- to maintain body temperature
- in *active transport*.

air: the mixture of gases that makes up the Earth's atmosphere. Without the atmosphere there would be no life on Earth.

- The pie chart shows the approximate composition of dry air.
- Air usually also contains water vapour.

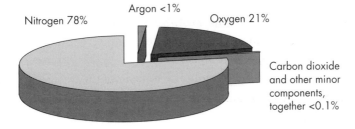

Nitrogen 78% Argon <1% Oxygen 21%

Carbon dioxide and other minor components, together <0.1%

albino: an organism lacking the normal colouring (pigments) in the skin and eyes, e.g. mice with white fur and pink eyes.

- Human albinos often need to wear dark glasses and to protect their skin from the sun.
- Albinos arose from a *mutation* in the gene that produces pigments.
- The albino allele is usually recessive.

alcohol: the common name for ethanol – the drug found in beer, lager, wines and spirits.

ETHANOL IS PRODUCED:

- in brewing by fermentation, which involves anaerobic respiration in yeast cells
- in industry by the addition of water to ethene.

EFFECTS OF ETHANOL ON THE BODY

- Ethanol affects the nervous system.
- It slows down our reactions, which is why it is dangerous to drive after drinking.
- Drinking excessive amounts of alcoholic drinks may lead to addiction.
- Long-term effects of drinking excessive amounts of ethanol include damage to the liver and to the brain.

alcohol emulsion test: a test for fats.
- A foodstuff is shaken with *ethanol*.
- The solid food is then allowed to settle and some of the liquid is poured into a tube containing water.
- If the water turns milky then the foodstuff contains fat.

algae: a group of simple plant-like organisms, e.g. the seaweeds that grow on rocky shores.
- Most can photosynthesise.
- They do not have flowers, stems, roots or leaves.
- They range in size from microscopic single-celled structures to large seaweeds.
- They make up most of the phytoplankton – the main *producers* in lakes and seas.

alimentary canal: another name for the gut of an animal – it is where food is digested.
The functions of the alimentary canal are:

- *ingestion* of food
- *digestion* of food
- *absorption* of the soluble products of digestion
- *egestion* of indigestible food.

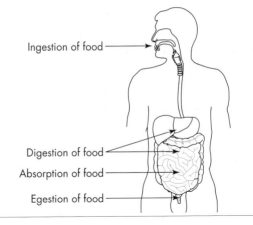

Ingestion of food

Digestion of food

Absorption of food

Egestion of food

---

alkali: see *acids and alkalis*.

---

alkali metals: metals in Group I of the *periodic table*. They do not look like metals, and they are not used to make typical metal objects, but their reactions and their compounds are very important both in industry and in your body.

- Alkali metals include lithium, sodium and potassium.
- They are the most reactive metals.
- Reactivity increases down the group.
- They react with non-metals to form ionic compounds in which the metal ion carries a 1⁺ charge.
- They react with water releasing hydrogen.
- Alkali metals form hydroxides which dissolve in water to give alkaline solutions.

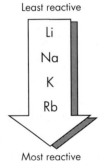

Least reactive

Li

Na

K

Rb

Most reactive

---

alkane: a family of *hydrocarbons*, including methane, which forms the largest part of the natural gas that we burn.

- The carbon atoms are joined by single *covalent bonds*.
- The general formula of alkanes is:
  C_nH_{2n+2}
- The simplest alkane is methane (CH_4).
- Ethane (opposite) has the formula C_2H_6.

---

alkene: a family of *hydrocarbons* that are very important in producing many of the plastics we use every day.

- There is at least one *covalent bond* in an alkene molecule.
- They are unsaturated.
- The general formula of alkenes is:
  C_nH_{2n}

- The simplest alkene, ethene (opposite), has the formula C_2H_4.
- They are very reactive.
- Many alkenes are used to make polymers, see *addition polymers*.

$$\begin{array}{c} H \\ \diagdown \\ C = C \\ \diagup \\ H \end{array} \begin{array}{c} H \\ \diagup \\ \\ \diagdown \\ H \end{array}$$

---

allele: one of the forms of a particular *gene*, e.g. there are two common alleles of the gene responsible for eye colour – the blue-eye allele and the brown-eye allele.

- The scientist Mendel noted that pea plants existed in two forms – tall and short.
- Height in peas is controlled by a single gene. There are two different forms of this gene.
- One form (the dominant allele) produces tall pea plants.
- The other form (the recessive allele) produces short pea plants.

---

alloy: a mixture containing at least one metal – most metallic objects we use every day are alloys rather than pure metals.

- The metals are blended to make best use of their individual properties.

EXAMPLES

- 'Silver' coins contain copper and nickel so that they are hardwearing and malleable.
- Brass is a mixture of copper and zinc – it is stronger than both copper and zinc and has a lower melting point than either.
- Solder contains lead and tin – it has a very low melting point.

---

alpha radiation: positively charged particles (*helium nuclei*) moving at high speed. It is what makes the smoke detector in your home work. You need to know the differences between alpha, *beta* and *gamma radiation*.

PROPERTIES

- easily stopped by paper or a few centimetres of air (β and γ radiation are more penetrating)
- can be deflected by magnetic fields
- may cause *ionisation* in materials (α radiation is much more strongly ionising than β and γ radiation)

protons

neutrons

MAIN USE

- in smoke detectors since it can travel only a few centimetres in air and is easily absorbed by smoke

alternating current (a.c.): an electric current that is continually reversing its direction. The mains supply to your home is an alternating current.
- Mains electricity is an alternating current
- with a frequency of 50 cycles per second (50 hertz).
- The graph shows one of these cycles.

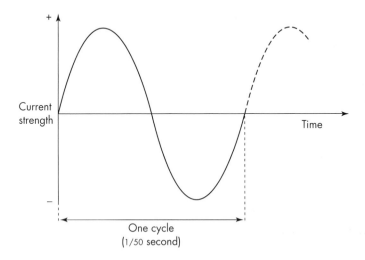

Current strength

Time

One cycle
(1/50 second)

aluminium, extraction: you need to remember that aluminium is extracted by *electrolysis* of its oxide (rather than using a furnace as in the extraction of iron).
- Aluminium is extracted from its ore – *bauxite*.
- Bauxite consists mainly of aluminium oxides.
- The ore is purified then melted in the electrolysis cell.
- Bauxite has a very high melting point so it is dissolved in molten cryolite to reduce energy costs.
- The electrodes are made of carbon (graphite).

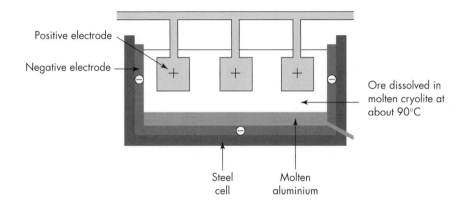

Positive electrode

Negative electrode

Ore dissolved in molten cryolite at about 90°C

Steel cell

Molten aluminium

- Aluminium is formed at the *cathode.*
- Oxygen is formed at the *anode.* This causes the graphite electrodes to gradually burn away, so they have to be replaced frequently.
- Ionic equation at the cathode:

  $Al^{3+} + 3e^- \longrightarrow Al$ (aluminium ions are reduced)
- Ionic equation at the anode:

  $2O^{2-} - 4e^- \longrightarrow 2O_2$

---

aluminium, reactions: You need to remember that aluminium is not as reactive as you might expect because a layer of aluminium oxide rapidly forms on its surface when in contact with air.

- This protective layer means that aluminium does not react with water, steam or dilute acids, even though the metal is very reactive.
- Aluminium will displace metals lower in the *reactivity series* from their *oxides*, e.g. in the thermit reaction:

  iron oxide + aluminium $\longrightarrow$ aluminium oxide + iron

  $Fe_2O_3 \quad + \quad 2Al \quad \longrightarrow \quad Al_2O_3 \quad + 2Fe$

---

aluminium, uses: the following properties make aluminium a very useful metal:

- its density is less than one third that of steel
- it has a high strength to weight ratio
- it has a high thermal conductivity
- it has a high electrical conductivity
- it does not easily rust or corrode (because of its protective layer of aluminium oxide).

ITS USES INCLUDE THE MANUFACTURE OF:

- aircraft and car bodies (high strength to weight ratio)
- cooking utensils and car engines (high thermal conductivity)
- high-voltage power transmission (high electrical conductivity and it has a high strength to weigh ratio)
- drinks containers (high strength to weight ratio and does not easily rust or corrode).

---

aluminium oxide: an oxide of aluminium with the formula Al_2O_3. It is our main source of aluminium.

- It is found mainly in the ore *bauxite.*
- It is an ionic compound with very strong ionic bonds
- which give it a very high melting point of 2000°C.

---

alveolus (pl. alveoli): the alveoli are the parts of the lung where oxygen gets into the blood. They are microscopic air sacs where:

- oxygen *diffuses* from the air into the blood capillaries
- carbon dioxide diffuses from the blood capillaries into the air.

Alveoli provide an <u>efficient surface for gaseous exchange</u> because:

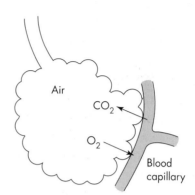

- the folding gives them a large surface area
- their walls are only one cell thick, reducing the distance that gases have to diffuse
- they are well supplied with gas capillaries
- they are lined with a liquid in which gases dissolve.

amino acids: the building blocks from which proteins (needed for growth) are made.

- Plants make amino acids from carbohydrates and nitrates.
- Animals use protease enzymes to digest proteins in their diet into amino acids; they then synthesise body proteins from these amino acids.
- In mammals, excess amino acids are broken down (*deamination*) by the liver, forming the excretory compound *urea*.

ammeter: you need to be able to recognise the circuit symbol for an ammeter, and how to connect an ammeter in a circuit.

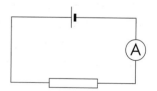

- An ammeter is used to measure the size of the electric current flowing in a circuit.
- It is connected in *series* with the other components.

ammonia: a colourless gas which turns red litmus blue. It is very important in the manufacture of artificial fertilisers.

- Its formula is NH_3.
- It is highly soluble in water.
- In solution in water, ammonia becomes ammonium hydroxide, NH_4OH.

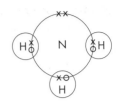

- Ammonium hydroxide is strongly basic and behaves in a similar way to the hydroxides of the *alkali metals*.
- Ammonia is an example of a *covalent compound* – the shared electron pairs are shown in the diagram.

---

ammonia, manufacture: ammonia is manufactured by the Haber process.

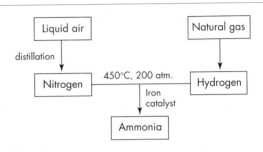

- Even at this temperature and pressure only some of the nitrogen and hydrogen react – the rest are recycled.
- The reaction between nitrogen and hydrogen is reversible:
  $$N_2(g) + 3H_2(g) \rightleftharpoons 2NH_3 \quad \Delta H = -92 \text{ kJ/mol}$$
- Increasing the pressure increases the proportion of ammonia in the equilibrium mixture.
- Increasing the temperature too high decreases the proportion of ammonia in the equilibrium mixture.
- The iron catalyst speeds up the rate at which equilibrium is reached.

---

ammonia, uses: Ammonia is used in the manufacture of nitric acid and artificial fertilisers.

MAKING NITRIC ACID

There are three stages:

1 ammonia + oxygen $\longrightarrow$ nitrogen monoxide + water (a hot platinum catalyst is needed for this stage)
2 nitrogen monoxide + oxygen $\longrightarrow$ nitrogen dioxide
3 nitrogen dioxide + oxygen + water $\longrightarrow$ nitric acid (HNO_3)

MAKING FERTILISERS

- Ammonium nitrate fertiliser is made by a *neutralisation* reaction between ammonia and nitric acid:
  ammonia + nitric acid $\longrightarrow$ ammonium nitrate
- Ammonium sulphate fertiliser is made by a neutralisation reaction between ammonia and sulphuric acid:
  ammonia + sulphuric acid $\longrightarrow$ ammonium sulphate

---

ammonium compound: a compound containing the ammonium ion (NH_4^+). Ammonium compounds are important both as natural and artificial fertilisers.
- The most important ammonium compounds are ammonium sulphate and ammonium nitrate, which are used as fertilisers.
- Ammonium compounds are formed in the *nitrogen cycle* when putrefying bacteria break down nitrogenous waste. They are then converted to nitrates by nitrogen-fixing bacteria.

ampere: the unit of electric *current*.
- Symbol A or amp.
- 1 ampere is the flow of 1 coulomb of electricity per second.

amphibians: a group of animals, including frogs and newts. They mostly live on land but need water to breed.

CHARACTERISTICS

- vertebrates (have backbones)
- eggs do not have shells
- external fertilisation
- aquatic young breathe via gills
- terrestrial adults breathe via skin and lungs

amplitude: a measure of the amount of energy in a wave.
- The amplitude is the height of the crest of the wave (the maximum displacement from the mean or rest position).

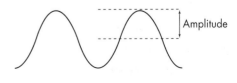

Amplitude

- The larger the amplitude, the more energy the wave contains.
- The larger the amplitude of a sound wave, the louder the sound.
- The larger the amplitude of a light wave, the brighter the light.

amylase: a substance (*enzyme*) that breaks down starch into simpler sugars, e.g. maltose. Without it you would not be able to digest the starch in foods such as bread.
- It is produced by animals, plants and microbes.
- It is secreted in mammals by the salivary glands, the pancreas and glands in the small intestine.
- The type of reaction it catalyses is known as *hydrolysis*, e.g.
  starch + water $\longrightarrow$ maltose

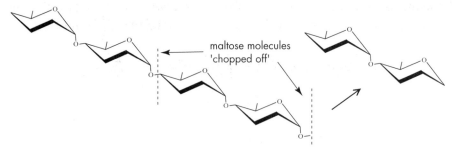

maltose molecules 'chopped off'

- Many amylases used in industry have optimum temperatures in the range 60–80°C – much higher than that of amylases in the guts of mammals.

anaemia: the condition when a person is pale and listless because they do not have enough *red blood cells*.
- It is most commonly caused by insufficient iron in the diet.
- It is most common when the need for iron rises, e.g. in childhood or during pregnancy.
- Iron is needed for the production of *haemoglobin* – the red pigment found in red blood cells.
- Symptoms are listlessness caused by insufficient oxygen being delivered to the organs by the blood.

anaerobic respiration: a process that results in muscle fatigue in animals and the production of alcohol by yeast cells.
- It is *respiration* which takes place in the absence of oxygen.
- During this reaction, glucose (a sugar) is <u>not</u> *oxidised*.
- Less energy is released than during aerobic respiration.
- In yeast, carbon dioxide and ethanol are formed:
    glucose ⟶ energy + carbon dioxide + ethanol
  This reaction is the basis of the brewing industry.
- In muscle, lactic acid is formed:
    glucose ⟶ energy + lactic acid
- Lactic acid is poisonous; it is one of contributors to cramp during exercise.
- Lactic acid is oxidised, mainly by the liver, into carbon dioxide and water.
- The amount of oxygen needed to oxidise this lactic acid is known as the *oxygen debt*.

angle of incidence and angle of reflection: you need to remember the law which governs how waves are reflected from surfaces.
    angle of incidence = angle of refraction, where:
- the angle between the direction of travel of the incident wave and a line drawn at right angles to the boundary line is the angle of incidence

● the angle between the direction of travel of the reflected wave and a line drawn at right angles to the boundary line is the angle of reflection.

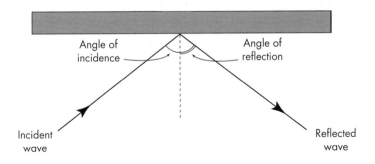

anion: you need to remember that in a solution of an *ionic compound* (or in a melted ionic compound) there are negatively charged *ions* called anions, and positively charged ions called *cations*.

● Anions move towards a positively charged electrode (*anode*).
● Example of anions include chloride ion (Cl^-); hydroxide ion (OH^-) and sulphate ion (SO_4^{2-}).

anode: the positively charged electrode in *electrolysis*.
● It is made from a metal or from a conductive non-metal such as graphite.

anther: the part of a flower where pollen grains are produced.
● Pollen grains contain the male gametes of the plant.
● *Meiosis* – reduction division – occurs in the anthers during the formation of the pollen grains.

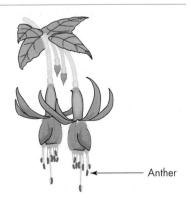

Anther

antibiotic: a chemical produced by one microorganism to kill another microorganism. We now use antibiotics such as *penicillin* to combat infectious diseases. They have saved hundreds of millions of lives.

- Fungi such as *Penicillium* are grown in fermenters to produce antibiotics industrially.
- Antibiotics are only effective against disease caused by bacteria and fungi.
- They cannot be used to treat viral infections because viruses live inside cells.
- Some disease-producing microbes have mutated and are now resistant to antibiotics.

antibody: a substance produced by the body to kill infectious microbes – without antibodies we would be defenceless against microbes.
- Antibodies are produced by *white blood cells* (lymphocytes).
- Antibody production is stimulated by molecules called *antigens* on the surface of the microbes.
- Once white blood cells have produced a particular antibody they can produce it again very quickly if the same microbe reinfects the body.
- In active *immunisation*, dead or weakened microbes are introduced into the body to stimulate antibody production.
- In passive immunisation, antibodies are introduced into the body to kill microbes already infecting the body.

antidiuretic hormone: see *ADH*.

antigen: a substance which the body recognises as foreign. Found on the outside of disease microbes, it causes that body to begin to defend itself against the microbe.
- An antigen is a molecule that triggers *white blood cells* (lymphocytes) to produce antibodies.
- Most antigens are proteins in the coats of microbes.
- Other antigens are large molecules that cause allergic responses.

antiseptic: a chemical which we use to kill microbes, e.g. in a cut or a graze.
- Antiseptics are safe to use on the outside of the body.
- They are less effective at killing microorganisms than disinfectants, but they are safer to use on the human body.
- Examples include carbolic acid, TCP and iodine solution.

antitoxin: when disease microbes multiply in the body they produce toxins (poisons) that make us feel ill. The body produces antitoxins to neutralise the effects of these toxins so that we begin to feel better.
- They are produced by *white blood cells*.
- Antitoxins can be introduced into the body to neutralise toxins, e.g. the tetanus injection consists of tetanus antitoxins.

- Commercial antitoxins are made by injecting horses with small doses of toxins, then extracting from its *blood plasma* the antitoxins made in response.

aorta: the main *artery* of the body.
- It supplies oxygenated blood to the other arteries of the body.
- It originates in the left *ventricle* of the heart.
- It has a *semi-lunar valve* at its base preventing backflow of blood into the ventricle.
- The walls of the aorta are very thick and elastic to cope with the great pressure produced when the ventricles contract.

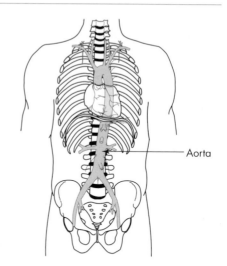

Aorta

apparent depth: the phenomenon which causes swimming pools to appear less deep than they really are.
- This is because light rays are refracted away from the normal as they pass from the water into the air.

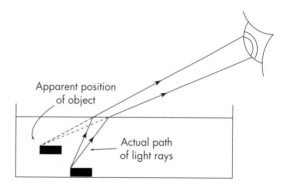

Apparent position of object

Actual path of light rays

Archimedes: a Greek scholar who lived 287–212 BC.
- He discovered the principle that a body immersed in a fluid apparently loses weight (equal to the weight of the liquid it displaces).
- He invented the Archimedes screw – a device for raising water from rivers into fields (still used in many developing countries).
- Archimedes also discovered the principle on which levers work.

armature: the part that rotates in an electric motor or electric generator.
- It is usually made from laminated soft iron supported by conducting wires.
- In an electric generator the armature is moved mechanically, and as it cuts through the magnetic field of the generator, an electric current is induced in its wires.

- In an electric motor a current is passed through the wires, causing the armature to rotate in the magnetic field of the motor.

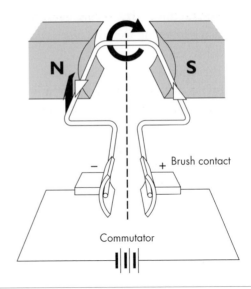

Brush contact

Commutator

---

artery: blood vessel that supplies blood to all the organs in the body. You need to know the differences between arteries, *veins* and *capillaries*.

- Arteries carry blood away from the heart.
- Arteries have thicker walls than veins.
- Their walls contain more elastic and muscular tissue than the walls of veins.

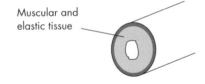

Muscular and elastic tissue

- Elastic tissue allows them to expand when the ventricles of the heart contract.
- Muscular tissue enables them to reduce the flow of blood by constricting.
- All arteries, <u>except the pulmonary artery</u>, carry oxygenated blood (blood with a high concentration of oxygen and low concentration of carbon dioxide).

---

arthritis: swelling (inflammation) of one or more joints in the body which may result in severe pain when bones move at the joint.

- Severe cases may be treated by joint replacement surgery, now commonly carried out on hip and knee joints in the elderly.
- Artificial materials such as stainless steel and carbon fibre are used to replace the affected bone surfaces.

---

arthropods: a group of animals which includes crustaceans, insects and spiders. Their characteristics include:

- invertebrates (do not have a backbone)
- an exoskeleton
- jointed limbs.

artificial selection: method by which we breed new strains of animals and plants. Our pet dogs, for example, have been bred from wolf-like ancestors.

- Humans choose desirable *characteristics*, and select for breeding animals and plants showing those characteristics.
- It is used principally to improve yields from animals and plants used for human food, e.g. grain size in cereal crops and milk yield in cows.

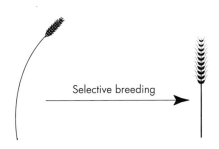

Selective breeding

- Selection for the desirable characteristic usually has to be repeated for many generations before significant changes can be seen.

asexual reproduction: reproducing by 'splitting' rather than by 'joining'.
- Reproduction that does not involve the fusion (joining) of sex cells (*gametes*).
- It is found mainly in microbes and plants.
- Natural examples in plants include the production of potato tubers and daffodil bulbs.
- Taking cuttings from chrysanthemums to produce new plants is an example of artificial asexual reproduction.
- All the offspring of asexual reproduction are genetically identical.
- These offspring are called *clones*.
- The usual type of cell division involved is *mitosis*.

atmosphere: the mixture of gases that surround a body, particularly a planet – without the atmosphere there would be no life on Earth.
- The gases are prevented from escaping into outer space by gravity.
- The original atmosphere of Earth was mainly carbon dioxide, with small amounts of water, methane and ammonia.
- When plants evolved, *photosynthesis* removed much of the carbon dioxide, replacing it with oxygen.
- Nitrogen was released into the atmosphere, mainly by organisms such as denitrifying bacteria.
- Some of the oxygen has been converted into ozone which absorbs harmful ultraviolet radiation from the Sun (see *ozone layer*).

atmospheric pressure: the pressure caused by the weight of the air above us – it is big enough to squash a can from which the air has been removed.

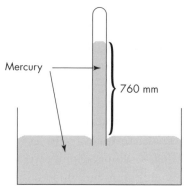

- The pressure exerted by the atmosphere at sea level is about 100 kN/m².
- This pressure is measured by *barometers*, e.g. mercury barometer.
- A height of 760 mm of mercury is known as Standard Atmospheric Pressure.
- Atmospheric pressure can be demonstrated by the 'crushed can' experiment and by Magdeburg hemispheres.

atom: the smallest particle of an element which can exist. You need to know the differences between atom, *ion*, *compound* and *molecule*.

- There are over 90 different sorts of atoms.
- Each atom has a central nucleus made up of *protons* and *neutrons*.
- Around the nucleus are *electrons*.
- The relative masses and relative charges of these particles are shown in the table:

Particle	Mass	Charge
Proton	1	+1
Neutron	1	0
Electron	Negligible	−1

- The number of electrons is equal to the number of protons.
- Atoms therefore have no overall charge.
- All atoms of a particular element have the same number of protons.
- Atoms of different elements have different numbers of protons.
- The electrons occupy particular energy levels (shells).
- They always occupy the lowest energy level available.
- An atom can be represented in the following ways, e.g. helium:

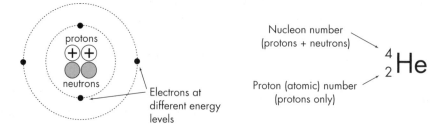

atomic mass: equal to the number of particles in the nucleus (the mass number) – remember it is the top number (4) in this way of representing an atom: ^4_2He

- It is the number of *protons* in the nucleus plus the number of *neutrons*, e.g. helium ^4_2He has 2 protons and 2 neutrons, so its mass number is 4.
- Chlorine ($^{35}_{17}\text{Cl}$) has 17 protons and 18 neutrons, so its mass number is 35.
- To calculate the number of neutrons, subtract the number of protons from the mass number.

atomic number (proton number): the number of *protons* in the nucleus of an atom. Remember that it is the bottom number (2) in this way of representing an atom: ^4_2He.

- So chlorine ($^{35}_{17}\text{Cl}$) has an atomic number of 17.

atria: the upper two chambers of the heart, as opposed to the *ventricles* which are the lower two chambers.

- Atria receive blood returning to the heart through the veins.
- The atria pump blood into the *ventricles*.
- They have much thinner walls than the ventricles.
- The right atrium receives deoxygenated blood from the *vena cava*.
- The left atrium receives oxygenated blood from the pulmonary vein.

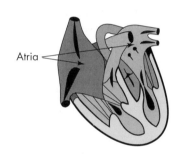

Atria

auxin: a substance that controls growth in plants. We now use synthetic auxins to control the growth of garden plants and food plants.

- Auxins cause young plant cells to elongate.
- They are important in tropic responses (see *phototropism* and *geotropism*).

COMMERCIAL USES INCLUDE:

- weedkillers – they disrupt the normal growth patterns of weeds; most commonly used to kill broad-leaved weeds in lawns
- cuttings – they promote the growth of roots on cuttings taken from the stems of plants such as chrysanthemums
- preventing fruit from dropping too early in orchards.

Avogadro's constant: the number of molecules that exists in one *mole* of any substance. This makes it possible to use moles in many chemical calculations.

- Its approximate value is 6×10^{23}.
- Equal volumes of gases at the same temperature and pressure contain equal numbers of molecules.

axon: if we think of the nervous system as a series of electric circuits, then the axons would correspond to the wires (but they are <u>not</u> metals).
- The axon is the long process of a *neurone* (nerve cell).
- It consists of *cytoplasm* and *membranes*.
- It is specialised for carrying *nerve impulses*.
- It is usually covered by an insulating sheath made out of fatty material.

background radiation: radiation that is always around us, in the air and in substances such as:

- rocks
- building materials
- food.
- In radioactivity calculations, always subtract the background radiation count from the observed count to find the actual amount of radiation being measured.

bacteria, decay: bacteria are responsible for the recycling of dead organisms and waste materials in nature. The leaves which fall off trees in autumn have nearly all disappeared by spring, due partly to the action of bacteria.

- The breakdown of materials by bacteria is by *digestion*.
- Bacteria produce digestive *enzymes* which pass out onto the material; the soluble products of digestion are then absorbed.
- Decay occurs fastest when conditions are warm, moist and there is oxygen available.
- Decay releases the nutrients in dead and waste materials.
- These nutrients are taken up and used by plants.
- Sewage works and compost heaps both depend upon decay by bacteria.

bacteria, disease: disease bacteria multiply rapidly inside the body and release *toxins* (poisons). This is what makes us feel ill.

PREVENTION OF INFECTION

- The skin acts as a barrier to the entry of bacteria.
- The breathing organs produce a sticky liquid called *mucus* which traps bacteria.
- The stomach produces hydrochloric acid which kills bacteria in food.

WHITE BLOOD CELLS PROTECT US BY:

- ingesting bacteria
- producing *antibodies* which kill bacteria
- producing *antitoxins* which neutralise bacterial toxins.

DOCTORS HELP US BY:

- *immunisation*
- using *antibiotics* such as *penicillin* to kill bacteria.

bacteria, in manufacturing: many of the foods and household products that we buy are made using *enzymes* from bacteria.
Enzymes made by bacteria are used in the manufacture of:

- *yoghurt*
- biological detergents
- baby foods
- slimming foods.
- Bacteria have been *genetically engineered* to produce highly complex molecules such as human *insulin*.

bacteria, structure: bacteria are microscopic organisms which have:

- cell wall
- cell membrane
- cytoplasm
- genetic material in a chromosome
- <u>no</u> nucleus.

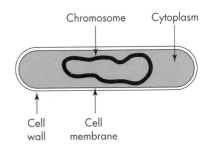

baking: if yeast is mixed into bread dough it will make the dough rise.

- This is due to the carbon dioxide given off during the *respiration* of yeast.
- The yeast is mixed with sugar solution so that the yeast is able to respire (see *aerobic respiration*).
- The sugar solution is mixed with the dough and left in a warm place to increase the rate of respiration of the yeast.
- The bubbles of carbon dioxide gas given off by the yeast make the bread rise.
- The reactions that give off carbon dioxide are brought about by *enzymes* (biological catalysts).

balancing equations: you are almost certain to be asked to balance a chemical equation. It is important that you learn the following rules:

- The total number of atoms of each element must be the same on both sides of a chemical equation.

EXAMPLE

Chlorine (Cl_2) reacts with hydrogen (H_2) to form hydrogen chloride (HCl).
The equation $Cl_2 + H_2 \longrightarrow$ HCl does not balance because there are 2 chlorine atoms and 2 hydrogen atoms on the left-hand side of the equation, but only 1 of each on the right-hand side.
By putting 2 in front of the HCl we get the same number of atoms on each side of the equation:

$$Cl_2 + H_2 \longrightarrow 2HCl$$

- You must <u>not</u> change the formula of any substance to balance an equation.
- You may <u>only</u> change the number of molecules of the substance.

barometer: a device used to measure *atmospheric pressure*. Changes in pressure mean that the weather will probably change.
There are two main types of barometer:
- mercury barometer (see *atmospheric pressure*)
- aneroid barometer.

An aneroid barometer comprises:
- a flexible metal container
- which has had most of the air drawn out of it
- and which changes dimensions with changes in atmospheric pressure.

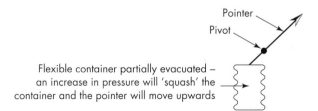

Pointer
Pivot
Flexible container partially evacuated – an increase in pressure will 'squash' the container and the pointer will move upwards

basal metabolic rate (BMR): the amount of energy the body needs to keep it 'ticking over', rather like a car engine waiting at a set of traffic lights.
- It is the least amount of energy needed to maintain the body's basic activities.
- Basic activities include breathing, heartbeat and maintaining a constant body temperature.
- BMR is usually calculated by measuring the person's oxygen consumption.
- This oxygen is used in *respiration*, which provides the person with energy.

basalt: a hard rock produced when volcanoes erupt.
- It is produced when molten rock (*magma*) from the *mantle* of the Earth cools down very quickly.

- When a volcano erupts, magma is forced out as lava.
- This lava cools quickly
- which results in small crystals in the basalt.
- It is an *extrusive igneous* rock.

bases: see *acids and alkalis*.

basic oxides: these *oxides* dissolve in water to form *bases*. You need to know the difference between *acidic oxides* and basic oxides.
- e.g. sodium oxide + water $\longrightarrow$ sodium hydroxide

  $Na_2O(s) \quad + H_2O(l) \longrightarrow \quad 2NaOH(aq)$
- Most basic oxides are oxides of metals.
- Some metal oxides such as copper oxide do not dissolve in water.
- These metal oxides do react with acids and are therefore bases.

battery: electrical *cells* in which chemical energy is converted into electrical energy. Batteries are used in appliances, e.g. torches, which cannot usefully be connected to a mains electricity supply.
- Batteries usually consist of two or more electrical cells connected in *series*.
- A car battery is a collection of lead–acid cells.
- Since the cells are connected in series, the output voltage of a battery is the sum of the voltages produced by the individual cells.

Cell   Battery

bauxite: the ore from which we get most of our *aluminium*.
- It is an ore of aluminium consisting mainly of aluminium oxide with impurities.

In the extraction of aluminium, bauxite is:
- purified
- dissolved in molten cryolite
- electrolysed using graphite electrodes.

becquerel (Bq): the unit for the amount of radioactivity of a substance.
- It is a measure of the rate of *decay* of a *radioactive* substance.
- One becquerel is the disintegration of one radioactive atom per second.

Bell, Alexander: a scientist who lived from 1847 to 1922.
- He was a teacher of deaf children whose interest in transmitting speech led him to invent the telephone in 1876.

Benedict's test: a test for reducing sugars.
- Benedict's solution is heated to boiling point with the test substance.
- A change in colour from blue to brick-red indicates a reducing sugar.
- Glucose and maltose both reduce Benedict's solution but sucrose does not.

beta radiation: one of the three types of radiation which may be emitted by a radioactive substance. You need to know the differences between *alpha*, beta and *gamma radiation*.
- Beta radiation is negatively charged particles emitted from the nuclei of radioactive atoms, moving at very high speeds.
- It consists of *electrons*.
- For each β particle emitted from a nucleus, one *neutron* becomes a *proton*.

PROPERTIES
- can penetrate air, paper and thin sheets of aluminium (α radiation is less penetrating and γ radiation is more penetrating)
- can be deflected by magnetic fields
- may cause *ionisation* in materials (much less strongly ionising than α radiation)

MAIN USE
- in thickness detectors, since the thicker the material the more β particles are absorbed

big bang: the theory that the universe began in one place, 10–20 billion years ago, and has been expanding ever since. You need to know why most scientists think this is how the universe was formed.

EVIDENCE FOR THE THEORY
- The light from other galaxies is shifted to the red end of the spectrum.
- The further away galaxies are from us, the bigger the 'red-shift'.
- This means that other galaxies are moving away from us very quickly, and the further away a galaxy is, the faster it is moving away from us.

bile: a liquid produced by the *liver* that helps us to digest *fats*.
- It is a green-yellow liquid produced by the *liver* and stored in the *gall bladder*.
- Bile is alkaline – this helps to neutralise the acidified food that passes into the small intestine from the stomach (see *acids and alkalis*).
- Bile salts emulsify fats (i.e. change large drops into smaller droplets). This gives *lipase* enzymes a greater surface area of fat to act upon.

- Bile pigments are waste materials formed by the breakdown of red blood cells.

biodegradable: a substance which is biodegradable will decay naturally in the soil. Biodegradable materials are 'environmentally friendly' because they are recycled naturally.

- Biodegradable substances are able to be broken down by microbes in the *environment* (see *bacteria, decay*).
- Most natural biological materials are biodegradable.
- Synthetic materials such as plastics are mainly non-biodegradable since no microbe produces enzymes that can digest them.
- Non-biodegradable pesticides may become concentrated in *food chains*, harming the organisms at the top of those food chains.

biofuel: a fuel produced by living organisms. Biofuels could help to solve the world's 'energy crisis'.

- Biofuels are *renewable energy resources*.

EXAMPLES

- Wood – some forests are grown specifically to provide wood for fuel. After harvesting the wood, the forest is replanted.
- Ethanol – in countries such as Brazil, sugar cane is grown to provide sugar which is then *fermented* to produce ethanol. Ethanol can be used to fuel motor vehicles.
- Methane – waste material from animals, e.g. human or cattle faeces, can be fermented *anaerobically* to produce the gas methane which can be burned as a fuel.

biological control: the use of living organisms rather than chemicals to control a pest. It is a natural control method which does not usually damage the *environment*.

- It usually involves using a natural *predator* of the pest.

EXAMPLES

- The viral disease, myxomatosis, has been used to control rabbit populations.
- A parasitic wasp is used to control whitefly in large glasshouses.

ADVANTAGES

- It does not pollute the environment.
- It is usually specific – only the pest is affected.

- It may be cheaper than other forms of control, since the control organism normally needs to be introduced only once.

DISADVANTAGES

- The control organism may have no natural predators (particularly if introduced from another country), and may itself spread out of control, e.g. the cane toad introduced to Australia.
- Other species may be (unintentionally) affected by the control organism.

biomass: the mass of living organisms in an area. It is an important measure when forests or crops such as sugar cane are grown to produce fuel.

- It is the amount of biological material in a given area, or of a given species in an area.
- Biomass is best calculated as dry mass (mass after all water has been evaporated off), since wet mass is highly variable.
- *Pyramids of biomass* are useful ways of describing the flow of materials in *food chains* and *food webs*.

bioreactor: a reaction vessel in which microbes are grown in ideal conditions to produce useful chemicals. Many of the chemicals we use, e.g. *antibiotics, detergents* and *biofuels,* are now made in this way, and many more are likely to be made like this in the future.

- The microbe is usually selected or *genetically engineered* to produce the required chemical.
- It is then provided with all the nutrients it needs.
- The temperature is kept at the optimum – often by cooling coils.
- Oxygen is required by most bacteria, but *anaerobic* conditions are used when producing biofuels.

biosphere: the parts of the Earth where organisms can survive without artificial support. There is no biosphere on the Moon because there is no air.

- The biosphere supplies many of the needs of living organisms, e.g. nutrients and gases.
- For millions of years, natural global cycles have kept conditions within the biosphere relatively constant.
- In more recent times, human activities have begun to alter the biosphere, e.g. *global warming*.

biotic factors: factors that are living, and affect other living organisms, as opposed to non-living factors that affect living organisms, e.g. water and air. Biotic factors include:

- availability of food
- *predation* or grazing
- *competition*.
- Light, temperature and pH are <u>not</u> biotic factors – they are said to be abiotic.

birds: animals that have feathers.
- They are *vertebrates* (have a backbone).
- They lay hard-shelled eggs.
- Along with mammals, they have a high, constant body temperature.
- Most have forelimbs which are adapted to give a large surface area for flight.

bitumen: a black solid or semi-solid often used in road building.
- It is a mixture of compounds *(hydrocarbons)*.
- The solid nature of bitumen is due to many of the hydrocarbons in the mixture having more than 50 carbon atoms in their chains.
- It occurs naturally in many parts of the world.
- It is what is left at the bottom of a fractionating column when the shorter-chain hydrocarbons have been evaporated off (see *fractional distillation*).
- It can be used as a fuel and as a cement, e.g. in road making.

biuret test: a test for *protein*.
- Sodium hydroxide solution is added to the test substance followed by a few drops of copper sulphate solution.
- A mauve colour indicates the presence of protein.

bladder: organ in which *urine* is stored until it leaves the body.
- Urine is made in the kidneys and passes down the *ureters* to the bladder.
- Urine leaves the bladder via the *urethra*.
- The muscle controlling the exit of urine from the bladder is a *voluntary* muscle that we learn to control during early childhood.

blast furnace: used in industry to make iron.
- It is a reactor used to extract iron from its ore.
- The ore is mainly *haematite* (iron(III) oxide).
- The other raw materials are coke (mainly carbon) and limestone.
- Limestone does not take part in the main reactions but gets rid of many impurities as a liquid called slag.

REACTIONS IN THE FURNACE

1 coke + oxygen $\longrightarrow$ carbon dioxide

$C(s) + O_2(g) \longrightarrow CO_2(g)$

2 carbon dioxide + coke $\longrightarrow$ carbon monoxide

$CO_2(g) + C(s) \longrightarrow 2CO(g)$

3 iron(III) oxide + carbon monoxide $\longrightarrow$ iron + carbon dioxide

$Fe_2O_3(s) + 3CO(g) \longrightarrow 2Fe(l) + 3CO_2(g)$

In this reaction, the carbon monoxide *reduces* the iron oxide to iron.

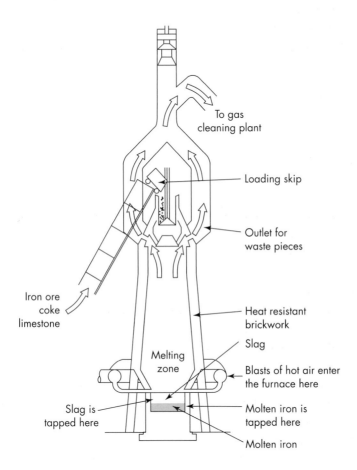

bleach: household chemical used to whiten or remove the colour from a material.

- Household bleaches usually contain sodium hypochlorite (NaOCl) which releases *chlorine* – a bleaching agent.
- The bleach used for removing hair colour usually contains hydrogen peroxide (H_2O_2).

blind spot: part of the eye, so-called because if an object is focused there we cannot see it.

- It is the part of the back of the eye *(retina)* where the *optic nerve* leaves the eye.
- Objects focused on the blind spot cannot be seen because there are no *receptor* cells *(rods* or *cones)* in this part of the retina.

blinking: an automatic action *(reflex action)* in which the eyelids close and then open again quickly when, for example, an object approaches the eye. Like many reflexes this helps to protect the body from damage.

MECHANISM OF BLINKING REFLEX

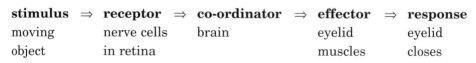

stimulus $\Rightarrow$	**receptor** $\Rightarrow$	**co-ordinator** $\Rightarrow$	**effector** $\Rightarrow$	**response**
moving object	nerve cells in retina	brain	eyelid muscles	eyelid closes

blood, cells: there are three main types of blood cell – red cells, white cells and platelets, and you need to know the differences between them.

	Red cells	**White cells**	**Platelets**
Shape	biconcave disc	variable	irregular
Nucleus	none	present	none
Haemoglobin	present	none	none
Function	Carry oxygen as oxyhaemoglobin: haemoglobin + oxygen $\rightleftharpoons$ oxyhaemoglobin Oxyhaemoglobin is formed as blood flows through lung *capillaries*; it splits up as blood flows through capillaries in other organs.	Protect the body by: 1 *ingesting* microbes 2 producing *antibodies* to kill microbes 3 producing *antitoxins* to neutralise the toxins produced by microbes.	Involved in the formation of *blood clots* at the site of a wound.

blood, circulation: how the blood, which carries the materials we need, is moved around the body.
- Blood is forced around the body by a muscular pump – the *heart*.
- Vessels carrying blood away from the heart are called *arteries*.
- Vessels carrying blood towards the heart are called *veins*.
- Arteries are connected to veins by *capillaries*.
- Mammals have a double circulation.

● The main advantage of a double circulation is that oxygenated blood from the lungs goes back to the heart to be repressurised before going to the other organs of the body.

blood, clotting: blood forms clots at the site of a wound – without it we would bleed to death from even a small cut.
● A protein called *fibrinogen* (dissolved in blood plasma) is converted to insoluble fibres called *fibrin* by an *enzyme* called thrombin (formed in blood plasma when the body is injured).

$$\text{fibrinogen} \xrightarrow{\text{thrombin}} \text{fibrin}$$

● The fibres form a mesh in which blood cells are trapped, forming the clot.
● The clot stops further blood loss and prevents the entry of microbes.
● *Haemophiliacs* lack a factor in the blood which is needed for the enzyme thrombin to work.

blood, defence: if disease microbes get past the body's outer defences, e.g. the skin, then they are dealt with by the blood system.
Blood defends the body in the following ways:
● Blood clots at the site of a wound prevent further blood loss and the entry of microbes.
● Some types of blood cells (*leucocytes*) *ingest* microbes.
● Other types of white cells (*lymphocytes*) produce *antibodies* to kill microbes.
● Once these white cells have produced antibodies against a particular microbe, they can quickly produce them again if those microbes reinfect the body. This makes the body *immune* to that microbe.
● Other types of white cells produce *antitoxins* to neutralise the poisons (toxin) produced by microbes.

blood, plasma: the liquid part of blood.
Its main functions are:
● transport of materials around the body (see *blood, transport*)
● forming blood clots (see *blood, clotting*).

blood, transfusion: the transfer of blood from one person to another. It is vital in saving the lives of people who have lost a lot of blood, e.g. during an operation or in an accident.
● The blood types of the two people must be matched otherwise the red blood cells will stick together (agglutinate) with fatal results (see *blood, types*).
● The compatibility table below shows which blood types can be mixed safely.

		Donor blood group			
		A	**B**	**AB**	**O**
Recipient	**A**	safe	no	safe	safe
blood	**B**	no	safe	safe	safe
group	**AB**	safe	safe	safe	safe
	O	no	no	no	safe

- Group O blood can be transfused into people of all groups – group O people are therefore known as universal donors.
- Group AB people can receive blood from any person – they are known as universal recipients.

blood, transport by: you need to know what substances are transported in the blood, how they are transported, where they enter the blood and where they leave the blood.

Substance	Transported as	Transported by	Transported from	Transported to
oxygen	oxyhaemoglobin	red blood cells	lungs	organs
carbon dioxide	hydrogen-carbonate ions	plasma	organs	lungs
urea	dissolved	plasma	liver	kidneys
soluble food	dissolved	plasma	small intestine	organs
hormones	dissolved	plasma	ductless glands	target organs

blood, types: it is vital to know a patient's blood type so that blood can be transfused safely (see *blood, transfusion*).
- A person's blood type depends on the types of *antigens* found on their *red blood cells* and the naturally occurring *antibodies* in the *plasma*.
- Antibody a will cause blood cells with antigen A to stick together (agglutinate).
- Antibody b will cause blood cells with antigen B to stick together (agglutinate).
- This is why group A blood cannot be transfused into a person with group B blood and vice versa (see *blood, transfusions*).

Blood group	Antigens present on red blood cells	Antibodies occurring naturally in blood plasma
A	A	b
B	B	a
AB	both A and B	neither a nor b
O	neither A nor B	both a and b

blood, vessels: structures which carry blood around the body. You need to know the differences between *arteries, veins* and *capillaries*.

Arteries	Veins	Capillaries
carry blood away from heart	carry blood towards heart	connect arteries and veins
carry oxygenated blood (except pulmonary artery)	carry deoxygenated blood (except pulmonary vein)	allow substances to diffuse into and out of tissues
thick walls	thin walls	walls one cell thick
very elastic	less elastic	inelastic
no valves	valves to prevent backflow of blood	no valves
blood flows in pulses	blood flow even	blood flow even
pressure of blood high	pressure of blood low	pressure of blood low

Bohr: a scientist who lived from 1885 to 1962.
- He studied with *Rutherford* and *Thompson*.
- He extended the Rutherford model of the *atom*.
- He discovered that the *electrons* in an atom occur in 'shells' (energy levels) and that
- the outer electrons of an atom are responsible for its chemical properties.

boiling point: the temperature at which a liquid bubbles rapidly.
- It is the temperature at which vapour forms within the body of a liquid.
- The bubbles in a boiling liquid contain the vapour formed within the liquid.
- At temperatures below the boiling point, evaporation only occurs at the surface of a liquid.
- Evaporation occurs when the particles of a liquid have enough energy to escape from the liquid and become a gas.
- Impurities raise the boiling point of a liquid.
- Reducing the pressure reduces the boiling point of a liquid.

bond breaking: breaking bonds in chemicals is rather like trying to pull two magnets apart – you need energy to do it.

- Bond breaking is always *endothermic*.

bond energy: the energy needed to make or to break a chemical bond (see *bond breaking*).

- The units are kJ per mole.
- This means the energy needed to make or break the number of bonds in one *mole* of the molecule.

(See also *chemistry calculations, bond energies.*)

bond making: since energy is always needed to break bonds (see *bond breaking*), it follows that energy must be released when bonds are formed.

- Bond making is always *exothermic*.

bonding: atoms form chemical bonds when they combine. You need to understand the differences between *ionic bonding* and *covalent bonding*.

IONIC BONDING

- *Atoms* can form chemical bonds by losing or gaining *electrons* to form electrically charged atoms called *ions*.
- Ionic bonds usually form between metals and non-metals, e.g. sodium and chlorine form the ionic compound sodium chloride.

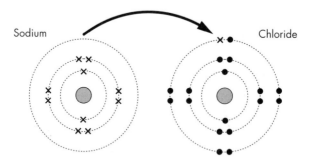

- The sodium atom loses an electron to become the sodium ion Na^+.
- The chlorine atom gains this electron to become the chloride ion Cl^-.
- Sodium chloride is an ionic compound held together by strong forces of attraction between the oppositely charged sodium and chloride ions.
- This is ionic bonding.
- The outer energy level of both ions is complete with electrons – like that of a noble gas.

- Ionic compounds form giant structures (giant ionic lattices) in which the strong forces between the oppositely charged ions result in the compounds having high melting points and high boiling points.

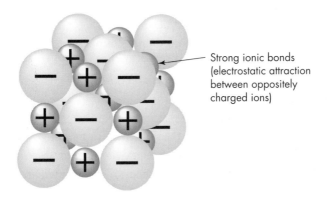

Strong ionic bonds (electrostatic attraction between oppositely charged ions)

COVALENT BONDING

- Atoms can form chemical bonds by sharing electrons.
- Atoms which share electrons often form molecules.
- Some compounds are made of molecules in which the atoms are held together because they share pairs of electrons, e.g. ammonia (NH_3).

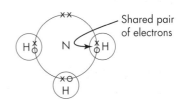

Shared pair of electrons

- The strong bonds <u>between the atoms</u> are called covalent bonds.
- The outer energy level of all four partner atoms is effectively complete with electrons – like that of noble gas.

Covalent molecular compounds

- The forces between the molecules are weak.
- The molecules do not carry an overall charge.
- These properties mean that simple molecular compounds are gases, liquids or solids which have low melting points, low boiling points and do not conduct electricity.
- Giant covalent structures, e.g. *diamond* and *graphite*, have large numbers of covalent bonds in their structures and therefore high melting and boiling points.

bone: forms the *skeleton*, which supports the body and enables the animal to move.

- Bone consists of 70% carbon compounds and 30% organic material.
- These substances make it both strong and elastic.

- Lack of either *calcium* or *vitamin D* in the diet of humans may lead to rickets.
- In rickets the bones are weakened due to a deficiency in calcium salts, and the leg bones may bend under the weight of the body.

bone marrow: the central part of long bones, important in the manufacture of blood cells.
- *Red blood cells, platelets* and some *white blood cells* (leucocytes) are made mainly in the bone marrow.

Boyle's law: you need to remember this law and to be able to use it in calculations.
- Boyle's law states that when the pressure on a gas increases and its temperature remains the same, its volume decreases.
- For a fixed mass of gas at a constant temperature, pV (pressure × volume) is a constant.
- Volume is inversely proportional to pressure, i.e.

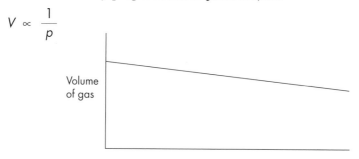

$$V \propto \frac{1}{p}$$

Volume of gas

Pressure applied to gas

- In a calculation, you will usually be given p_1, V_1 and either p_2 or V_2 and asked to use $p_1 \times V_1 = p_2 \times V_2$ to calculate the unknown variable.
- If you find it difficult to cross-multiply, remember these forms of the equation:

$$p_2 = \frac{p_1 \times V_1}{V_2} \quad \text{and} \quad V_2 = \frac{p_1 \times V_1}{p_2}$$

EXAMPLE

Air in a syringe has a volume of 50 cm³ and a pressure of 100 Pa. Calculate the pressure of the air in the syringe if the volume is reduced to 25 cm³ and the temperature remains constant.

To do this calculation use:

$$p_2 = \frac{p_1 \times V_1}{V_2}$$

Substitute the values you know:

$$p_2 = \frac{100 \text{ Pa} \times 50 \text{ cm}^3}{25 \text{ cm}^3}$$

$$= 200 \text{ Pa}$$

Bragg: William Henry and William Lawrence Bragg were scientists (father and son) who used X-rays to study crystals.

- Their work enabled scientists to measure exactly the distances between atoms in crystals.
- *Watson* and *Crick* used many of the Braggs' techniques to discover the structure of *DNA*.

brain: the part of the *nervous system* which has overall control of the body, consciousness, thought and memory. You may need to know the functions of parts of the brain:

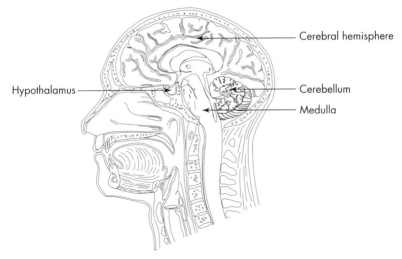

Part of brain	Function
cerebral hemispheres	consciousness, thought and memory
cerebellum	muscular coordination
medulla	control of unconscious activities, e.g. heartbeat
hypothalamus	control of temperature regulation and of hormone secretion

brakes, hydraulic: braking system used in modern cars that applies an equal braking force to all four wheels.

- When the driver presses the brake pedal, hydraulic liquid is sent from a master cylinder to the brakes on all the wheels.

- Movement of the driver's foot creates a force which acts on the master piston.
- The master piston exerts a pressure on the hydraulic liquid.
- The hydraulic fluid transmits this pressure to the slave piston.
- The slave piston exerts a force on the brake disc.

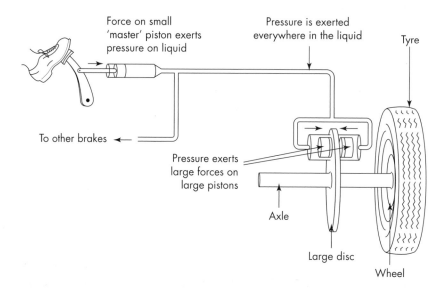

- Because the area of the slave piston is greater than the area of the master, the force exerted by the slave cylinder is greater than the force acting on the master cylinder.
- This is because:

$$\frac{\text{force}_f}{\text{area}_a} = \frac{\text{force}_F}{\text{area}_A}$$

EXAMPLE

In a hydraulic brake system the area of the master cylinder is 4 cm² and the area of the slave cylinder is 16 cm². If a force of 1000 N acts on the master cylinder, what force will act on the slave cylinder?

Rearrange the above equation:

$$\text{force on master cylinder} = \frac{\text{force}_f \times \text{area}_A}{\text{area}_a}$$

substitute the values: $= \dfrac{1000\ \text{N} \times 16\ \text{cm}^2}{4\ \text{cm}^2}$

work out answer: $= 4000\ \text{N}$ (don't forget the unit!)

---

braking distance: the distance a vehicle travels <u>after</u> the brakes are applied. The greater the speed of a vehicle:

- the greater the braking force needed to stop it within a certain distance
- the greater the distance needed to stop it with a certain braking force.

---

brass: a mixture (*alloy*) of copper and zinc used to make a wide variety of objects, such as musical instruments.

PROPERTIES

- harder than copper
- lower melting point than either copper or zinc
- easy to mould and to shape

---

breathing: forcing air into and out of the lungs – not to be confused with respiration.

To inhale:

- The intercostal muscles (muscles between the ribs) contract, pulling the *ribcage* upwards.
- At the same time the *diaphragm* muscles contract causing the diaphragm to flatten.
- These two movements cause the volume of the *thorax* to increase.
- This increase in volume results in a decrease in pressure inside the thorax.
- As a result of this decrease in pressure, atmospheric air enters the lungs.

To exhale:

- Both intercostal muscles and diaphragm muscles relax.

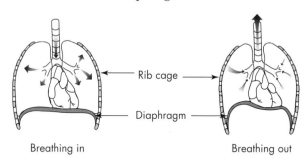

Breathing in   Breathing out

---

breeding: choosing the parents of the next generation.

- It is a way of improving varieties of animals or plants by selecting parents with the desired characteristics (see *artificial selection*).

---

brewing: making alcoholic drinks such as beer using *fermentation*.

- The reactions that produce alcohol and carbon dioxide are brought about by *enzymes* (biological catalysts).

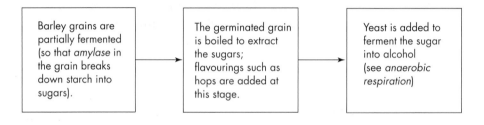

| Barley grains are partially fermented (so that *amylase* in the grain breaks down starch into sugars). | → | The germinated grain is boiled to extract the sugars; flavourings such as hops are added at this stage. | → | Yeast is added to ferment the sugar into alcohol (see *anaerobic respiration*) |

brine, electrolysis: an important industrial process that yields several useful chemicals.

- The electrolysis of brine (sodium chloride solution) yields hydrogen gas, chlorine gas and sodium hydroxide solution.

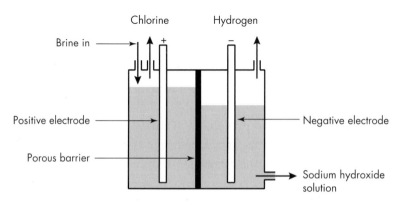

The porous barrier:
- keeps hydrogen gas and chlorine gas apart
- allows sodium ions to pass through, but not chloride ions
- prevents chlorine reacting with sodium hydroxide.

IONIC EQUATIONS FOR THIS CELL
- *ionisation* of some water molecules:
    $$H_2O(l) \rightleftharpoons H^+(aq) + OH^-(aq)$$
- sodium chloride exists in solution as $Na^+(aq)$ and $Cl^-(aq)$ ions
- chlorine gas is formed at the anode:
    $$2Cl^-(aq) - 2e^- \longrightarrow Cl_2(g)$$
- hydrogen gas is formed at the cathode:
    $$2H^+(aq) + 2e^- \longrightarrow H_2(g)$$
- $Na^+(aq)$ ions and $OH^-(aq)$ ions are left in solution – this is sodium hydroxide solution.

brine, products: hydrogen gas, chlorine gas and sodium hydroxide solution are obtained from the *electrolysis* of brine.

- Hydrogen gas is used in the manufacture of ammonia and margarine.
- Chlorine gas is used in the manufacture of disinfectants, bleaches and some plastics (PVC), and to kill microbes in drinking water and swimming pools.
- Sodium hydroxide is used in the manufacture of soap, paper and ceramics.

bromine (Br): a reddish brown liquid; a *halogen*. You may be asked to compare the properties of bromine with other elements in the same group of the periodic table.

PROPERTIES

- non-metallic element
- in Group VII of the periodic table
- consists of *molecules* made up of pairs of *atoms* (Br_2)
- forms *ionic salts* with metals
- forms *molecular compounds* with other non-metals
- it is more reactive than iodine but less reactive than chlorine
- it is less reactive than chlorine because its outer electron energy level is at a higher level than that of chlorine, therefore it finds it less easy to gain an electron.

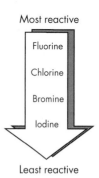

Most reactive

Fluorine

Chlorine

Bromine

Iodine

Least reactive

bronchioles: fine tubes through which air passes in the lungs.
- A bronchiole is a branch of a *bronchus*.
- The narrowest bronchioles terminate in a bunch of *alveoli*.
- They carry air to and from the alveoli.
Bronchioles are lined by:
- cells which produce mucus – which traps microbes
- cells with cilia (tiny 'hairs') which move the mucus out of the lungs.

bronchitis: inflammation of the *bronchioles* and *bronchi* resulting in difficult or painful breathing.
- It is caused by infection and by air pollution.
- It is much more common in smokers than in non-smokers.

bronchus (pl. bronchi): a branch of the windpipe (*trachea*) which itself branches to form narrower *bronchioles*.
- It has rings of *cartilage* in its walls for support.

Brownian movement: the way in which tiny particles suspended in a liquid or gas are seen to move about erratically.

The diagram shows Brownian movement of a
pollen grain suspended in water.

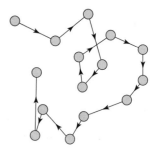

- The pollen grain moves as it is hit by water
  molecules.
- This movement provides evidence for the
  constant, random movements of the molecules in a liquid or a gas.

burning (combustion): rapid reaction, usually giving off both heat and
light.

- It is an *oxidation* reaction.
- When fossil fuels burn, the principal reaction is:

  carbon + oxygen $\longrightarrow$ carbon dioxide

  $C(s)$ + $O_2(g)$ $\longrightarrow$ $CO_2(g)$

- burning is an *exothermic* reaction (thermal energy is released).

cacti: a group of spiny, fleshy plants that live mainly in hot deserts.
- They are adapted for living in dry conditions.

ADAPTATIONS

- The leaves are reduced to spines – this reduces the area for evaporation of water.
- The stem is swollen to store water after periods of rain.
- The spines protect the plant from animals seeking water.
- The stem is covered by a thick layer of wax – this reduces the rate of evaporation of water.
- The roots are very long and cover a large area, to absorb as much water as possible.

calcium (Ca): a silvery-white metallic element, found as compounds in common rocks such as limestone.
- It is in Group II of the periodic table.
- It is an alkaline earth metal – these metals are less reactive than the *alkali metals*.
- It is the fifth most abundant element in the Earth's crust.
- It occurs mainly as *calcium carbonate* (limestone, chalk), calcium sulphate (gypsum), calcium fluoride (fluorite) and calcium phosphate (rock phosphate).

calcium, in the body is needed for:
- formation of bones and teeth
- blood clotting
- transmission of nerve impulses
- muscle contraction.

SOURCES IN THE DIET

- milk
- milk products e.g. cheese, yoghurt

EFFECT OF DEFICIENCY

- rickets (leg bones bend since they are too soft to support the body)

calcium carbonate, CaCO$_3$ is a natural compound found mainly in rocks such as *chalk, limestone* and *marble*.

- All these rocks were initially formed from the skeletons of animals which lived in the sea millions of years ago.
- It is an important raw material in the manufacture of glass, concrete, cement, iron and paper.
- It can be used to *neutralise* soils and water.
- When heated it decomposes to form calcium oxide (quicklime):

calcium carbonate $\longrightarrow$ calcium oxide + carbon dioxide

$$CaCO_3(s) \longrightarrow CaO(s) + CO_2(g)$$

---

cancer is an abnormal growth in the body. Such growths can prove fatal but many forms are now treated successfully if discovered early enough.

- Cancer is formed by abnormal, uncontrolled division of cells in the body, often resulting in a tumour.
- It is caused by a *mutation* – a change to the genes which control cell division.
- The chance of mutation is increased by exposure to *ionising radiation,* e.g. ultraviolet light, and to certain chemicals.
- Too much sunbathing increases the risk of skin cancer.
- Smoking increases the risk of lung cancer.

---

capacitor: a device for storing electrical *charge* used in almost all electronic circuits. It is rather like a small, rechargeable battery.

- Capacitors are made from two strips of metal separated by an insulating material such as plastic.
- If one of the metal strips is charged positively, then the other strip will become negatively charged (by *induction*).
- The capacitor now stores this charge.
- Because it takes time to build up the charge, capacitors can be used as timing devices in simple circuits.

---

capillary: the smallest type of blood vessel in the body. You need to know the differences between arteries, veins and capillaries (see *blood, vessels*).

- A capillary is a microscopic blood vessel used to exchange materials with the tissues.
- Blood flows from *arteries* to capillaries to *veins*.

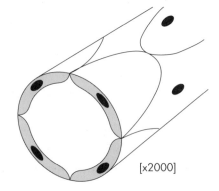

[x2000]

- Capillary walls are one cell thick.
- Molecules such as glucose, oxygen and carbon dioxide are exchanged between the blood in the capillaries and the fluid that surrounds the tissues (*tissue fluid*).

carbohydrase: an *enzyme* which is needed to break down the *carbohydrate* in your diet.
- Carbohydrases break down large carbohydrate molecules such as starch into smaller carbohydrate molecules such as glucose.
- In the human digestive system carbohydrases are produced by the *salivary glands,* the *pancreas* and the *small intestine.*
- In plants carbohydrases are produced in seeds and in storage organs, e.g. potato tubers.

EXAMPLES OF CARBOHYDRASES

- *amylase* which breaks down starch to maltose
- *maltase* which breaks down maltose to glucose
- *invertase* which breaks down sucrose to glucose and fructose

carbohydrates are compounds used mainly to provide living organisms with energy. We get carbohydrates from the cereals, fruits and root vegetables we eat.
- *Starch* is an insoluble carbohydrate stored by plants.
- *Glycogen* is an insoluble carbohydrate stored by animals.
- *Cellulose* is a structural carbohydrate in plant cell walls.
- *Glucose* is a soluble carbohydrate used in *respiration* to obtain energy.

carbon (C) is an important element because the *carbohydrates, fats* and *proteins* which make up the bulk of living organisms all contain carbon atoms.
- Carbon is in Group IV of the *periodic table.*
- It occurs naturally as *diamond* and *graphite*
- It occurs widely as compounds, e.g. *carbon dioxide* and *carbonates*
- It is the element found in all organic compounds – those compounds found mainly in living organisms
- Carbon can displace some metals (e.g. lead) from their oxides:

lead oxide + carbon $\longrightarrow$ lead + carbon dioxide

$2PbO(s) + C(s) \longrightarrow 2Pb(s) + CO_2(g)$

carbon cycle: the flow of carbon compounds through plants, animals, decomposers and fuels. It is like a huge natural recycling programme.
- Plants remove carbon dioxide from the air by *photosynthesis.*

- All living organisms return carbon dioxide to the atmosphere via *respiration*.
- The carbon materials in dead organisms are *digested* by *decomposers* (*bacteria* and *fungi*).
- Some plant materials form *fuels*; carbon dioxide is returned to the atmosphere when fuels are burned.

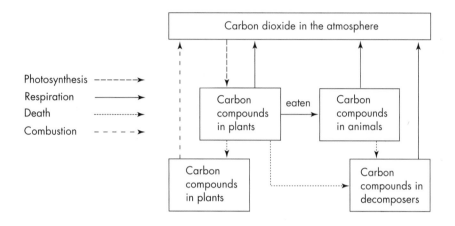

carbon dioxide is a colourless, odourless gas, formula CO_2. Used by plants to manufacture food it is ultimately the source of all the food on Earth. Carbon dioxide is:

- found naturally in the atmosphere (approximately 0.003% by volume)
- absorbed by plants during *photosynthesis,* forming *carbohydrates*
- released during *aerobic respiration* in all living organisms and during *anaerobic respiration* in yeast
- released during *combustion* of fuels
- detected by lime water test in which it turns limewater milky.

MAIN USES

- making 'fizzy' drinks
- in baking – it makes bread and cakes rise
- in fire extinguishers
- as 'dry ice'

carbon monoxide is a colourless, odourless poisonous gas, formula CO. Carbon monoxide is:

- formed when carbon compounds are burned in a limited oxygen supply
- an important part of tobacco smoke
- poisonous because it combines irreversibly with *haemoglobin*, preventing haemoglobin from carrying oxygen in the blood

- important in the *blast furnace* where it reduces iron(III) oxide to iron.

  iron(III) oxide + carbon monoxide $\longrightarrow$ iron + carbon dioxide

  $Fe_2O_3(s)$ + $3CO(g)$ $\longrightarrow 2Fe(l)$ + $3CO_2(g)$

carbonates are compounds containing the carbonate ion ($CO_3{}^{2-}$). Found in many common rocks such as limestone they:
- occur naturally, mainly as ores of the *alkaline earth metals*, e.g. calcium carbonate and magnesium carbonate
- decompose when heated, e.g.

  calcium carbonate $\longrightarrow$ calcium oxide + carbon dioxide

  $CaCO_3(s)$ $\longrightarrow$ $CaO(s)$ + $CO_2(g)$
- react with dilute acids, releasing carbon dioxide and water, e.g.

  calcium carbonate + dil. hydrochloric acid $\longrightarrow$ calcium chloride + water + carbon dioxide

  $CaCO_3(s)$ + $2HCl(aq)$ $\longrightarrow CaCl_2(aq) + H_2O(l) + CO_2(g)$

  This is a *neutralisation* reaction.

carnivore: an animal whose diet consists mainly of other animals e.g. a lion.
- Carnivores are also known as secondary *consumers*.
- The teeth of carnivores are adapted to their diet; they have long, pointed *canine* teeth for gripping prey and for tearing flesh and sharp *premolar* and *molar* teeth which work with a shearing action.

carrier: a person who can pass on a hereditary disease to a child but does not suffer from the disease themselves.
- Some hereditary diseases are caused by *recessive* alleles, e.g. cystic fibrosis.
- A person who has the *dominant allele*, say C, does not suffer from the disease; there are two 'healthy' genotypes CC and Cc.
- Only people with two *recessive* alleles cc have the disease.
- People who have the genotype Cc are known as carriers.
- If two carriers have a child there is a 25% chance that the child will suffer from the disease.

		Parent 1 (carrier)	
		C	c
Parent 2 (carrier)	C	CC	Cc
	c	Cc	cc child suffers from disease

cartilage: a tissue which helps movement in joints.
- In most moveable joints the ends of the bones are covered with cartilage.
- Cartilage is a smooth material, which reduces friction between the moving bones.
- Cartilage is often lubricated by *synovial fluid*.

catalase is an *enzyme* found in liver cells. Catalase breaks down hydrogen peroxide into water and oxygen:

$$\text{hydrogen peroxide} \longrightarrow \text{water} + \text{oxygen}$$
$$2H_2O_2(aq) \longrightarrow 2H_2O(l) + O_2(g)$$

catalyst: a substance that increases the rate of a chemical reaction without being used up during the reaction. Catalysts are important in speeding up reactions both in our body cells (*enzymes* are catalysts) and in industry.
- Catalysts are used over and over again to speed up the conversion of reactants to products.
- Different reactions need different catalysts. For example an iron catalyst is needed in the production of ammonia but a platinum catalyst is needed in the production of nitric acid.

cathode: the negatively charged electrode in *electrolysis*, it is made from a metal or from a *conductive* non-metal such as graphite. You need to know the difference between *anode* and cathode.

cathode ray oscilloscope: an instrument we can use to 'see' waves. Waves such as sound waves are changed into electrical voltages which are displayed on a screen rather like that in a television set.

cation: a positively charged particle (*ion*) that moves towards a negatively charged electrode (*cathode*). You need to know the difference between cation and *anion*.
- Examples of cations include the hydrogen ion (H^+), aluminium ion (Al^{3+}) and copper ion (Cu^{2+}).

⊕ → Cation

Cathode

cell, animal: the basic building block of an animal. You need to know the functions of the following cellular parts and the differences between animal cells and plant cells.

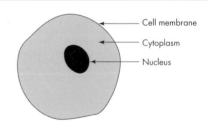

Cell membrane
Cytoplasm
Nucleus

Part	Function
cell membrane	controls the passage of substances in and out of the cell
cytoplasm	where most chemical reactions take place
nucleus	controls the activities of the cell; contains hereditary material
mitochondria	where *respiration* takes place

cell, electrical: converts chemical energy into electrical energy. Useful if an appliance (e.g. a torch) cannot practically be connected to a mains electricity supply. The cell consists of:

- an *anode* (positive electrode) – the carbon rod in a zinc–carbon cell
- a *cathode* (negative electrode) – the zinc case in a zinc–carbon cell
- *electrolyte* (solid, liquid or paste) – ammonium chloride paste.

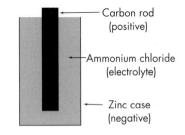

When the cell is connected in an electric circuit, chemical energy is transferred into electrical energy and electrons are forced round the circuit (from the zinc around the circuit to the carbon).

- Cells connected in series are known as a *battery*.

cell, plant: the basic building block of a plant. You need to know the functions of the following parts and the differences between *animal cells* and plant cells.

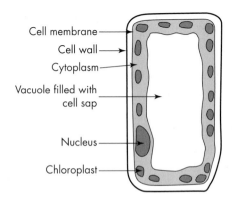

Part	Function
cell membrane	controls the passage of substances in and out of the cell
cytoplasm	where most chemical reactions take place
nucleus	controls the activities of the cell; contains hereditary material
mitochondria	where *respiration* takes place
cell wall	made of *cellulose*; strengthens the cell
chloroplast	absorbs energy from light to make food
vacuole	the cell sap inside it supports the cell

cell division is the process by which cells divide. You need to know the similarities and differences between the two types of cell division – *mitosis* and *meiosis*.

- In *mitosis* (division of body cells) the genetic information in both the daughter cells is identical to that of the parent cell.
- In *meiosis* (division forming *gametes* or sex cells) the number of *chromosomes* is halved during cell division and the genetic information in each daughter cell is slightly different.

cell membrane: controls the passage of substances in and out of a cell. You need to know the processes by which substances move through the membrane – *diffusion, active transport* and *osmosis*. The cell membrane:
- forms the outer boundary of the cytoplasm
- is *partially permeable* – small molecules pass through quickly, large molecules slowly, if at all
- allows many substances to pass through by *diffusion*
- allows some substances to be transported through the membrane against a concentration gradient – this is known as *active transport* (or *active uptake*).

cell sap: the fluid in the *vacuole* of a plant cell which keeps young plants upright.
- Cell sap usually contains a high concentration of mineral salts.
- Water therefore enters it by *osmosis*.
- Pressure (*turgor pressure*) of the cell sap against the *cytoplasm* and thus the *cell wall*, helps to support the cell.

cell wall: a structure found on the outside of plant cells but not animal cells. It keeps large plants such as trees and shrubs upright.
- The cell wall is made mainly of *cellulose* which strengthens the cell.

- *Xylem* tissue cells have a waterproof substance called lignin in their walls which helps xylem to transport water.
- The cell wall is completely permeable to most substances.

cellulose: a carbohydrate which strengthens plant *cell walls* – very important in the support of plants.
- Cellulose has long molecules which are twisted, rather like a rope, to form strong fibres.
- Most animals do not posses digestive enzymes to break down cellulose; they rely on microbes in their gut to produce these enzymes.

cement is any substance which joins other materials together when it hardens – vital in the building industry.
- Building cement is made by roasting powdered limestone with powdered clay in a rotary kiln.
- When this cement is mixed with water and sand it forms mortar which is used to hold bricks together when it hardens.
- When this cement is mixed with water, sand and crushed rock it hardens to form concrete.

centre of gravity: see *centre of mass*.

centre of mass: the point through which the entire *mass* of an object seems to act. It is the position of the centre of mass which determines how easily an object will fall over.
- An object balances if it is supported at its centre of mass.
- An object with a low centre of mass is more stable than an object with a high centre of mass, for example a racing car is more stable than a double-decker bus.

centripetal force is the force that causes an object to move along a circular path rather than in a straight line. A centripetal force acts towards the centre of a circle. It is like being on a moving roundabout; so long as you hold on to the roundabout you move along a circular path. If you let go you are thrown off along a straight path. When you hold on a centripetal force is acting on you.

cerebellum: part of the *brain* which coordinates movement of the voluntary muscles, for example it coordinates the muscles we use when running, walking, swimming, jumping or standing still.

cerebral hemispheres: parts of the *brain* which coordinate higher activities such as thinking, memory and emotions. The cerebral hemispheres also process most of the information obtained from the body's receptors.

CFCs are compounds of carbon, fluorine and chlorine used as coolants in refrigerators and propellants in aerosol cans. Their use is affecting the *ozone layer*.
- When released into the atmosphere CFCs rise and are then broken down by the action of sunlight, releasing chlorine.
- This chlorine destroys ozone in the ozone layer, allowing more dangerous ultraviolet rays to reach the surface of the Earth.
- Because of this, the use of CFCs is now banned.
- CFCs have got <u>nothing</u> to do with the *greenhouse effect* or *global warming*.

chain reaction: a reaction in which the products of the reaction initiate further reactions. This is the basic reaction in some types of *nuclear reactor* and atomic bombs.
- If a *neutron* hits a uranium-235 atom the atom splits up into two smaller atoms and releases three neutrons.
- Each of these three neutrons can cause a further uranium-235 atom to split up, resulting in a reaction which goes faster and faster.
- If a chain reaction is not controlled, an explosion results – this is what happens in an atomic bomb.

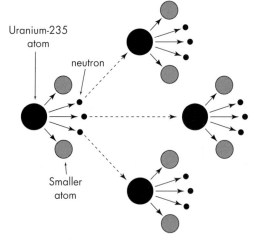

- In a nuclear reactor rods of graphite are used to absorb some of the neutrons and thus keep the reaction under control.

chalk is a soft, white form of *limestone*. It is:
- almost pure calcium carbonate ($CaCO_3$)
- a *sedimentary* rock
- made from the shells of small marine animals which lived hundreds of millions of years ago.

change of state: a physical change in a substance, for example ice changing into water or water changing into steam.

- You need to know the properties of solids, liquids and gases in terms of the movement of particles and how changes to the movement of particles bring about *melting* and *evaporation*.

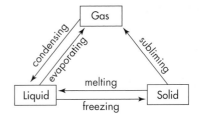

PROPERTIES OF SOLIDS, LIQUIDS AND GASES

Solids	Liquids	Gases
definite shape	take the shape of the container	spread into all the space available to them
definite volume	definite volume	–
not easily compressed	not easily compressed	easily compressed
particles very close together	particles close together	particles well spread out
particles cannot move – only vibrate	particles can move around each other	particles can move around each other

- If energy is supplied to a solid the particles vibrate more violently and may become free to move; this is melting.
- If energy is supplied to a liquid the particles move around more quickly and some may have enough energy to escape from the surface of the liquid and become a gas; this is evaporation.

---

characteristic: an observable feature of an organism. You need to know how characteristics are *inherited* (genetics) and how they change (*mutation* and *evolution*).
- Characteristics include height and colour of eyes.
- Some characteristics are controlled by *dominant alleles*, others by *recessive alleles*.

---

charge: when certain objects are rubbed together they become electrically charged and will attract small objects placed near them. You have to understand charge to understand how electric *current* flows through solids and liquids.
- There are two types of charges – positive (+) and negative (–).
- Like charges repel each other; unlike charges attract each other.
- A material which gains *electrons* becomes negatively charged.
- A material which loses electrons becomes positively charged.
- In a solid *conductor*, the flow of charge (current) is the flow of electrons.
- *Ions* are electrically charged particles.

- In a liquid conductor the flow of charge (current) is the flow of ions.
- A large build-up of charge may cause lightning flashes or sparks in dangerous situations (e.g. during refuelling an aeroplane).

Charles' law describes how temperature affects the volume of a gas – the important thing to remember is that it is *absolute temperature*.

Here are three ways of stating Charles' law:

- at constant pressure, the volume of a gas is proportional to its *absolute temperature*
- $V \propto T$ (at constant pressure)
- for a 1°C rise in temperature the volume of a gas increases by 1/273 of its volume at 0°C.

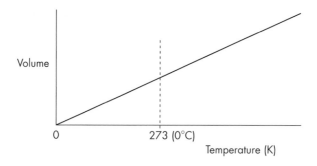

cheese: a food made by using *enzymes* to clot milk.

- The enzymes used include rennet from calves' stomachs and similar enzymes from yeast.
- The clotted part of milk is called curds.
- Curds are salted, pressed to remove water, then left to mature.

chemistry calculations, bond energies: you have to calculate the total energy involved in making new bonds and the total energy involved in breaking bonds.

EXAMPLE OF A BOND ENERGY CALCULATION

The symbol equation shows the reaction between methane and oxygen:

$$CH_4 + 2O_2 \longrightarrow CO_2 + 2H_2O$$

The structural formulae below show the bonds in each molecule involved:

$$H-\overset{\overset{\displaystyle H}{|}}{\underset{\underset{\displaystyle H}{|}}{C}}-H \ + \ 2[O=O] \ \longrightarrow \ O=C=O \ + \ 2[H-O-H]$$

The table gives the energies of the bonds:

Bond	Bond energy (kJ mol^{-1})
C – H	413
C = O	805
O = O	498
O – H	464

Use the information to calculate the energy released when the formula mass of methane (1 mole) is completely oxidised.
- First add up the total energy involved in breaking the bonds on the left-hand side of the equation:

energy change in breaking bonds = (4 × C – H bonds) + (2 × O = bonds)
$$= (4 \times 413) + (2 \times 498)$$
$$= 3466 \text{ kJ}$$

- Then add up the total energy involved in forming new bonds on the right-hand side of the equation:

energy change in forming bonds = (2 × C = O bonds) + (4 × O – H) bonds
$$= (2 \times 805) + (4 \times 464)$$
$$= 2648 \text{ kJ}$$

energy change $= (3466 \text{ kJ} – 2648 \text{ kJ})$
$$= +818 \text{ kJ}$$

- Since the energy change has a positive value, the reaction is said to be *exothermic*.

chemistry calculations, concentrations: remember that a one *molar* solution (1 M) contains the *relative formula mass (RFM)* of the substance in 1000 cm^3 of the solution. For example, to make 250 cm^3 of a molar solution of a substance you dissolve 0.25 of the RFM of the substance in water, then make up the solution to 250 cm^3.

EXAMPLE OF CALCULATION
What mass of sodium chloride would be needed to make 250 cm^3 of a 0.5 M solution of sodium chloride?
- First calculate the RFM of sodium chloride:

RFM NaCl = 23 + 35.5 = 58.5
- 1000 cm^3 of a molar solution of NaCl contain 58.5 g NaCl
- 1000 cm^3 of a 0.5 M solution of NaCl contain (58.5/2) = 29.25 g NaCl
- 250 cm^3 of a 0.5 M solution of NaCl contain (29.25/4) = 7.31 g NaCl.

chemistry calculations, formulas: you need to know how to calculate the ratios of atoms (or of *moles*) in a compound from data gives the formula of that compound.

EXAMPLE OF CALCULATION

Analysis of a sample of sodium oxide showed that it contained 2.3 g of sodium and 0.8 g of oxygen.
Use this information to calculate the formula of sodium oxide.

Method using ratio of masses

Divide each reacting mass by the relative atomic mass of the atom:

	Na	O
ratio of masses	2.3	0.8
ratio of atoms	(2.3/23)	(0.8/16)
	= 0.1	= 0.05
simplest ratio	2	1

Formula is therefore Na_2O.

Method using moles

moles of Na = (2.3/23) = 0.1
moles of O = (0.8/16) = 0.05
ratio of moles = (0.1 to 0.05) = 2 to 1
Formula is therefore Na_2O.

---

chemistry calculations, moles: remember that one mole of any element contains the same number of atoms as one mole of any other element; also that one mole of a compound contains this same number of molecules.

EXAMPLE 1

- number of moles of atoms $= \dfrac{mass}{RAM\ (relative\ atomic\ mass)}$

How many moles are there in 24 g of carbon?

$$moles = \frac{mass}{RAM}$$

$$= \frac{24}{2}$$

$$= 2\ moles$$

EXAMPLE 2

- number of moles of molecules $= \dfrac{mass}{RFM\ (relative\ formula\ mass)}$

How many moles are there in 22 g of carbon dioxide (CO_2)?

$$moles = \frac{mass}{RFM}$$

$$= \frac{22}{(12 + 16 + 16)} = \frac{22}{44}$$

$$= 0.5 \text{ mole}$$

chemistry calculations, percentage composition: you need to know how to calculate the percentage by mass of an element in one of its compounds.

$$\% \text{ mass of element} = \frac{relative\ atomic\ mass \text{ of element} \times 100}{relative\ formula\ mass \text{ of compound}}$$

EXAMPLE

Calculate the percentage of nitrogen in ammonia (NH_3).

$$\% \text{ of nitrogen} = \frac{\text{RAM of N} \times 100}{\text{RFM of } NH_3}$$

$$= \frac{14 \times 100}{(14 + 3)}$$

$$= \frac{1400}{17}$$

$$= 82.35\%$$

chemistry calculations, reacting mass: to calculate this you multiply the *relative atomic mass* or *relative formula mass* by the number of atoms/molecules of that substance in a balanced equation of a chemical reaction.

EXAMPLE

In a blast furnace, iron(III) oxide is reduced by carbon monoxide:

$$Fe_2O_3 + 3CO \longrightarrow 2Fe + 3CO_2$$

Calculate the mass of iron that could be obtained from 32 000 tonnes of iron(III) oxide.

● First calculate proportion of iron in iron(III) oxide:

$$= (2 \times 53)/(2 \times 53) + (3 \times 16)$$

$$= 0.7$$

● Then calculate this proportion of the given mass of iron(III) oxide:

$$= 0.7 \times 32\ 000 \text{ tonnes}$$

$$= 22\ 400 \text{ tonnes}$$

chemistry calculations, relative atomic mass (RAM): this is simply mass of an atom of an element compared with the mass of a hydrogen atom. Being a ratio it has no units.
- The symbol for RAM is A_r.
- Examples are: H = 1, O = 16, Cl = 35.5.
- You will always be given the A_r of elements, either in a data book or in the question itself.

chemistry calculations, relative formula mass: this is the sum of all the *relative atomic masses* (A_r) in the formula of a substance. It has the symbol M_r.

EXAMPLE
Calculate the relative formula mass (M_r) of iron(III) oxide (Fe_2O_3).
Add (the A_r of iron × number of atoms of iron) to (the A_r of oxygen × the number of atoms of oxygen).
   = $((2 \times 56) + (3 \times 16))$
   = 160

chemical effects of a current: passing a current through a liquid causes the release of a substance(s). This is the basis of *electrolysis*, which is a very important production method in industry (e.g. for producing chlorine).
- One effect is the release of substances at the *electrodes* when a current is passed through an *electrolyte*.
- Electrolytes are solutions of *ionic compounds* or melted ionic compounds.
- The current in an electrolyte is carried by movement of ions towards the electrodes.
- At the electrodes the ions may be deposited or released. For example, copper is deposited from copper sulphate solution onto the cathode, and chlorine is released from sodium chloride solution at the anode.

chloride is the *ion* formed when a chlorine atom gains an electron:
   $Cl + e^- \longrightarrow Cl^-$
- Test for chlorides: they give a white precipitate of silver chloride when mixed with silver nitrate solution.

chlorine (Cl) is a greenish-yellow gas.
- Chlorine is a *halogen*.
- It is a non-metallic element.
- It is in Group VII of the periodic table.
- It consists of Cl_2 *molecules*, which is made up of pairs of chlorine *atoms*.

chlorine, manufacture of: chlorine is made by the electrolysis of brine (sodium chloride solution). (See *brine, electrolysis of.*)

chlorine, reactions of: in reaction, chlorine:

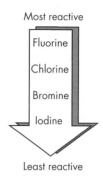

Most reactive

Fluorine

Chlorine

Bromine

Iodine

Least reactive

- forms *ionic salts* with metals, e.g. sodium chloride (NaCl)
- forms *molecular compounds* with other non-metals, e.g. chlorine oxide (Cl_2O)
- is more reactive than bromine but less reactive than fluorine
- is less reactive than fluorine because its outer *electron energy level* is higher than that of fluorine so it finds it less easy to gain an electron.

chlorine, uses of: chlorine is used mainly as *bleach* and disinfectant.

- The active ingredient in household bleach is sodium hypochlorite (NaOCl) solution.
- Chlorine dioxide (ClO_2) solution is used as a bleach in the paper industry.
- Chlorine gas is used as a disinfectant in swimming pools and for the public water supply.

chlorophyll gives green plants their colour and enables them to manufacture food.

- Chlorophyll is the green pigment found in the *chloroplasts* of plant cells.
- In *photosynthesis* it absorbs light energy and converts it into chemical energy.

chloroplasts are the parts of a plant cell where food is manufactured.

- Chloroplasts are disc-shaped structures found in green plant cells.
- There are usually 40–50 per cell.
- Chloroplasts contain *chlorophyll*.
- They are where all the reactions of *photosynthesis* take place.

cholesterol: a fatty material found in the blood system and the brain – too high a level in the blood can lead to diseases of the blood vessels.

- Cholesterol is an essential material in the manufacture of many materials (e.g. sex hormones).
- High levels of cholesterol may appear in the blood if the diet contains too much fat.
- High blood levels may lead to deposits of fatty materials in the walls of blood vessels.

● These deposits narrow the blood vessels, increasing the risk of heart attacks and strokes.

chromatography is a method of separating compounds based on the different rates at which substances spread on a support such as paper. An example is separating the dyes in ink.

In paper chromatography:

● drops of the mixture of compounds are placed near the bottom of the paper and allowed to dry
● the bottom of the paper is dipped in a suitable solvent
● as the solvent moves up the paper the different compounds move at different speeds
● drops of marker substances are sometimes used to identify compounds from the mixture.

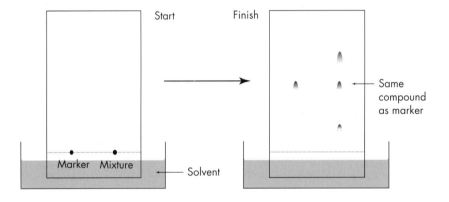

chromosome: where genetic information is stored in cells. All the information needed for you to develop from a tiny, fertilised egg is contained on 46 microscopic chromosomes.

● A chromosome is a thread-like structure which carries the *genes* that control *characteristics*.
● It is found in the *nuclei* of plant and animal cells.
● Chromosomes are usually present in pairs.
● Bacteria have chromosomes, but do not have nuclei.
● Chromosomes are copied before a cell divides.
● In most species the number of chromosomes in a *gamete* (sex cell) is half the number in a body cell.
● A gamete contains one member of each pair of chromosomes.

cilia are the microscopic, hair-like projections from the surface of a cell, important in moving things along surfaces inside the body.

- In the breathing organs, cilia move the *mucus* that traps microbes towards the throat.
- Smoking tobacco may paralyse these cilia.
- In some aquatic animals cilia are used to create feeding currents.
- Some unicellular organisms use cilia for locomotion.

ciliary muscles are the muscles near the front of the eye used in focusing. They work by changing the shape of the lens rather than moving the lens backwards and forwards as in a camera.
- They are attached to the *suspensory ligaments*.
- To focus on near objects the ciliary muscles contract – this reduces the tension in the suspensory ligaments and the lens becomes more spherical.
- When the eye is focused on distant objects the ciliary muscles are relaxed.

circuit, parallel: a circuit in which the *electron* flow is shared between components wired in parallel with each other. You have to know the differences between series circuits and parallel circuits.
In a parallel circuit:
- some electrons flow through one *resistor* and others flow through other resistors
- the *current* which flows through each resistor depends on the size of the resistors – the smaller the resistance the greater its share of the current

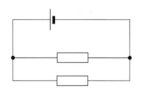

- the total current through the whole circuit is the sum of the currents passing through the resistors
- there is the same *potential difference* across each resistor.
(See also *circuit, series*.)

circuit, series: a circuit in which all the *electrons* flow through every component. You have to know the differences between series circuits and parallel circuits.
In a series circuit:
- all the electrons flow through all *resistors*
- therefore the same *current* flows through each resistor
- the total *potential difference* of the *cell* is shared between the resistors.
(See also *circuit, parallel*.)

circuit, symbols: you have to remember the most common symbols used in electrical circuit diagrams, which are shown on the following page.

Conductors crossing with no connection		Transformer	
Junction of conductors		Ammeter	
Normally open switch		Milliammeter	
Normally open push switch		Voltmeter	
Normally closed switch		Fuse or circuit breaker	
Normally closed push switch		Fixed resistor	
Primary or secondary cell		Variable resistor	
Battery of cells		Heater	
Power supply		Thermistor	
Light dependent resistor (LDR)			

circuit breaker: a safety device in an electric circuit used to protect humans and the circuit itself from damage.

● It is effectively a switch used in place of a *fuse* to disconnect the supply voltage to a circuit if a fault develops and an excessive *current* flows.

TYPES OF CIRCUIT BREAKER

● An *electromagnetic* switch which operates when a current flowing through a coil produces a magnetic field strong enough to attract an iron rod which in turn causes a break in the circuit.

● A bimetal strip circuit breaker operates when the heating effect of a current flowing through the strip causes it to bend away from a contact and thus break the circuit.

classification of species: the way in which organisms are divided into groups. Most syllabuses do not now require you to know the names of the different groups, but you need to know that differences between groups of organisms have come about by *evolution*.

● Starting with large groups such as 'animals' , organisms are divided into smaller and smaller groups ending with individual species.

● Classification may also take into account how organisms have evolved.

clone: a group of individuals which are genetically identical. It is now possible to create clones of many types of organism, but there is controversy as to whether we should create human clones. You should be able to explain the pros and cons of using cloning techniques.
- Clones are produced by *asexual* (or vegetative) *reproduction*.

Cloning methods include:
- taking cuttings from plants
- tissue culture – using small groups of cells from part of an organism
- embryo transplants – splitting up embryos into groups of identical cells then transplanting these into host mothers
- transferring identical nuclei or identical DNA into eggs from which the original nuclei have been removed.

clot: a solid deposit produced by the blood at the site of a wound to stem bleeding and prevent infection. (See *blood, clotting*.)

coal is a solid fuel which, in the UK, is used mainly in power stations.
- Coal consists largely of *carbon*.
- It is a fossil fuel.
- It is a *non-renewable energy resource*.
- It formed hundreds of millions of years ago.
- It formed in the absence of oxygen by the action of heat and pressure on the remains of plants and animals.
- It usually contains sulphur, resulting in the production of *sulphur dioxide* which leads to *acid rain*.
- It contributes to the *greenhouse effect* when burned, since carbon dioxide is produced.

coke is a solid fuel made by heating *coal* to very high temperatures. In the UK it is used mainly in industry.
- Coke is a much purer form of carbon than coal.
- It is a *non-renewable energy resource*.
- It is used mainly in *blast furnaces* to produce iron.

combustion: the rapid *oxidation* of a substance. (See also *burning*.)

comet: an object made up of ice and rock that orbits the Sun. Comets are not often seen because their orbits rarely bring them close to the Sun. Typical comets have:

- a very elliptical orbit
- a luminous tail when close to the Sun.

community: all the populations of animals and plants that live together in a particular place (*habitat*).

- One example is a woodland where there are populations of trees, shrubs and herbs and the animals that depend on these.
- The organisms in a community can be arranged into *food chains* and *food webs* which show their feeding relationships.

commutator: a slit metal ring mounted on the *armature* of an *electric motor* or *generator*.

Its main effect is to reverse the flow of the current in the coils of the motor or generator.

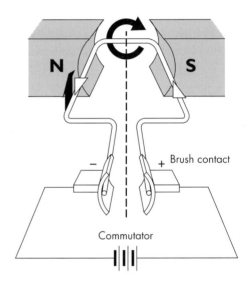

- In a direct current motor the effect of the commutator is to continually reverse the direction of the current flowing through the coils of the armature.
- In a generator the effect of the commutator is to continually reverse the direction of the current flowing from the generator to the external wires.

competition occurs when there are not enough resources to go round the organisms in a *community*.

PLANTS MAY COMPETE WITH EACH OTHER FOR:

- space
- light
- water
- mineral ions.

ANIMALS MAY COMPETE WITH EACH OTHER FOR:

- food
- shelter
- breeding space.

Competition is important in *evolution* by *natural selection*. The most successful competitors are most likely to survive, breed and pass their genes onto the next generation.

compound: a substance in which *atoms* of two or more *elements* are chemically combined by *bonding*. You need to know the differences between *atoms, elements* and *compounds*.
- *Ionic bonding* occurs when atoms gain and lose electrons to form ions.
- *Covalent bonding* occurs when atoms share electrons.

compound, covalent: a compound formed when *atoms* share electrons (see *bonding, covalent*).
- Examples include ammonia (NH_3) and methane (CH_4).
- Covalent compounds have low melting and boiling points because the forces between the *molecules* are weak.
- They do not conduct electricity because the molecules have no overall charge.

compound, ionic: a compound formed when *atoms* gain and lose electrons to form *ions* (see *bonding, ionic*).
- Examples include sodium chloride (NaCl) and aluminium oxide (Al_2O_3).
- Ionic compounds have high melting and boiling points because of the strong forces between ions.
- They conduct electricity when melted or in solution because their ions carry charges.

compression: part of a *longitudinal wave* – like the part of a 'slinky' where the coils are close together.
- It is represented by the part of a *sound* wave where the particles that transmit the wave are very close together, as opposed to *rarefaction* where the particles are further apart.
- The distance between two adjacent regions of compression is the wavelength of a sound wave.

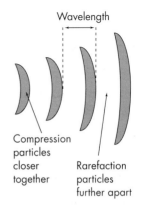

Wavelength

Compression particles closer together

Rarefaction particles further apart

concentration gradient: the difference in concentration of a substance between two areas, it is the reason for much of the movement of materials into and out of living cells.

X   Y

- There will be a net movement of molecules from Y towards X.
- To make molecules move from X to Y (against the concentration gradient) requires an external source of energy.

condensation is the changing of a gas into a liquid, e.g. during the formation of dew. You need to be able to explain condensation in terms of the movement of particles.
Condensation happens when gas is cooled and:
- the gas particles lose energy
- the distance between the particles becomes smaller
- the attractive forces between the particles become larger.
Cooling devices called condensers are used to condense gases in chemical processes (e.g. *fractional distillation*).

condensation reaction: a reaction where two *molecules* of the same type combine with the loss of a small molecule such as water. Many *polymers* such as nylon and the large molecules that make up our bodies are made by condensation reactions.
- One example is: glucose + glucose $\longrightarrow$ maltose + water.
- Glucose molecules are added to the ends of the molecule in the same way until a very long molecule of starch is formed.

conditioning is a simple form of learning; much of our learning as very young children is by conditioning.
- Conditioning was discovered by a scientist called Pavlov.
- In one experiment he rang a bell every time he gave food to dogs.
- After repeating this many times the dogs would produce saliva every time he rang the bell, whether or not he gave them food.
- The dogs had learned to associate the sound of the bell with being fed.

conduction, electricity: the movement of charged particles through a material which allows the transfer of electrical energy from place to place.
- In solids an electric current is the movement of *electrons* through the material.
- The easier it is for electrons to move the better a conductor the material is.

- Electrons move from negative to positive, not from positive to negative as early scientists thought (see *conventional current*).
- In liquids the current is carried by movement of *ions*.
- Negatively charged ions move towards the *anode*, positively charged ions towards the *cathode*.

conduction, heat: the transfer of thermal energy through a substance without the substance itself moving (e.g. the transfer of thermal energy through the base of a pan to the liquid inside). Make sure you know the differences between *conduction*, *convection* and *radiation*.
- Metals are generally good conductors of thermal energy.
- Most liquids are poor conductors of thermal energy.
- Gases are very poor conductors.
- In a conductor, thermal energy is transferred quickly from particles to their neighbours.
- Metals are good conductors because they have *free electrons*.
- When energy is transferred to free electrons their *kinetic energy* increases and they move through the metal, transferring their energy quickly to neighbouring electrons.

cones: nerve cells in the eye which enable us to see things in colour.
- Cones are the *receptor* cells for colour vision.
- They are located mainly in the region of the *fovea* (yellow spot) of the *retina* of the eye.
- They only work in bright light (*rods* work in dim light).

conglomerate: a rock composed mainly of stones, e.g. pebbles.
Conglomerate is:
- a *sedimentary* rock
- formed under pressure when pebbles and smaller particles are cemented together to make a rock.

conjunctiva: a thin membrane that protects the front of the eye.
- It produces mucus to keep the front of the eye moist.
- It sometimes becomes infected by microbes resulting in the disease conjunctivitis.
- Conjunctivitis is a contagious disease passed on by, for example, two people sharing a towel.

conservation of energy: energy cannot be created or destroyed, only transferred from one form into another. When we 'use' energy we do not lose it – it merely spreads around into the surroundings.

- You should know the different forms of energy: *light, sound, thermal, electrical, chemical, nuclear, kinetic* and *potential*.
- You should be able to describe devices that transfer one form of energy into another (e.g. an electric light bulb transfers electrical energy into light energy and thermal energy).
- In energy transfers, only some of the energy is transferred as useful energy; the rest is 'lost', usually as thermal energy.
- The proportion of useful energy transferred by a device is known as its *efficiency*.

constrict: become narrower; the opposite of *dilate*. Be careful not to confuse constrict and dilate when describing changes in the cross-section of *blood vessels*.

- *Arteries* and arterioles have muscle in their walls which can contract to make these vessels narrower.
- When a blood vessel constricts, the rate of blood flow through it is reduced.
- When the *pupil* of the eye constricts it allows less light into the eye.

Dilated   Constricted

constructive boundary: where the plates which make up the Earth's *crust* are moving apart and new rock is being added to the crust. You need to know the differences between constructive boundaries and *destructive* boundaries.

- These boundaries are mainly on the floors of the oceans.
- *Magma* (hot molten rock) rises to fill the gap and produces new crust.
- The main rock produced in the new crust is *basalt*.

consumer: an organism that eats other organisms. You are a consumer whether you eat a potato or a burger.

- Consumers that eat plants are called primary consumers or *herbivores*, e.g. rabbits, cows.
- Consumers that eat primary consumers are called secondary consumers or *carnivores*, e.g. foxes, lions.

contact process: an industrial process for the manufacture of *sulphuric acid*.

Sulphur is burned in air:
$$S(s) + O_2(g) \longrightarrow SO_2(g)$$
sulphur + oxygen $\longrightarrow$ sulphur dioxide

Sulphur dioxide is mixed with oxygen then passed over a vanadium catalyst at 500°C to form sulphur trioxide:
$$2SO_2(g) + O_2(g) \rightleftharpoons 2SO_3(g)$$
sulphur dioxide + oxygen $\rightleftharpoons$ sulphur trioxide

The sulphur trioxide is passed through 98% sulphuric acid – the sulphur trioxide reacts with the water in the acid to produce sulphuric acid:
$$SO_3(g) + H_2O(l) \longrightarrow H_2SO_4(aq)$$
sulphur trioxide + water $\longrightarrow$ sulphuric acid

continental plate: part of the Earth's *crust* that makes up a continent. You need to know the differences between continental plates and *oceanic plates*.
- Continental plates are thicker and less dense than oceanic plates.
- Continental plates are made mainly of *granite*-type rocks.
- They move slowly due to *convection currents* in the Earth's *mantle* on which they float.
- When continental plates collide, mountain ranges form (e.g. the Alps and the Himalayas).

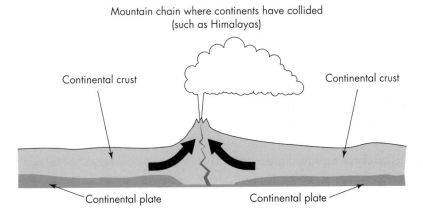

Mountain chain where continents have collided (such as Himalayas)

- All the continental plates were once joined to form a huge super-continent called *Pangea*.

continuous variation: variation in a *characteristic* such as height, where there is a smooth range of measurements. (Compare this with variation in, for example, tongue rolling ability, where individuals can be divided into just two groups – those who can roll their tongues and those who can't (see *discontinuous variation*).

- Continuous variation means that the *gene* controlling the characteristic exists as several *alleles*.
- It may also mean that the environment has a large effect on the characteristic.

contraceptive: something which is used to prevent pregnancy. Contraceptives include:

- barrier methods which prevent *sperm* reaching the *egg* (e.g. condoms fit onto the penis of the male, diaphragms fit on the neck of the womb of the female)
- birth control pills which may contain two female *hormones*; *oestrogens* which prevent the release of eggs by inhibiting the production of the hormone *FSH*, and *progesterone* which causes thick mucus to block the neck of the womb preventing the sperm from passing through
- IUDs (intrauterine devices) which are small coils of metal or plastic which are fitted inside the womb; these either prevent fertilisation or prevent the fertilised egg from attaching to the wall of the womb.

contraction: getting shorter, for example in muscles – the opposite of relaxation. Your biceps muscle contracts in order to bend your arm.

- Muscles can only do work by contracting – they can pull a bone but they cannot push it.
- Muscles often occur in pairs – one to pull the bone in one direction, the other to pull the bone in the opposite direction.

convection is the transfer of energy by movement of gases or liquids, for example when milk is warmed in a pan, thermal energy from the warm milk near the base of the pan is transferred to the rest of the milk mainly by convection. Make sure you know the differences between *conduction, convection* and *radiation*.

- In convection the liquid or gas flows from a region where the temperature is high to a region where the temperature is lower.

It moves because:

- particles move faster when they are hot.
- This causes expansion.
- The warmer regions are therefore less dense than the cooler regions
- so the warmer regions move up through the cooler regions.

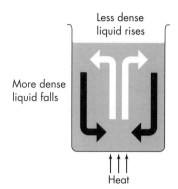

Less dense liquid rises

More dense liquid falls

Heat

---

conventional current: the direction that early scientists thought that a current flowed in a circuit.

- They thought that something flowed from positive to negative.
- We now know that *electrons* flow from negative to positive.

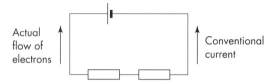

Actual flow of electrons

Conventional current

---

coordinator: the role of the *brain* or *spinal cord* in simple *reflex actions*.

- The path of impulses in a reflex action such as blinking is:

receptor (light-sensitive cell in eye) $\longrightarrow$ *coordinator* $\longrightarrow$ *effector* (muscle in eyelid)

- The coordinator is the brain for reflexes involving parts of the head.
- The coordinator is the spinal cord for reflexes involving parts of the body from the neck downwards.

Copernicus: a Polish scientist, who lived from 1473 to 1543 and proposed the Sun-centred theory of the universe. His theory stated that:

- the Sun is at the centre of the universe
- the Earth rotates once daily on its own axis and revolves round the Sun once a year
- the other planets revolve round the Sun
- other stars are in a fixed sphere.
- His theory replaced earlier theories which placed the Earth at the centre of the universe and was suppressed by the Church. It was not until the seventeenth century that *Newton* developed this theory further.

copper (Cu): a brown-red metal with widespread uses in everyday life.
- Copper is a good *conductor* of heat and electricity.
- It is a *transition* metal.
- It is therefore less reactive than metals in Groups I and II of the periodic table.
- It is important in many *alloys* (e.g. *brass*).

---

copper, extraction: because copper is relatively unreactive it exists as the free metal in many ores; it also occurs as sulphides. Copper ore is crushed and impurities removed by:
- flotation
- smelting (heating to a high temperature) during which the sulphur in copper sulphides is removed as sulphur dioxide.
- The liquid produced by smelting contains about 98% copper; this is purified by electrolysis (see *copper, purification*).

---

copper, purification: copper is purified by *electrolysis*.
- Impure copper is used as the *anode*; pure copper as the *cathode*.
- Copper *ions* change to copper atoms at the cathode.
- As these copper ions leave the solution they are replaced by copper ions formed at the anode.
- The ionic equation at the cathode is $Cu^{2+} + 2e^- \longrightarrow Cu$
- The ionic equation at the anode is $Cu - 2e^- \longrightarrow Cu^{2+}$

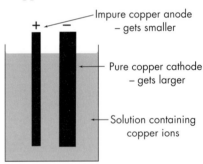

Impure copper anode – gets smaller

Pure copper cathode – gets larger

Solution containing copper ions

---

copper, reactions: copper is a *transition metal* and is therefore relatively unreactive.
- It reacts slowly with oxygen to form copper(II) oxide:

    copper + oxygen $\longrightarrow$ copper(II) oxide
    $2Cu(s) + O_2(g) \longrightarrow 2CuO(s)$
- It is near the bottom of the *reactivity series* of metals and can therefore be displaced from its salts by metals higher up the series (e.g. zinc):

    copper sulphate + zinc $\longrightarrow$ zinc sulphate + copper
    $CuSO_4(aq) + Zn(s) \longrightarrow ZnSO_4(aq) + Cu(s)$

---

copper, uses: the uses of copper depend on its good *conductivity* for both heat and electricity and the fact that it is not very reactive.

It is therefore used:
- in electrical wiring because of its high electrical conductivity and the fact that it is *ductile* (easily drawn into wires)
- to make cooking utensils because of its high thermal conductivity, because it is malleable (easily shaped) and because it is unreactive
- to make jewellery and ornaments because it is attractive and unreactive
- in many alloys, particularly in coinage, because it is unreactive.

copper sulphate is a blue (when hydrated) crystalline salt, formula $CuSO_4$.
- If the blue crystals are heated, water is given off, resulting in a white powder of anhydrous (without water) copper sulphate.
- If water is added to this powder it turns back to blue crystals of hydrated copper sulphate.

hydrated copper sulphate $\rightleftharpoons$ anhydrous copper sulphate + water
$$CuSO_4.5H_2O(s) \rightleftharpoons CuSO_4(s) + 5H_2O(g)$$
- This reaction is used as a test for water.

core (of the Earth): the central part of the Earth. No one has ever been there but scientists have worked out its structure from the behaviour of *seismic waves*. The Earth's core:
- is just over half the Earth's radius in diameter
- has a liquid outer part
- has a solid inner part
- is made mainly from iron with some nickel
- is very dense, 10–13 g/cm³
- is very hot; approximately 6000°C.

core, electromagnetism: part of a *transformer* or *electromagnet*.
- The core is usually made out of iron or steel.
- In a transformer the core connects the primary coil and the secondary coil by *induction* of a current.
- In an electromagnet the core increases the strength of the magnetic field produced by the coil.

cornea: the window at the front of the *eye* that allows light to enter.
- The cornea is the transparent part of the *sclera* (white) of the eye.
- Most *refraction* (bending) of light in the eye occurs at the junction between the cornea and air.
- If the cornea turns cloudy it can usually be replaced with a transplanted cornea – this is what is meant by 'donating your eyes'.

coronary artery: a blood vessel which supplies blood to the *heart* muscle itself, bringing with it the glucose and oxygen which the heart muscle needs to keep beating.

- Heart muscle is supplied with oxygen and nutrients by *capillaries* which branch off the coronary arteries.

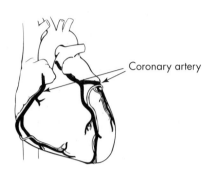

Coronary artery

- The coronary arteries branch off from the *aorta* – the main blood vessel of the heart.
- Blockage of a coronary artery results in a heart attack (*coronary thrombosis*) since the supply of oxygen and nutrients is cut off to parts of the heart muscle.

coronary thrombosis: blocking of the blood supply to some of the muscles of the heart, causing a heart attack.

- Fatty deposits build up on the inner wall of the *coronary arteries.*
- This reduces the blood supply to the heart muscle and may cause heart pain (angina).
- If part of this deposit breaks away it may block the artery in a narrower region, stopping the blood flow to part of the muscle.
- This part of the heart muscle may then die causing a heart attack.

corrosion: the wearing away of the surface of a metal due to a chemical reaction (e.g. rusting).

- Corrosion is usually due to the action of both water and oxygen.
- The metal is converted to an oxide or a hydroxide.
- It may be prevented by painting, or by galvanising (coating iron with a layer of zinc).

cotyledon: the part of a seed which stores food.

- Seeds need to store nutrients for growth until the leaves of the new plant open up and begin to *photosynthesise.*
- In many plants the cotyledons are brought above ground during *germination* and become the first leaf of the new plant.
- These 'seed leaves' begin to photosynthesise until the true leaves develop.

coulomb (C): the unit of electrical *charge*. You need to remember the following equation:

   charge (C) = current (ampere, A) × time (second, s)

- One coulomb is the amount of charge transferred when a current of one amp flows for one second.

covalent bond: the kind of bonding which occurs when atoms share *electrons* (see also *bonding*).

covalent giant structures are structures containing large numbers of atoms joined by *covalent bonds*. You need to know how the giant structures of diamond and graphite are related to their properties.

- In diamond each carbon atom forms four covalent bonds with its neighbours.
- This makes diamond very hard and gives it a very high melting point.

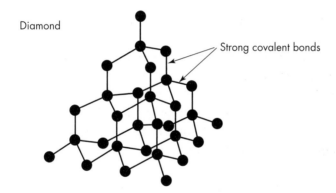

Diamond

Strong covalent bonds

- In graphite each carbon atoms forms three covalent bonds with its neighbours, forming sheets of carbon atoms that can slide over each other; this makes it a useful lubricant.

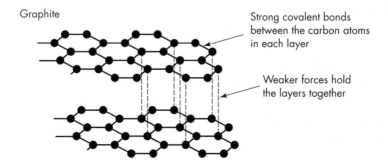

Graphite

Strong covalent bonds between the carbon atoms in each layer

Weaker forces hold the layers together

- There are also *free electrons* in graphite which makes it a good electrical *conductor* (see also *bonding*).

covalent simple molecular structures are substances with low melting and boiling points (e.g. ammonia, methane). You need to know why they are mainly gases or liquids.
- In these structures there are strong forces between the atoms, but very weak forces between the molecules – this is why they are mainly gases or liquids.
- They do not conduct electricity since they have no overall charge.
(See also *bonding*.)

cracking: making the products of crude oil into more useful substances.
- Cracking is the breaking down of long-chain molecules (hydrocarbons) into shorter, more useful molecules.
- It usually involves both heating and using a catalyst (see *crude oil, cracking of*).

Crick, Francis: a scientist, born in 1916, who was a member of the team which discovered the structure of *DNA*.
- Other members of the team were James Watson, Maurice Wilkins and Rosalind Franklin.
- They used techniques such as making X-ray diffraction patterns of crystals, a method originally developed by the *Braggs*.
- Their work led eventually to great advances in biotechnology.

critical angle: the smallest *angle of incidence* at which light is reflected from a surface rather than passing through it (see also *refraction*). For a glass/air surface this is approximately 42°.

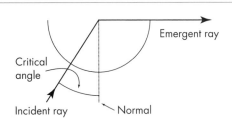

crude oil is the thick, black liquid from which we get the petrol to run our cars.
- Crude oil was formed in the Earth's *crust* from the remains of organisms which lived millions of years ago.
- It is a *fossil fuel*.
- It is a mixture of many compounds, making it an important raw material for the chemical industry.

Crude oil was formed by:
- the action of heat and pressure
- over millions of years
- on the remains of marine animals and plants
- in the absence of oxygen.

crude oil, cracking of distillation products: this is done to make the products of distillation more useful.
- Cracking is done by heating the high boiling point *fractions* from the distillation of crude oil as they are passed over a *catalyst*.
- Long-chain *hydrocarbon* molecules are broken down into shorter, more useful molecules, such as petrol.
- The process greatly increases the amount of petrol obtained from crude oil.

crude oil, extraction of: you need to know how oil has become trapped so that we can extract large quantities of it.
- Oil is less dense than water so it slowly rises up to the top of porous rock layers where it becomes trapped under non-porous rock layers.
- Gas is often trapped on top of the oil.
- We drill into the Earth's *crust*, into pockets of trapped oil.
- The pressure of gas present may be sufficient to force the oil to the surface, otherwise oil has to be pumped to the surface.

crude oil, fractional distillation of: this consists of separating the useful products from crude oil.
- The oil is first *evaporated* by heating.
- It is then allowed to *condense* at different temperatures in a fractionating column.

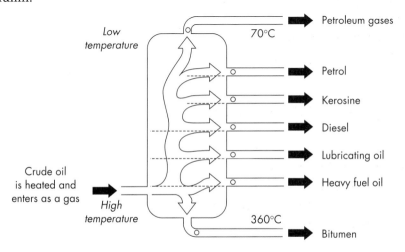

- The different liquids condensing at different temperatures are called fractions.
- The temperature in the column varies from about 400°C at the bottom to about 100°C at the top.
- Fractions condensing at low temperatures near the top of the column contain short-chain *hydrocarbons* such as petrol.
- The liquids condensing at high temperatures near the bottom of the columns contain larger, long-chain hydrocarbons such as diesel oil and lubricating oil.

crust: the solid, rocky, outer portion of the Earth; it is the only part of the Earth which humans have seen.
- The Earth's crust is about 100 km in depth.
- It floats on the *mantle*.
- It is composed largely of rocks; the main elements found in these rocks are oxygen, silicon, aluminium, iron, calcium , sodium, potassium and magnesium.

crustaceans are animals such as shrimps, crabs and woodlice.

CHARACTERISTICS OF CRUSTACEANS

- exoskeleton (external skeleton)
- body divided into segments
- each segment has a pair of jointed limbs
- the head bears a pair of antennae (feelers) and a pair of compound eyes

cryolite: a mineral used in the manufacture of *aluminium*.
- It is used to dissolve *alumina*, which is the aluminium ore.
- It has a lower melting point than alumina, therefore it saves energy used for heating in the manufacture of aluminium.

crystal: the structure formed when a liquid cools slowly to form a solid or when a hot, saturated solution is cooled.
- Crystals have a regular shape caused by a regular arrangement of particles within the crystal.
- *Ionic compounds* form crystals with very high melting points because of the very strong ionic bonds between the ions.

crystallisation: a process which forms crystals when a substance or a solution is cooled. You should know how the rate of cooling affects the size of crystals, both in the laboratory and when *igneous* rocks are formed.

- Rapid cooling leads to small crystals.
- Slow cooling leads to large crystals.
- Crystals may form in a saturated solution if the solution is 'seeded' with a small crystal.

Curie, Marie: a French scientist (1867–1934) who, with her husband, discovered that uranium was *radioactive*. The Curies:
- discovered the elements polonium and radium
- were the first scientists to realise that radioactive elements disintegrate and change (transmute) into other elements.
- Unfortunately Marie Curie died due to the effects of radiation, which were unknown when she began her work.

current is the flow of *electrons* through a *conductor* (a material that allows this flow). You should know how a current flows through a wire and how it flows through a liquid containing *ions*.
- Where the current flows through wires, electrons flow from the negative terminal to the positive terminal.
- Early scientists thought that the current flowed from the positive to the negative – this is known as *conventional current*.
- A current that flows in one direction is known as a *direct current* (d.c.).
- A current that flows alternately in both directions is called an *alternating current* (a.c.).
- The unit of current is the *ampere*, symbol A.
- Current in a conducting liquid is carried by the movement of *ions* (see *electrolysis*).

cuticle: a skin that reduces the rate of *evaporation* of water from an organism, so helping it to conserve water. Types of cuticle include:
- the waxy covering on plants, often very thick in those that live in dry conditions
- the outer part of human skin, which consists of several layers of dead cells.

cuttings: used to produce plants that are identical to the parent plant (*clones*), quickly and cheaply.
- A cut-off part of a plant stem or leaf will often produce roots first and then a new plant.
- The end of the cutting is often dipped in *hormone* powder to speed up root formation.
- Cuttings are an example of *asexual* (vegetative) *reproduction*.

• New plants obtained in this way are identical to the parent because they contain identical genetic information; every cell division is by *mitosis*, which replicates the genetic information.

cystic fibrosis is a hereditary disease that affects the lungs and pancreas.
• Humans with the condition produce a thick liquid called *mucus* that blocks the lungs and pancreas.
• It is caused by a *recessive allele* c.
• People with the condition are *homozygous* recessive cc.
• People *heterozygous* for the allele, Cc, are known as *carriers*; they do not suffer from the disease.
• If two carriers have a child there is a 25% chance that the child will inherit the disease and a 50% chance that the child will be a *carrier*.

PUNNETT SQUARE FOR THESE POSSIBILITIES

		Gametes – parent 1	
		C	c
Gametes – parent 2	C	CC	Cc
	c	Cc	cc – inherits disease

cytoplasm is the part of a cell which does most of the cell's work. It is:
• where many of the chemical reactions to make new substances take place
• found in the cells of animals, plants and bacteria
• bounded by the *cell membrane*.

Dalton, John: a British scientist who lived 1766–1844. He developed the ideas that:

- each *element* was made up of its own type of *atoms*
- compounds contained different kinds of atoms
- different atoms had different weights.

However he thought that:

- atoms were solid spheres, rather like billiard balls
- atoms could not be divided.

We now know that atoms are far from 'solid' and contain *protons, neutrons* and *electrons*.

Darwin, Charles: a British scientist who lived 1809–1882. He was largely responsible for developing the theory of *evolution* by *natural selection*.

OBSERVATIONS

- Most organisms produce large numbers of offspring
- but populations remain fairly stable
- therefore there must be a struggle to survive.

THEORY

- Organisms show *variation*.
- Some variations make the organism better adapted to the environment.
- These better adapted organisms are more likely to survive to breed.
- Their offspring will inherit these variations.

MODERN VIEW

- Scientists working in this century have discovered mechanisms of variation and heredity which support Darwin's theory.

dating: finding out the age of fossils, rocks and minerals. Dating is used to give us information about the order in which rocks and organisms developed on Earth. Also used to date human remains and artefacts.

METHODS

- Before methods using radioactivity became available, scientists estimated the age of rocks by the sequence in which rocks developed, as seen in exposed layers of rock and the types of fossils they contained.

- Carbon-14 method:
  after an organism has died, the carbon-14 (radioactive carbon) in its body breaks down at a known rate, but because of the rate of breakdown this method can only be used for remains up to about 50 000 years old.
- Rubidium–strontium method:
  this depends on the decay of rubidium-87 to strontium-87 and is used to date *igneous* and *metamorphic* rocks.
- Uranium–lead method:
  this depends on the decay of uranium to lead; uranium has a very long half-life so this method is useful for estimating the age of igneous rocks.

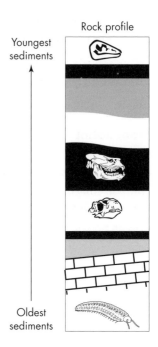

Rock profile

Youngest sediments

Oldest sediments

Davy, Humphrey: a British scientist (1775–1829), most famous for his experiments on electrolysis in which he:
- was the first person to isolate sodium and potassium
- discovered boron
- showed that diamond was a form of carbon.
- He also showed that it is hydrogen that gives acids their properties.

DDT: a chemical used to kill insects (insecticide) which is now banned in the UK.

ADVANTAGES

- very effective in killing insects
- saved millions of deaths from malaria

DISADVANTAGES

- non-*biodegradable* – it is not broken down by living organisms
- accumulates in *food chains* – the animals at the top of the food chains may accumulate lethal concentrations of DDT
- responsible for large reductions in populations of *predators* such as birds

---

deamination is what eventually happens to the *amino acids* in the protein you eat.

- Breakdown of excess amino acids takes place in the *liver* and results in the formation of *urea*.
- Urea contains nitrogen and is therefore known as a *nitrogenous* waste product. It is excreted by the *kidneys* in the *urine*.
- Be careful not to confuse the roles of the liver and kidney in producing and getting rid of urea.

decay, biological: the breakdown of dead organisms and waste products is a natural recycling process and the reason why the Earth is not littered with the remains of dead animals and plants.
- *Bacteria* and *fungi digest* the dead and waste material using *enzymes* which pass out of their bodies.

CONDITIONS FAVOURING DECAY ARE:

- warmth
- moisture
- oxygen.

DECAY IS USEFUL BECAUSE:

- it makes nutrients such as mineral ions available for use by plants
- decay organisms can be used to break down sewage into less harmful materials.

decay, radioactive: the spontaneous disintegration of the nuclei of some elements – the cause of much of the *background radiation* on Earth. When an unstable nucleus splits up:
- it emits radiation
- a different atom – with a different number of protons – is produced.

EXAMPLES

- $^{238}_{92}$uranium decays to form $^{234}_{90}$thorium by emitting *alpha radiation* ($^{4}_{2}$helium nucleus); note that the *nucleon number* is reduced by 4 and the *proton number* by 2 when an atom loses an alpha particle.
- $^{234}_{90}$thorium decays to form $^{234}_{91}$proactinium by emitting *beta radiation* (an electron); note that the proton number is reduced by 1 when an atom loses a beta particle, but the nucleon number remains the same. This is because a proton disintegrates to form a neutron and a beta particle.

decibel (dB): the unit, symbol dB, used to measure sound intensity.
- When the intensity of a sound doubles, it increases by 10 dB on the decibel scale.

- Decibel meters are used in industry and near airports to monitor sound pollution.
- Human conversations reach about 70 dB and a jet plane taking off registers about 140 dB, so the noise from the jet plane sounds about 128 times louder than the conversation (80 dB = 2×, 90 dB = 4×, 100 dB = 4× etc. ...).

decomposition, electrolytic: the breakdown of a chemical (either molten or dissolved) when an electric current is passed through it. Electrolytic decomposition is very important in many industrial processes (see *aluminium, production of; brine, electrolysis of; copper, purification of*).

- An example is the electrolytic breakdown of molten lead bromide:
    lead bromide $\longrightarrow$ lead + bromine
- at the anode bromide ions each lose an electron and bromine molecules are formed:
    $2Br^-(aq) - 2e^- \longrightarrow Br_2(g)$
- at the cathode lead ions each gain two electrons to form lead atoms:
    $Pb^{2+}(aq) + 2e^- \longrightarrow Pb(s)$

decomposition, thermal is the breakdown of a chemical when it is heated. It is important in many industrial processes (e.g. the production of cement). When calcium carbonate is heated it decomposes to form calcium oxide and carbon dioxide:

calcium carbonate $\longrightarrow$ calcium oxide + carbon dioxide
$$CaCO_3(s) \longrightarrow CaO(s) + CO_2(g)$$

demagnetisation: the destruction of magnetism in a piece of iron or steel.

- In magnetised iron, groups of iron atoms called domains (see *magnetism*) line up parallel to each other.
- This arrangement can be destroyed in three ways: by hammering the iron, by heating the iron to above 800°C or by passing an *alternating current* through it.

denature: to alter the properties of a substance. A common example is the change in egg white to a solid when an egg is boiled.

- Denaturation usually means that the compound will no longer carry out its function.
- Enzymes have complex three-dimensional shape, part of which is the *active site*.
- If human enzymes are heated to above 45°C or placed in solutions which are too acid or alkaline, the shape of the enzyme molecule changes and this alters the shape of the active site so the enzyme will then be inactive.

- Many enzymes used in industrial processes can withstand temperatures much higher than 45°C.

denitrifying bacteria are microbes which convert nitrates in the soil into nitrogen gas which escapes into the atmosphere (see *nitrogen cycle*). Farmers try to keep the activity of these bacteria to a minimum.
- These bacteria thrive in soil which is poorly drained, where there is little oxygen.
- They decrease soil fertility because crops need nitrates for healthy growth.

density: mass per unit volume of a substance, that is the mass of a standard volume. The more dense a substance, the 'heavier' it feels.
- Units are usually g/cm^3 or kg/m^3.
- The density of water is 1 g/cm^3.
- Density is calculated by dividing the mass of a body by its volume.

EXAMPLE
A piece of iron has dimensions 5 cm $\times$ 4 cm $\times$ 2 cm and a mass of 320 g. Calculate its density.

$$\begin{aligned} density &= mass/volume \\ &= 320 \text{ g}/(5 \times 4 \times 2) \text{ cm}^3 \\ &= 320 \text{ g}/40 \text{ cm}^3 \\ &= 8 \text{ g/cm}^3 \end{aligned}$$

depressant: any drug which slows down the nervous system.
- Alcohol is a depressant so it slows down our reactions – that is why it is not safe to drive after drinking alcohol.
- Alcohol in small quantities depresses inhibitions which is why many people drink alcohol at parties.

destructive boundary: a region where two plates of the Earth's crust collide and one is forced underneath the other. Mountains and volcanoes are often formed at destructive boundaries. You need to know the differences between destructive boundaries and *constructive boundaries*.
- A destructive boundary occurs where *oceanic plates* and *continental plates* collide.
- The thinner, denser oceanic plate is forced under the thicker, less dense continental plate.
- The continental plate is often forced upwards to form mountains.
- As it is forced into the *magma* the rocks of the oceanic plate melt, which is why it is called a destructive boundary.

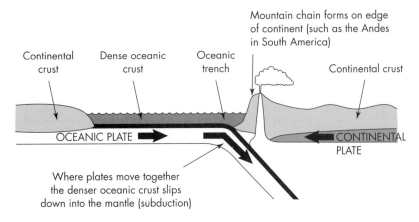

Mountain chain forms on edge of continent (such as the Andes in South America)

Continental crust | Dense oceanic crust | Oceanic trench | Continental crust

OCEANIC PLATE ➡ CONTINENTAL PLATE

Where plates move together the denser oceanic crust slips down into the mantle (subduction)

- Magma is often forced out of the volcanoes which form at these boundaries.

detergent: a chemical which gets rid of dirt (e.g. soap powder and washing-up liquid).
- *Soaps* were the original detergents – they help water to dissolve greasy substances.
- Soapless detergents were developed in the middle of this century – they are better than soap for use where only *hard water* is available.

detritus feeder: an animal that feeds on dead or waste matter. Earthworms, for example, feed on dead leaves which have fallen to the ground. Detritus feeders are important in the natural recycling of materials.
- Detritus feeders are mainly animals such as earthworms and *arthropods*.
- Decomposition of dead matter occurs much more quickly if detritus feeders are present because they break up large pieces of material into smaller pieces which can then be digested by *bacteria* and *fungi*.

diabetes is a condition which results in high levels of sugar in the blood. It is caused when the *pancreas* does not make enough *insulin*.
- Insulin lowers blood sugar levels by stimulating the liver to convert glucose to *glycogen*.
- The condition is treated by restricting intake of *carbohydrates* and possibly by daily injections of insulin.
- Starchy foods are better than sugary foods for diabetics because they are digested and absorbed more slowly.

dialysis: separating materials by using a membrane which allows small molecules to pass through but not larger ones. The principle is used in kidney machines (see *kidney, artificial*).

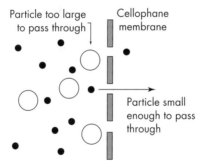

Particle too large to pass through

Cellophane membrane

Particle small enough to pass through

diamond: a precious stone; one form of the element *carbon*.

- Diamond is formed in the Earth by extreme heat and pressure.
- It is one of the hardest substances on Earth –10 on *Moh's harness scale*.
- It is very hard because of the strong covalent bonds between the carbon atoms.

(See also *covalent giant structures*.)

diaphragm: the sheet of muscle that we use to breathe.

The diaphragm separates the body cavity of mammals into two halves – the upper *thorax* from the lower *abdomen*.

DURING BREATHING IN:

- the diaphragm muscles contract
- causing the diaphragm to flatten
- so increasing the volume of the thorax
- and decreasing the pressure so that air moves into the lungs.

DURING BREATHING OUT:

- the diaphragm muscles relax
- the diaphragm returns to its dome shape
- so decreasing the volume of the thorax
- and increasing the pressure so that air moves out of the lungs.

diesel: a *fuel* produced from *crude oil*, used mainly in motor vehicles such as lorries and buses.

- Diesel is obtained from crude oil by fractional distillation (see *crude oil, distillation of*).
- Diesel has a higher boiling point than petrol since it consists of longer-chain *hydrocarbons* (about 15–10 carbon atoms).

diet, balanced: a diet that provides a body with just sufficient of all the necessary nutrients. Without a balanced diet we do not stay healthy.

CONTENTS OF A BALANCED DIET

- sufficient *carbohydrates* to provide energy needs
- sufficient *protein* for growth and/or repair of body tissues
- sufficient *fats* for cell membranes and insulation
- sufficient *vitamins* for health
- sufficient *mineral ions* (e.g. *calcium* and *iron*)
- sufficient *fibre*
- sufficient water

diffraction is the reason that radio and television signals cannot sometimes be heard in the shadow of a hill and sound sometimes cannot be heard in the shadow of a building.

- It is the spreading out of waves after passing through a gap or around the edge of an obstacle.

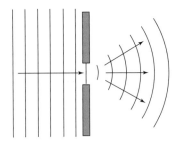 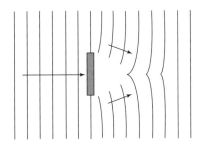

diffusion is the spreading out of a substance to fill all of the space available to it; it is the reason why everyone in a laboratory can quickly smell a gas produced in a single experiment.

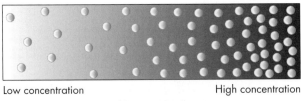

Low concentration   High concentration

Net movement

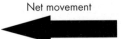

- Particles show a net movement from a region of high concentration to a region of low concentration.
- Particles move because they have energy – the more energy they have the faster the rate of diffusion.

digestion: the means by which food is broken down so that it can be absorbed by body cells.

- It is the breakdown of large, insoluble food molecules into smaller, soluble molecules that can be absorbed into the body/blood of the organism.
- Food may first be broken down into smaller pieces by teeth – this is physical rather than chemical digestion.
- Proteins are digested into amino acids.
- Carbohydrates are digested into sugars.
- Fats are digested into fatty acids and glycerol.

(See also *digestive enzymes* and *digestive system*.)

digestive enzymes: substances produced by the body to breakdown food into small, soluble molecules.

- Enzymes are produced by glands.
- They pass along ducts to mix with food.
- Enzymes produced by the stomach work best in acid conditions.
- All the other digestive enzymes work best in alkaline conditions.

Enzyme	Produced by	Action
Carbohdrase (amylase)	salivary glands pancreas small intestine	starch $\longrightarrow$ sugars (maltose)
Protease	stomach pancreas small intestine	protein $\longrightarrow$ amino acids
Lipase	pancreas small intestine	fat $\longrightarrow$ fatty acid + glycerol

digestive system: the organs which digest food and absorb the soluble products into the blood.

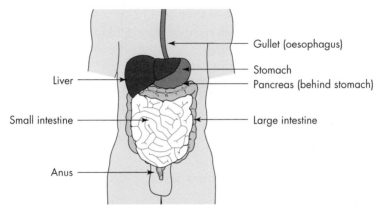

93

Organ	Job
Mouth	teeth and tongue break food into smaller pieces; digestion of starch begins
Salivary glands	produce saliva which contains *carbohydrase* enzyme
Oesophagus	transports food from mouth to stomach
Stomach	produces gastric juice which contains *protease* enzyme and hydrochloric acid (where protein digestion starts)
Pancreas	produces pancreatic juice which contains protease, carbohydrase and *lipase* enzymes
Liver	produces bile
Small intestine	produces intestinal juice which contains *protease, carbohydrase and lipase* enzymes; where digestion of carbohydrates, fats and proteins is completed and most soluble foods are absorbed into the bloodstream
Large intestine	where most water is reabsorbed into the blood; where *faeces* (waste matter) are produced
Anus	where faeces leave the body

dilate: get wider; the opposite of *constrict*.

- Blood vessels dilate when the muscles in their walls relax.
- When a blood vessels dilates the rate flow of blood flow through it is increased.
- When the *pupils* of the eye dilate it allows more light to enter the eye.

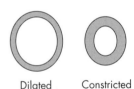

Dilated   Constricted

dinosaurs: a group of animals (*reptiles*) which appeared about 230 million years ago and became extinct about 65 million years ago. Some were the largest animals that have ever walked on land.

- Dinosaurs are known because of their *fossils*.
- They may have become extinct because they could not cope with the changes in climate that occurred.

diode: a device that allows an electric current to flow through it in one direction but not in the opposite direction. A computer 'chip' consists essentially of thousands of diodes.

USES

- to protect electrical equipment from damage, e.g. a battery being connected the wrong way round

- in circuits that convert *alternating current* into *direct current*

---

direct current (d.c.): an electric current that flows continuously in one direction, as opposed to an *alternating current* which is continually changing direction.
- Most generators (including the one on your bike) produce alternating current.
- A device such as a *diode* is needed to change alternating current into direct current.
- Cells and batteries produce a direct current.
- Direct current is the continuous flow of electrons from the cathode to the anode in a circuit.

---

discontinuous variation: the kind of variation where individuals can be placed into two (or a few) distinct groups, e.g. some people can roll their tongue, others cannot; eyes are brown or blue. Compare this with *continuous variation* where there is a smooth range of measurements, such as human weight or height.

---

disease, deficiency: a disease caused by something lacking in the diet rather than microbes, metabolic imbalance or genetic causes.

Deficiency disease	Caused by lack of	Symptoms
anaemia	iron	tiredness caused by low number of red blood cells
night blindness	vitamin A	unable to see in dim light
rickets	calcium or vitamin D	leg bones are soft and become deformed
scurvy	vitamin C	bleeding gums

---

disease, immunity: the reason why you do not necessarily catch an infectious disease (e.g. why you do not normally catch measles twice). Resistance to an infectious disease may occur:
- naturally after we have recovered from the disease (natural immunity)
- artificially, through immunisation (artificial immunity).

NATURAL IMMUNITY

- When *microbes* invade the body *white blood cells* (lymphocytes) eventually produce *antibodies* which kill the microbes.

- If the same microbes enter the body again, the white cells can quickly produce antibodies to kill them.

ARTIFICIAL IMMUNITY

- Dead or weakened microbes are introduced into the body; white blood cells (lymphocytes) eventually produce antibodies which can kill the microbes.
- If the actual disease microbes then enter the body, the white cells can quickly produce antibodies to kill them.

disease, inherited: a disease which is inherited from a person's parents rather than caused by microbes.

- An example of a disease caused by a *recessive allele* is *cystic fibrosis*. A child can only inherit the disease if both parents possess the recessive allele for the disease.
- An example of a disease caused by a *dominant allele* is *Huntington's disease*. A child can inherit the disease if only one parent possesses the allele for the disease.
- An example of a *sex-linked* disease is *haemophilia*. This disease is caused by a recessive allele carried on the *X chromosome* but not on the *Y chromosome*.

disease, transmission of: how we catch diseases caused by microbes. There are three main methods of catching diseases:

CONTAGIOUS DISEASES

- Diseases which you can catch by contact with someone else.
- The disease organisms (e.g. *bacteria, fungi* or *viruses*) are passed from one person to another by physical contact (diseases such as AIDS are spread by contact of the sex organs) or by using the same towel, for example.

AIR-BORNE DISEASES

- Passed on when microbes breathed out by an infected person are breathed in by another person.
- Examples are colds and flu where the virus is transmitted in tiny droplets of water passed into the air when an infected person coughs or sneezes.

FOOD- AND WATER-BORNE DISEASES

- Passed on when microbes pass out of an infected person's body in the faeces.
- They may then enter drinking water if faeces are not properly disposed of (e.g. cholera)
- They may be passed onto food via the infected person's hands if the hands are not washed after visiting the toilet (e.g. *Salmonella* food poisoning).

disinfectant: a substance used to destroys microbes, for example in toilets and drains. Disinfectants are usually much more concentrated than *antiseptics* and are therefore used to clean baths and sinks rather than to treat wounds.

dispersion is the splitting of light into its different colours – a rainbow represents natural dispersion.
- White light is a mixture of seven visible colours – red, orange, yellow, green, blue, indigo and violet in that order.
- These can be split up by passing white light through a prism.

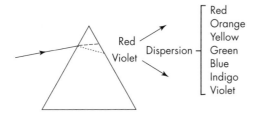

- Red light is bent (refracted) the least, violet the most because violet light is slowed down much more than red light as it passes from air into the prism.

displacement is how far something moves. It is:
- the amount by which an object is moved from its original position in a particular direction
- different from distance because it has <u>direction</u>
- a *vector* quantity.

displacement reaction of halogens occurs when one halogen displaces another halogen from a compound.
- Halogens become less reactive the further down Group VII they are.
- So halogens higher up the group can displace those lower down from their compounds.
  An example is where chlorine displaces iodine from potassium iodide solution:

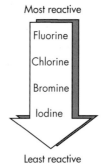

chlorine + potassium iodide $\longrightarrow$ potassium chloride + iodine

$$Cl_2(aq) + 2KI(aq) \longrightarrow 2KCl(aq) + I_2(s)$$

displacement reaction of metals occurs when one metal displaces another metal from a compound.

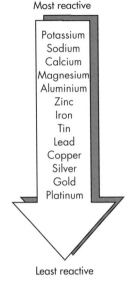

Most reactive

Potassium
Sodium
Calcium
Magnesium
Aluminium
Zinc
Iron
Tin
Lead
Copper
Silver
Gold
Platinum

Least reactive

- The more reactive metals can displace less reactive metals from their compounds.
- So metals higher up a *reactivity series* can displace metals which are lower down the series.
- An example of this is where aluminium will displace iron from iron oxide:

$$\text{aluminium} + \begin{matrix}\text{iron}\\\text{oxide}\end{matrix} \longrightarrow \begin{matrix}\text{aluminium}\\\text{oxide}\end{matrix} + \text{iron}$$

$$2Al(s) \quad +Fe_2O_3(s) \longrightarrow Al_2O_3(s) \quad +2Fe(s)$$

- Similarly magnesium will displace copper from copper sulphate solution:

$$\text{magnesium} + \begin{matrix}\text{copper}\\\text{sulphate}\end{matrix} \longrightarrow \begin{matrix}\text{magnesium}\\\text{sulphate}\end{matrix} + \text{copper}$$

$$Mg(s) \quad +CuSO_4(aq) \longrightarrow MgSO_4(aq) \ + \ Cu(s)$$

distance–time graph: a graph that shows how far an object, travelling in a straight line, is from a particular point.

EXAMPLE OF A DISTANCE–TIME GRAPH FOR A MODEL ELECTRIC CAR

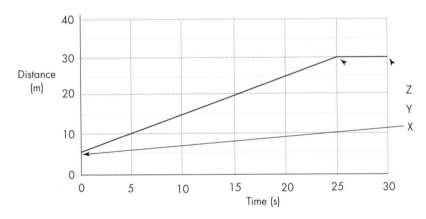

- Between X and Y the model car is moving at a steady speed – the graph is rising.
- Between Y and Z the car is stationary – the graph is horizontal.

EXAMPLE
To calculate speed from a distance time graph:
- work out the distance travelled between X and Y
    = (30 – 5) m = 25 m

- work out the time taken to travel this distance
    = (25 – 0) s – 25 s
- speed = distance travelled (m)/time taken (s)
    = 25 m/25 s
    = 1 m/s

---

distillation: separating a substance from a mixture by boiling the mixture to evaporate one of the substances then condensing it. An example is obtaining pure water from seawater.

- Distillation can only be used when the substances have different boiling points.
- The condenser usually has some method of cooling (e.g. running water) so that the vapour condenses quickly.
- Water can be separated from seawater by boiling seawater then condensing the pure water vapour – the salt in seawater does not evaporate.
- In distilling alcoholic spirits, alcohol has a lower boiling point than water so the vapour produced when the mixture boils contains more alcohol than water.

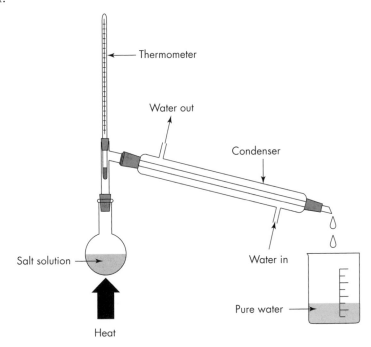

DNA (deoxyribonucleic acid): the chemical that carries the genetic code dictating the characteristics of organisms. All the information required for you to develop from an egg is carried as a simple '4-letter' code on the DNA molecules in your cells.

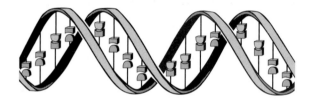

- DNA molecules carry coded information.
- DNA molecules are found in *chromosomes* (except in viruses).
- A *gene* is a section of a DNA molecule.
- The coded information in a gene determines the order in which amino acids are joined to produce a protein.
- In *genetic engineering* sections of DNA molecules are removed from the cells of one organism and inserted into the cells of another organism.

dominant: an *allele* of a *gene* is said to be dominant if it controls the development of a characteristic even when it is present on only one of the chromosomes in a pair. An example is the allele responsible for *Huntington's disease*.
- You can inherit Huntington's disease even if only one of your parents has the Huntington's allele.
- Dominant is the opposite of *recessive*, in which an allele controls development only when it is present on both chromosomes, for example the allele responsible for *cystic fibrosis*, where both parents need to carry the allele before you have a chance of inheriting it.

double bond: a bond where two atoms share two pairs of electrons, as opposed to a single bond where two atoms share one pair of electrons.
- Because the electrons are shared a double bond involves *covalent bonding*.
- Molecules containing double bonds are very reactive.
- They are said to be *unsaturated*, as opposed to *saturated* compounds, which have only single bonds.
- *Alkenes* such as *ethene* contain double bonds.

$$\begin{matrix} H & & & H \\ & \diagdown & & \diagup & \\ & & C = C & \\ & \diagup & & \diagdown & \\ H & & & H \end{matrix}$$

double circulation: a circulation system in which blood flows from the heart to the lungs then back to the heart before being pumped to the rest of the organs (see *blood, circulation*).
- More efficient than single circulation found in, for example, fish, because blood is supplied to the body organs at high pressure.
- Double circulation is found in mammals.
- When blood is pumped to the lungs it loses pressure as it passes into the lung capillaries.

- Blood is returned to the heart to be repressurised before passing through the arteries to the rest of the body organs.

double glazing: two sheets of glass, sealed around the edges, with an air gap between them. It reduces the heat loss through windows by up to 50%.

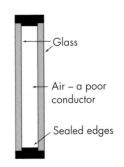
Glass
Air – a poor conductor
Sealed edges

- It works because the layer of air trapped between the panes is an *insulator* – gases are poor conductors of heat.
- Since double glazing is comparatively expensive to fit, cheaper methods such as loft insulation and cavity wall insulation are usually more cost-effective.

Down's syndrome is an inherited condition in which a person has 47 *chromosomes* rather than 46. The person does not develop normally, either physically or mentally. Down's syndrome cannot be cured, but modern approaches to the condition mean that there is no reason why the person should not live a long, fulfilling life.

- It is caused by a fault in the formation of an egg (during *meiosis*) which results in the egg having 24 rather than 23 chromosomes.
- This egg is fertilised by a sperm carrying the normal 23 chromosomes.

drug, contraceptive: 'the pill' – a drug taken by women designed to prevent pregnancy.

- Most contraceptive pills contain the hormone *oestrogen*.
- Oestrogen inhibits the production of the hormone *FSH* whose function is to stimulate production of eggs by the ovary.
- The woman does not release eggs and therefore cannot become pregnant.

drug, fertility: a drug which helps a woman to become pregnant.

- One type of fertility drug contains the hormone *FSH*.
- FSH stimulates eggs to mature in the woman's ovaries.
- It is given to women whose natural FSH levels are too low.
- Too high a dose of FSH may lead to multiple births.

drug abuse: taking drugs for reasons other than medical. Many drugs change the chemical processes in the body so that a person might become addicted to them and suffer withdrawal symptoms without them.

- Solvent abuse may lead to damage to the *liver, lungs* and *brain*, often causing death.
- Alcohol abuse may cause damage to the liver and brain.

- Smoking tobacco increases the risk of lung cancer, lung diseases such as *emphysema* and diseases of the heart and blood vessels.

ductile: able to be drawn into a fine wire without breaking. An example is the copper used to make electrical wiring, which is ductile as well as being a good electrical conductor.

dynamic equilibrium: the situation in a reversible reaction (symbol $\rightleftharpoons$ rather than $\longrightarrow$) in which the forward and backward reaction have the same rate.

- In some chemical reactions the products of the reaction can react to form the original reactants.
- When the rate of reaction is the same in both directions then the reactions are said to be in dynamic equilibrium.
- In the reaction A + B $\rightleftharpoons$ C + D at dynamic equilibrium, the rate of formation of C and D is the same as the rate of formation of A and B.
- The relative amounts of (A + B) and (C + D) in the equilibrium mixture depend on the external conditions.
- Industrial processes such as the *Haber process* are carried out in conditions which favour the production of products (C + D).

dynamo: a machine that converts kinetic (movement) *energy* into electrical energy – like the dynamo on your bike.

- A coil of wire is rotated in a *magnetic field* (or vice versa, as in a typical bicycle dynamo).
- As the wire cuts through the magnetic field a *voltage* is produced at the ends of the wire.
- This induced voltage is connected to a circuit by brush contacts.
- The current produced in the circuit is an *alternating current*.
- The size of the induced voltage can be increased by: increasing the speed of movement, increasing the strength of the magnetic field or increasing the number of turns of wire in the coil.

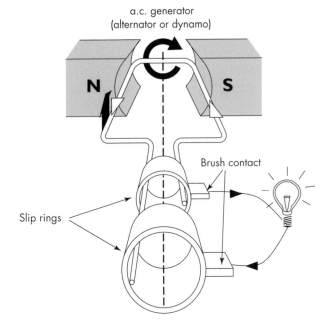

a.c. generator
(alternator or dynamo)

N

S

Brush contact

Slip rings

ear: the part of the body sensitive to sound and to balance. The ear contains receptors sensitive to:

- sound waves
- gravity
- movement.

Sound waves cause the ear drum to vibrate.

- These vibrations are transmitted to the inner ear by ossicles
- where they are detected by *receptor* cells that are sensitive to vibrations
- which send *nerve impulses* to the brain.

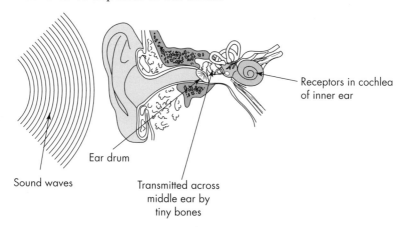

Receptors in cochlea of inner ear

Ear drum

Sound waves

Transmitted across middle ear by tiny bones

Earth, structure of: The Earth is divided into three main regions: the outer *crust*, the *mantle* and the inner *core*.

CRUST

- The crust is the solid, rocky, outer portion of the Earth.
- It is about 100 km in depth.
- It floats on the mantle.
- It is composed largely of rocks.

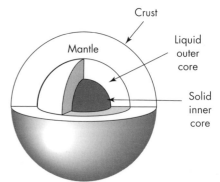

Crust

Mantle

Liquid outer core

Solid inner core

MANTLE

- The mantle is the molten rock (magma) extending almost half way to the centre of the Earth.
- It is extremely viscous (non-runny).
- Convection currents in the mantle cause movements of the plates which make up the crust.

CORE

- The core is the central part of the Earth.
- It is just over half the Earth's radius in diameter.
- Its outer part is liquid.
- Its inner part is solid.
- It is made mainly from iron with some nickel.

(See also *plate tectonics*.)

---

earth, electrical: a connection in an electric circuit that leads directly to the earth.

- Appliances with a metal case must be earthed because the metal case is a conductor of electricity.
- The earth pin of the plug is connected to the case via a yellow and green wire.
- If a fault in the appliance connects the case to the live supply, a very large current flows to earth and the *fuse* blows.
- This prevents the user getting a serious electric shock.

---

earthquake: vibrations in the Earth's *crust* caused when two of the plates which make up the crust suddenly slip past each other.

- The plates move due to *convection currents* in the *magma*.
- Movement of the plates is restricted by *friction*.
- When the plates suddenly move past each other shock waves are produced.
- These shock waves travel through the crust (see *seismic waves*).

---

echo: hearing a sound repeated after it has been reflected from a solid object (e.g. a wall or a submarine).

- Echoes can be used to calculate distances and to calculate the speed of sound.

EXAMPLE 1

Using echoes to calculate distance, in this example the depth of a submarine

A ship receives an echo in 0.2 seconds. How deep is the submarine?

(The speed of sound in water is 1500 m/s)

Equation: speed (m/s) = distance (m)/time (s)

Rearrange equation: distance = speed × time

= 1500 m/s × 0.2 s

= 300 m

Remember that the sound has travelled to the submarine and back, so divide the distance by 2: = 150 m

EXAMPLE 2

Using echoes to calculate the speed of sound

A boy stands 85 m from the wall. He hears an echo from the wall after 0.5 s. (Remember that the sound travels to the wall and back, so double the distance.)

Equation: speed (m/s) = distance (m)/time (s)

= 170 m/0.5 s

= 340 m/s

eclipse is when one object in the sky obscures another, e.g. the Moon obscures the Sun.

- In a solar eclipse the Moon comes between the Earth and the Sun forming a shadow of the Moon on Earth, where the Sun is obscured.

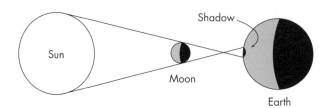

- In a lunar eclipse the Earth comes between the Sun and the Moon, casting a shadow of the Earth on the Moon.

ecosystem: a pond is an example of an ecosystem – the water and the mud form the *habitat* of this ecosystem and the organisms that live in the pond are the *community* of the ecosystem.

- Other examples of ecosystems are forest, seashore, desert and moorland.
- The organisms found there are adapted to live in that ecosystem.
- Ecosystems are affected by changes in conditions, e.g. temperature and rainfall.
- Many ecosystems are affected by humans. Human activities may pollute the ecosystem or remove resources from it, and when we build factories, homes, roads etc. we destroy ecosystems.

effector: if one of your fingers touches something hot you pull the finger away immediately. Pulling the finger away is a response and the arm muscles that bring about the response are called the effectors.
Effectors in animals are:
- muscles which contract to move parts of the body
- glands which produce *hormones* or *enzymes*.
- Most responses in plants occur by growth; the stem tip or the root tip is usually the effector.

efficiency is how good a machine is at transferring energy.
- Efficiency is the ratio of the amount of energy we get out of a device (output) to the amount of energy we put in (input).
- When energy is transferred, only part of it is transferred where it is wanted; the rest is wasted (transferred in a non-useful way). For example, an electric bulb is designed to transfer electrical energy into light energy, but much of the electrical energy is transferred as thermal energy.
- Efficiency is the fraction of the energy supplied to a device which is usefully transferred:

$$\text{efficiency} = \frac{\text{useful energy transferred by device}}{\text{total energy supplied to device}}$$

- There is no unit for efficiency as it is a ratio. Give the answer as a number only.
- You will usually be asked why the efficiency of a device is less than 1.0. It is because most devices waste energy by transferring it to the environment (*by conduction, convection* and *radiation*) and because any moving device will transfer energy as a result of *friction*.

egg: the reproductive cell produced by a female animal or the female part of a plant.
- Eggs and *sperm* (male reproductive cells) are called *gametes*.
- Eggs are usually produced by *meiosis* which means that eggs contain half the number of *chromosomes* of body cells, that is only one of each pair of the genes.
Eggs differ from sperms in that they are usually:
- bigger than sperm because they contain food reserves
- not motile – it is usually the sperm that swim to reach the eggs.

Einstein, Albert: a German-born scientist who lived from 1879 to 1955. He discovered the relationships between:

- energy and matter ($E = mc^2$ where E = energy, m = mass and c = velocity of light in a vacuum)
- space and time
- gravitation and acceleration.
- His theories were summarised in his theories of relativity which revolutionised the way that physicists regarded the universe.

elastic behaviour means behaving like an elastic band or a rubber.
- It involves returning to the original shape after being stretched or compressed.

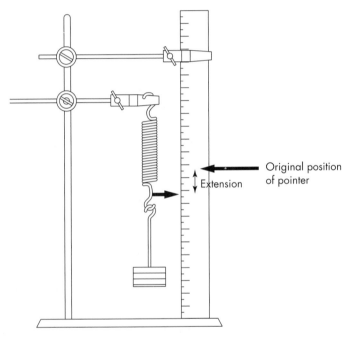

Extension

Original position of pointer

- The extension of a spring is directly proportional to the stretching force applied – this is known as *Hooke's law*.
- The steeper the slope of the graph the more elastic (stretchy) the material.

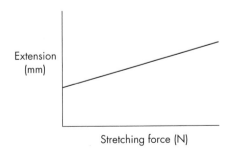

Extension (mm)

Stretching force (N)

elastic limit: the point at which elastic behaviour breaks down, as in a spring that has been stretched too far.

- If a very heavy stretching force is applied to an elastic material the material may not return to its original shape and its shape may be changed permanently.
- The limit to which the material can be stretched without being changed permanently is known as the elastic limit.

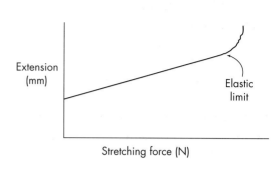

electric charge: see *charge*.

electric current: see *current*.

electric field: when charged particles are brought towards each other they exert a force on each other; this force is due to the electric force (called an electric field) around each particle.
- The charge on a particle is either positive or negative.
- Like charges repel so the particles move apart.
- Unlike charges attract so the particles move closer together.

electric meter: meter that measures how much electrical energy has been transferred by appliances.
The amount of electrical energy that has been transferred depends on:
- how long an appliance is switched on
- how fast the appliance transfers energy (the power of the appliance).
- The power of an appliance is measured in watts (W) or kilowatts (kW) 1 kW = 1000 W. The total amount of energy transferred is measured in kilowatt-hours (kWh), also called Units.
     energy transferred (kWh or Units) = power (kW) × time (h)
- Always remember to convert power to kilowatts and time to hours.

EXAMPLE
How many Units of energy are transferred by a 200 W lamp lit for 30 minutes?
     energy transferred (Units) = power (kW) × time (h)
                                          = 0.2 kW × 0.5 h = 0.1 Unit

- The cost of electricity is calculated by:
     total cost = number of Units × cost per unit

electric motor: see *motor (electric).*

electrical cell: see *cell, electrical.*

electricity: the effects caused by *charge.*
- If the charge is stationary its effects are known as *static electricity.*
- If the charged particles move then an electric *current* is said to flow.

electrode: the terminals used in *electrolysis.*
- They are used to connect an electrical power supply to a liquid which will conduct electricity (electrolyte).
- The electrode connected to the positive part of the supply is called the *anode.*
- The electrode connected to the negative part of the supply is called the *cathode.*
- Electrodes are often made of *graphite* or a low-reactive metal, e.g platinum.

electrolysis: the process of using an electric current to decompose a liquid or dissolved substance. Many important industrial processes depend on electrolysis (see *brine, electrolysis of*).
- A liquid which contains ions and conducts electricity is called an electrolyte.
- Electrolysis is only possible for ionic compounds.
- Negatively charged ions (*anions*) move towards the positive electrode (*anode*).
- Positively charged ions (*cations*) move towards the negative electrode (*cathode).*
- When ions reach electrodes they are deposited or released.

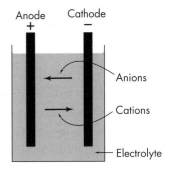

- The mass and/or volume of a substance deposited or released increases when either the current increases or the time for which the current flows increases.

electrolyte: a liquid which can be decomposed by electricity (e.g. brine – see *brine, electrolysis of*).
- Electrolytes contain *ions.*
- They are solutions of *ionic compounds* or molten electron compounds (see also *electrolysis*).

electrolytic decomposition: see *decomposition, electrolytic.*

electromagnet: a device used in moving iron or steel in electric bells, magnetic door catches and scrap yards.

- A soft iron core becomes magnetic when an electric current is passed through a coil of wire wound round it.
- The strength of an electromagnet may be increased by increasing the number of turns on the coil or increasing the size of the current passing through the coil.
- The electromagnet loses its magnetism when the current is switched off.
- Electric bells and magnetic door catches have springs to oppose the effect of the electromagnet.

electromagnetic induction: the means by which an electric current is produced in a generator; it is where our mains electricity comes from.

- When a magnet is moved into a coil of wire which is part of a complete circuit, a current is produced in the wire. This is called induction.
- If the magnet is moved out of the coil, the direction of the current is reversed.
- A current is only induced when the magnet (or the coil) is moving.
- Electricity is generated by rotating a coil of wire in a magnetic field or rotating a magnet inside a coil of wire (see *dynamo*).
- When a coil of wire cuts through a magnetic field a voltage is produced between the ends of the wire – it is this induced voltage that causes a current to flow if the wire is part of a complete circuit.

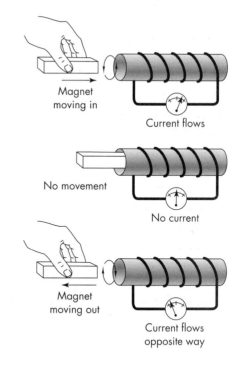

Magnet moving in

Current flows

No movement

No current

Magnet moving out

Current flows opposite way

- A changing magnetic field produces a induced voltage in a coil – this is how a *transformer* works.

electromagnetic radiation: waves (for example light and radio waves) which transfer energy.

- Electromagnetic waves can travel through a vacuum.
- They all travel at the same speed through space.
- The different types of waves have different wavelengths and different frequencies.
- The different types of radiation make up the electromagnetic spectrum.

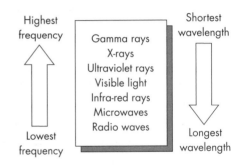

(See individual entries for radiation.)

electron: the smallest particle in an *atom*.

- Electrons are negatively charged particles.
- Atoms form chemical bonds by losing, gaining or sharing electrons.
- The chemical properties of elements depend on the arrangement of electrons (*electron configuration*) in their atoms.
- The flow of an electric current in a wire is due to the movement of electrons.
- Transfer of energy by conduction is mainly due to electrons.
- *Beta radiation* consists of electrons.

electron configuration is the reason why different elements have different properties.

- It is the pattern in which *electrons* are arranged in an *atom*.
- Electrons are arranged in energy levels in an atom.
- Electrons always occupy the lowest possible energy level.
- The lowest energy level can hold up to two electrons.
- The second energy level can hold up to eight electrons.
- The third energy level can hold up to eight electrons.
- An argon atom is shown opposite. All its energy levels are complete. Its electron configuration can be written as 2,8,8.
- The sodium atom opposite has the electron configuration 2,8,1.

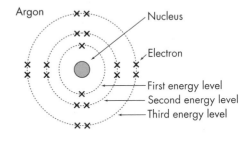

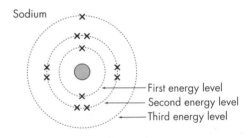

- You should be able to draw the electron configurations of the first 20 elements in the *periodic table*. The periodic table can be seen as an arrangement of the elements in terms of their electron configuration.

---

electroplating consists of depositing a thin layer of one metal on the surface of another by using an electric current. An example is the chromium plating on a bike.

- The process is a form of *electrolysis*.
- Usually a metal which will not corrode is deposited on a metal which might corrode, e.g. steel cutlery is often plated with silver.
- The metal which needs to plated (e.g. the steel) is the *cathode* in the cell.
- The metal used for plating (e.g. silver) is the *anode* of the cell and a solution of a silver compound is the *electrolyte*.

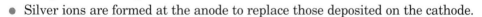

Silver anode +   Steel cathode −

Electrolyte – solution containing silver ions

- The ionic equation at the cathode, where silver is deposited is:

$$Ag^+ + e^- \longrightarrow Ag$$

- Silver ions are formed at the anode to replace those deposited on the cathode.

---

electroscope: a piece of apparatus used to demonstrate that an object has an electric charge.

- There are two conductors in an electroscope, one fixed and one moveable.
- When a charged object (e.g. a negatively charged piece of polythene) touches the top of the electroscope, electrons are transferred to both conductors.
- Since like charges repel, the moveable conductor is repelled from the fixed conductor.

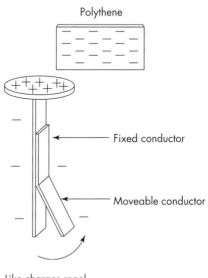

Polythene

Fixed conductor

Moveable conductor

Like charges repel

---

electrostatics, theory of: this explains why your comb will attract small pieces of paper after you have combed your hair.

- Electrostatics is about stationary electric charges on an object, as opposed to moving electric charges in an electric current.
- Many materials can become electrically charged if they are rubbed.
- If a polythene rod is rubbed with a wool cloth it becomes negatively charged because electrons are rubbed from the wool onto the polythene.
- If a glass rod is rubbed with a silk cloth it becomes positively charged because electrons are rubbed off the glass onto the silk.
- Objects with the same type of electric charge repel each other.
- Objects with opposite electric charges attract each other.

electrostatics, uses and dangers

USES

- Smoke produced by burning fuels in power stations can be cleaned by passing it between charged metal plates. The air particles between the plates become charged and attract dust particles. The charged dust particles are then attracted to the plates.
- Paint particles leaving a sprayer are positively charged; if the object being painted is given a negative charge the paint particles will be attracted to it.

DANGERS

- When petrol passes out of a hose it becomes positively charged. If this charge builds up it can cause a spark which would cause an explosion. Aircraft are connected to earth during refuelling to prevent this happening.

element: a substance that cannot be split into simpler substances by chemical means. You need to know the difference between element, *atom* and *compound*.
- Elements contain only one type of *atom*.
- There are about ninety naturally occurring elements.
- All atoms of the same element have the same number of *protons*; atoms of different elements have different numbers of protons.
- Atoms of the same element may have different numbers of *neutrons* – these different forms are called *isotopes* of the element.

embryo: an unborn offspring (e.g. a chicken inside the egg or you before you were born).
- Embryos of most mammals develop in the womb of the mother where they receive nutrients and oxygen from the mother's blood.
- Embryos of most other animals develop inside eggs – these eggs contain all the nutrients needed by the embryo before it hatches.

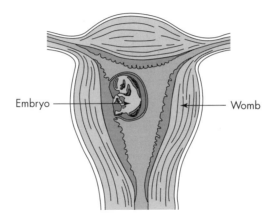

- Plant embryos are found in the seeds of the plant.

embryo transplant: the splitting apart of cells from a developing animal and the placing of these groups of cells in the womb of a host mother to develop. It is used to produce *clones* of animals.
- The embryo is usually produced by fertilising eggs in the laboratory, allowing the fertilised eggs to divide several times, then dividing the groups of cells before they begin to specialise.
- All the embryos produced from one fertilised egg in this way are genetically identical (clones).
- This is because the fertilised egg divides by *mitosis*.
- In mitosis the genetic information is copied before the cells divide.

emitter: a surface which gives out radiant energy – an important property to bear in mind when designing objects that get hot when used.
- Dark, matt surfaces are good emitters of radiant energy.
- Light, shiny surfaces are poor emitters of radiant energy, which is why metal teapots are shiny.

emphysema is a disease of the lungs in which the patient is short of breath and finds breathing difficult. In emphysema:
- the passages leading to the *alveoli* become narrower
- the surface area of the alveoli becomes reduced
- less oxygen is transferred into the blood.
- One cause of emphysema is tobacco smoking.

emulsify: to break down drops of a liquid into smaller droplets. Salad cream is an emulsion made by breaking down vegetable oil into tiny droplets.

In digestion:
- *bile* breaks down fat drops into droplets
- the droplets have a larger surface area for the enzyme *lipase* to act upon
- fat digestion is therefore speeded up.

enamel, tooth: the outer, white part of a tooth – the part of a tooth that you can see.
- Enamel is the hardest substance in the body.
- It is made of a bone-like material.
- Calcium is needed in the diet for the healthy development of enamel.
- Tooth decay occurs when bacteria feeding on food on the teeth release acid which dissolves the enamel.

endothermic reaction: a chemical reaction that absorbs energy. In a laboratory you would probably have to heat the chemicals to make them react under these circumstances.
In a chemical reaction:
- breaking chemical bonds requires energy
- forming chemical bonds releases energy
- if the energy needed to break the bonds is greater than the energy released when bonds are formed, then the reaction is endothermic
- therefore energy must be supplied (usually in the form of heat) for the reaction to proceed.

(See also *exothermic reaction*.)

energy, chemical: the energy contained in all substances, including petrol and food. Chemical energy is a form of *potential* energy.

energy, electrical: the energy transferred by a battery or a dynamo.
- The rate of transfer of electrical energy in an appliance is give by:

$$\text{rate of energy transferred} \atop (\text{watts, W}) = \text{potential difference} \atop (\text{volts, V}) \times \text{current} \atop (\text{amperes, A})$$

energy, heat: now called thermal energy, it is the energy that an object has due to its temperature.
- The higher the temperature the more energy have the particles which make up the substance.

energy, kinetic: this is the energy of a moving object.

● The energy of a moving object is given by:

$$\text{kinetic energy (joules, J)} = \frac{1}{2} \times \text{mass (kilograms, kg)} \times \text{speed}^2 \text{([metres/second]}^2, \text{[m/s]}^2)$$

energy, light: a form of energy that can be detected by the human eye.

● Light is a form of *electromagnetic radiation*.

● Light transfers energy without any matter being transferred.

energy, nuclear: energy transferred by the splitting or joining of atomic nuclei (e.g. in an nuclear power station or an atomic bomb).

● Very large amounts of energy are transferred when atomic nuclei split – much larger than the energy transferred when chemical bonds are made or broken.

● In a nuclear power station the energy transferred when uranium nuclei split is used to heat water and convert it to steam – this steam drives the generators.

energy, potential: energy which is stored, for example in the spring of a toy when you have just wound it up.

● If a spring is stretched it has stored elastic potential energy – this energy is usually transferred to kinetic energy when the spring is released.

● If an object is lifted it has stored gravitational potential energy – this energy is usually transferred to kinetic energy if the object falls back to Earth.

● A battery has stored chemical potential energy – this is transferred to electrical energy when the battery is connected in a complete electric circuit.

energy, sound: this is the energy you transfer to air molecules when you shout.

● It is the energy transferred from molecule to molecule as sound waves pass through gases, liquids or solids.

● The molecules which transfer the sound energy are in approximately the same place before and after the sound wave has passed.

energy level diagram: a diagram which shows the amount of energy transferred when chemical bonds are broken or made. You may be given one of these diagrams in the examination and asked to say what the various parts of it mean.

● Breaking chemical bonds requires energy.

- Energy is released when chemical bonds are formed.
- In *exothermic reactions* more energy is transferred when bonds in the products are formed than when the bonds of the reactants are broken.

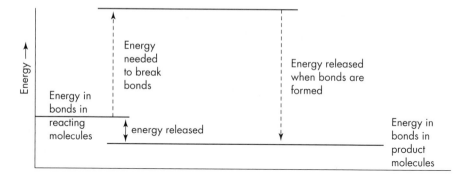

- In *endothermic reactions* more energy is transferred when bonds in the reactants are broken than when bonds in the products are formed.

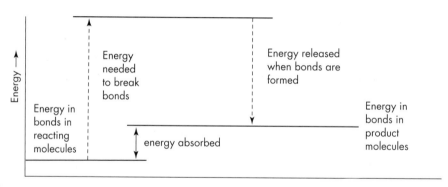

energy transfer in food chains: the transfer of *energy* from the Sun to plants and then from plants to the animals in *food chains*.

In the food chain   grass $\longrightarrow$ antelope $\longrightarrow$ lion:

- the total amount of energy in the antelopes is less than that in the grass
- the total amount of energy in the lions is less than that in the antelopes.
- This is because animals cannot digest all of the food that they eat – some energy is present in the *faeces* they pass out of their bodies.
- Most of the energy in the food is transferred to the environment, via respiration, during movement and as heat loss.
- This heat loss to the environment is highest in mammals and birds, which maintain a constant, high body temperature.

In agriculture the efficiency of energy transfer is increased by:

- reducing the number of stages in food chains
- restricting the movement of animals

- controlling the temperature of the environment in which the animals are kept.

environment: the external conditions which affect living organisms, for example air, soil and water.

The environment provides plants with:
- energy (from the Sun)
- carbon dioxide and oxygen (from the atmosphere)
- water and mineral ions (from the soil).

enzymes are biological *catalysts* – chemicals produced by living organisms to speed up chemical reactions within cells. Your saliva contains an enzyme, amylase, which speeds up the breakdown of starch to sugar.
- All enzymes are *proteins*.
- Living organisms produce thousands of different enzymes.
- These enzymes mean that chemical reactions in cells occur quickly in warm conditions rather than needing very high temperatures.
- Enzymes work by lowering the *activation energy* of the reaction.
- Enzymes are specific – they each speed up the rate of a particular reaction.
- Each enzyme has an *active site* into which reacting molecules fit.

enzymes, in digestion: digestive enzymes break down large, insoluble molecules into smaller, soluble molecules (see *digestive enzymes*).

enzymes, in food manufacture: enzymes are used in, for example, *baking*, *brewing* and *yoghurt manufacture*.

The enzymes are produced by:
- yeasts (a single-celled fungi) in baking and brewing
- bacteria in yoghurt manufacture.

enzymes, in home and industry: enzymes are found in biological detergents and purified enzymes are used to make baby foods, syrup and slimming foods.
- Biological detergents contain *protease* enzymes to digest protein stains and *lipase* enzymes to digest greasy stains on clothes.
- Protease enzymes are used to pre-digest proteins in baby foods (so that babies can digest the food more easily).
- *Amylase* (*carbohydrase*) enzymes are used to convert starch into sugar syrup.
- Isomerase enzymes are used to convert glucose into fructose; fructose is much sweeter than glucose and is used as a sweetener in low-sugar foods.

enzymes, properties of: you have to be able to explain why enzymes only work in a narrow range of conditions.

- Enzymes are proteins and so will only work over a fairly narrow range of temperature and pH.
- Enzymes have an optimum temperature – the temperature at which they work best. For many enzymes the optimum temperature is 35–40°C.
- Most enzymes are denatured (the shape of the *active site* is changed) by temperatures above 40°C and therefore are inactivated at high temperatures.
- Enzymes also have an optimum pH – usually between 6.5 and 7.5.
- Enzymes in our stomach have an optimum pH of about 2.0 whereas those in the small intestine have an optimum pH of about 7.5.

epidermis: the outer layer of many living organisms, for example the surface layers of your skin.

- Epidermis is often specialised for preventing excess water loss.
- The epidermis of our skin is composed mainly of dead cells.
- The epidermis of a plant leaf is covered by a waxy *cuticle* which reduces the rate of water loss.
- Special cells (*guard cells*) in the epidermis of plant leaves surround holes (called *stomata*) that allow gases to enter and leave the leaf.

equations, balancing: this consists of making sure that the number of atoms of each element is the same on both sides of an equation.

- You are usually asked to complete and balance an ionic half-equation.

EXAMPLE

Balance the equation for the combustion of methane.

$$CH_4 + O_2 \longrightarrow CO_2 + H_2O$$

You must make sure that there are the same numbers of carbon, hydrogen and oxygen atoms on each side of the equation. To do this two molecules of oxygen are needed on the left-hand side and two molecules of water on the right. Thus:

$$CH_4 + 2O_2 \longrightarrow CO_2 + 2H_2O$$

equations, ionic: equations involving ions. You must make sure that the number of charges balance on both sides of the equation.

- You are usually asked to complete and balance an ionic half equation.

EXAMPLE

Complete the ionic half-equation for the formation of aluminium at the cathode during the electrolysis of aluminium oxide (Al_2O_3):

$Al^{3+} + ...e^- \longrightarrow ...$

You need to give:

- the number of electrons – which must equal the number of positive charges on the aluminium
- the symbol for the aluminium atom (which is electrically neutral). Thus:

    $Al^{3+} + 3e^- \longrightarrow Al$

---

equations, word: you may be asked to describe a chemical reaction in words (rather than using symbols), for example reactants $\longrightarrow$ products.

- If you are asked to write a word equation you are usually given the names of all the substances – you have to put these substances on the correct side of the equation.

EXAMPLE

Hydrogen gas is released in the reaction between magnesium and hydrochloric acid. Complete the word equation for the reaction:

.... + ... $\longrightarrow$ .... + magnesium chloride

- Magnesium and hydrochloric acid are the reactants so they go on the left-hand side of the equation.
- Hydrogen is a product so it goes on the right-hand side of the equation. Thus:

    magnesium + hydrochloric acid $\longrightarrow$ hydrogen + magnesium chloride

---

equilibrium reaction: you can recognise a *reversible reaction* because the symbol $\rightleftharpoons$ is used rather than the symbol $\longrightarrow$.

- In some chemical reactions the products of the reaction can react to form the original reactants – these reactions are called reversible reactions.
- An example of a chemical reaction is the production of ammonia:

    nitrogen + hydrogen $\rightleftharpoons$ ammonia

    $2N(g) + 3H_2(g) \rightleftharpoons 2NH_3(g)$

- An equilibrium is reached when the reaction occurs at the same rate in each direction.
- In *exothermic* reactions increasing the temperature <u>decreases</u> the yield of products of a reversible reaction.
- In *endothermic* reactions increasing the temperature <u>increases</u> the yield of products of a reversible reaction.

---

erosion is the wearing away of rocks by the action of, for example, rain, wind and changes in temperature. This is why old stone statues have lost much of their fine detail.

- Rain may be acid because carbon dioxide and sulphur dioxide from the atmosphere dissolve in it; this acid dissolves some substances in the rock.

- If wind contains tiny particles like sand then the action of the wind is rather like that of sandpaper.
- Changes in temperature cause rocks to expand or contract, leading to cracking.

ethane: a gas with the formula C_2H_6. An important raw material in the plastics industry.
- Ethane is a *hydrocarbon*.
- It is an *alkane* and therefore contains no double bonds (*saturated*) and is relatively unreactive.
- It is found in natural gas.
- It can be *cracked* to form *ethene*.

ethanoic acid is the acid found in vinegar, formula CH_3COOH.
- It is a weak acid (see *acids and alkalis*).
- It is used in the manufacture of plastics, paints and aspirin.
- Ethanoic acid was originally produced by the action of bacteria on wine, beer or cider.

ethanol is the alcohol found in beer, wine and spirits, formula C_2H_5OH. (See also *alcohol*.)

ethene is a gas with the formula C_2H_4. It is important in making plastics.
- Ethene is a *hydrocarbon*.
- It is an *alkene* and therefore contains a double bond (*unsaturated*) making it fairly reactive.
- It is produced from oil by fractional distillation.
- It is widely used in the chemical industry to make, for example, polymers such as poly(ethene).

eutrophication is one of the effects of sewage or fertilisers on rivers and lakes. It is a process that leads to the death of animals such as fish.
- Eutrophication is the result of the introduction of excessive amounts of nutrients, such as nitrates and phosphates, into rivers or lakes.
- This causes rapid growth of plants that live in the water.
- Many of the plants die due to competition for light.
- This leads to an increase in the numbers of microbes that feed on dead plants.
- The increased numbers of microbes rapidly use up the oxygen in the water, leading to the suffocation of fish and other aquatic animals.

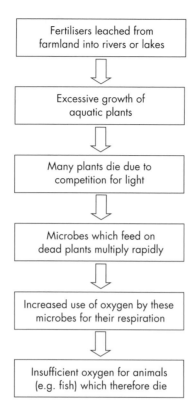

evaporation: changing from a liquid into a gas (see *changes of state*). In evaporation:

- heating a liquid transfers energy to the particles
- the particles move around more quickly
- particles which have enough energy overcome the attractive forces between the particles and escape from the liquid to become a gas.

evolution: the theory that all living things on Earth have developed from simple life forms which first appeared more than 3 billion years ago.

- Much of the evidence for evolution comes from the study of *fossils* which show how organisms have changed over millions of years.

You need to know the following main features of the theory of evolution by *natural selection*:

- Organisms show *variation*.
- Some variations make organisms better *adapted* to the environment.
- These organisms are more likely to survive to breed.
- Their offspring will inherit these variations.

(See also *Darwin, Charles*.)

excretion: getting rid of waste materials from the body (e.g. urine).
- Carbon dioxide produced by *aerobic respiration* is lost mainly through the lungs when we breathe out.
- Urea, produced by the breakdown of excess amino acids (*deamination*), is removed by the *kidneys* in the *urine*.

exercise is activity using muscles, for training or to improve health.

EXERCISE IMPROVES HEALTH BY:
- keeping muscles toned
- keeping tendons supple
- keeping the joints working smoothly
- maintaining an efficient supply of blood to the heart muscle and the lungs.

DURING EXERCISE:
- the heart rate speeds up, delivering blood to the muscles at a faster rate
- the breathing rate increases, increasing the rate at which oxygen enters the blood in the lungs
- both these changes result in a faster rate of delivery of oxygen to the muscles, and therefore a faster rate of *aerobic respiration* in the muscles, leading to faster energy transfer.

exothermic reaction: a chemical reaction which transfers energy as heat to the environment.
- In the laboratory you would <u>not</u> normally need to heat the chemicals to make them react.
- In exothermic reactions the energy released from forming new bonds in the products is greater than the energy needed to break existing bonds in the reactants.

expansion: most materials increase in size when they are heated, for example metal bars get longer.
- Engineers must allow for expansion when building large metal structures such as bridges.
- Liquid-in-glass thermometers use the expansion of liquid to measure temperature.
- Expansion of gas due to increase in temperature is governed by *Charles' law*.

explosive reactions are chemical reactions that cause an explosion, as in a 'banger' firework. In explosive reactions:

- a large amount of gas is produced quickly
- a large amount of energy is transferred to the environment.
- The sudden production of large amounts of gas produces a sudden increase in pressure – an explosion.
- Explosive reactions are *exothermic*.
- Most involve rapid *combustion*.

extinction is when all the members of a species of animal or plant have died out. Dinosaurs, for example, became extinct millions of years ago. Extinction of a species may occur:
- if the environment changes (e.g. gets too dry or too cold)
- because of competition, predation or disease.

extrusive rocks are rocks formed when volcanoes erupt. You need to know the difference between extrusive rocks and *intrusive rocks*.
- Extrusive rocks are formed when molten rock (*magma*) from deep in the Earth cools quickly after erupting from a volcano.
- One example is basalt.
- The crystals in the rock are small because the magma cools quickly after being erupted.

eye, focusing of: the main point to remember is that the shape of the lens is changed to focus on light at different distances.
- The eye bends (*refracts*) light so that it focuses on the retina.
- Most refraction occurs as light passes from air into the cornea.

TO FOCUS ON NEAR OBJECTS:

- the *ciliary muscles* contract
- this decreases the tension in the suspensory ligaments
- the lens becomes more spherical, focusing light on the retina.

TO FOCUS ON DISTANT OBJECTS:

- the ciliary muscles relax
- the tension in the suspensory ligaments increases
- the lens is pulled into a more elongated shape.

eye, structure of: you need to able to label a section of the eye and to describe what each part does.

Structure	Function
ciliary muscle	contracts to focus the eye on near objects
fovea	contains mainly *cones* which are sensitive to colour
pupil	the aperture of the iris – narrow in bright light, wide in dim light
cornea	transparent part of the sclera – where most *refraction* (bending) of light occurs
lens	helps to focus light on the retina
iris	the coloured part of the eye – controls the amount of light reaching the retina
suspensory ligaments	hold the lens in place
retina	contains receptors sensitive to light (*rods* and *cones*)
sclera	the white of the eye – a tough outer coat
optic nerve	contains sensory neurones that carry nerve impulses from the receptors in the retina to the brain

- The diagram shows the inside of the eye:

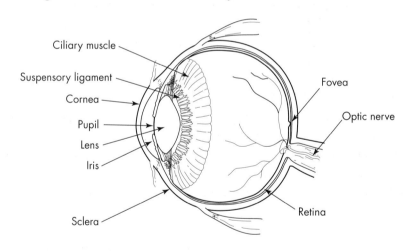

faeces: waste matter, mainly indigestible material, which leaves the body via the anus.
- Faeces are formed in the large intestine which absorbs water from the indigestible material.
- The indigestible material is mainly *roughage* – cellulose fibres from plant material.

Faraday, Michael: a British scientist who lived 1791–1867. Amongst other things, he discovered:
- *electromagnetic induction*, which led to the method of generating electricity
- the laws governing *electrolysis*.

farming, environmental effects: see *fertilisers* and *pesticides*.

fat is a food material used mainly as an energy source. Do not forget that we need fats in our diet – we only have problems if we eat too much of them.
- Fats are found in foods such as meat, milk, cheese, butter and margarine.
- Fats are needed to make cell membranes.
- A layer of fat under the skin *insulates* animals that live in cold conditions.
- Some nerve cells have an insulating layer of fat.
- Too much fat in the diet may lead to fat being deposited in the lining of blood vessels, increasing the risk of heart attacks.
- Fat is digested by lipase enzyme into fatty acids and glycerol.

fatigue is why your muscles get tired during exercise.
- Fatigue is partly due to insufficient *glycogen* (an energy-storing compound) in the muscles – athletes try to build up maximum glycogen stores in their muscles before an event.
- It is also due to the build-up of *lactic acid* in the muscles (see *anaerobic respiration*).

fatty acid: part of a fat molecule. We need fatty acids to make *cell membranes* and *nerve cells*.

- Fatty acids are formed, along with glycerol, during the digestion of fats by the body.
- All fats contain glycerol, but different fats contain different fatty acids.

faulting: fractures in the Earth's *crust*. Some faults are enormous – the Great Rift Valley in Africa can be seen from the Moon with the naked eye.
- Faulting occurs most often when the (*tectonic*) plates which make up the Earth's crust slide slowly past each other (e.g. the San Andreas fault in California).
- When the plates slide past each other earthquakes may occur.

feedback: the modification of a process by the effects of that process; you are most likely to be asked about negative feedback.

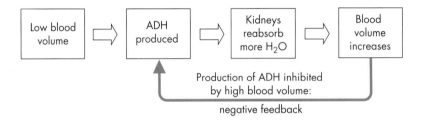

- One example of this is the control of *ADH* production. The effects of ADH production in turn reduce the production of ADH.

fermentation: the process by which most alcoholic drinks are made.
- Fermentation is a chemical change brought about by *enzymes*.
- Enzymes produced by yeast ferment sugars to produce alcohol (*ethanol*) – this is the basis of the brewing and wine-making industries.
- Most fermentation processes occur in the absence of oxygen (see *anaerobic respiration*).
- Yoghurt is made by the fermentation of sugars in milk, producing lactic acid which gives yoghurt its sour taste.

ferns: a group of plants that have roots, stems and leaves but which do not produce flowers.
- Ferns usually live in damp places.
- They produce spores by *asexual reproduction*.

fertilisation: what happens when a *sperm* enters an *egg* – this is how life is started.

- Fertilisation is the joining (fusion) of two sex cells (*gametes*).
- It occurs in the oviduct in mammals and in the ovum in plants.
- The cell produced by fertilisation is called the zygote.
- The number of chromosomes in the zygote is double that of the sperm or the egg.
- The zygote usually divides continually by *mitosis* to form the *embryo*.

fertiliser, manufacture: you need to know how fertilisers are made from ammonia.
- Most *artificial fertilisers* are made by reacting ammonia with an acid.
- Ammonia is made by the *Haber process*.
- Some of the ammonia is oxidised to form nitric acid.
- Ammonia is then reacted with nitric acid to form ammonium nitrate:

  ammonia + nitric acid $\longrightarrow$ ammonium nitrate

  $NH_3(aq) + HNO_3(aq) \longrightarrow NH_4NO_3(aq)$
- Water is evaporated off leaving the solid fertiliser.

fertiliser, NPK: the most common *artificial fertiliser*, used by farmers to increase the yield of crops. NPK fertilisers contain nitrogen compounds, phosphorus compounds and potassium compounds.
- Nitrogen is needed by plants to produce proteins.
- Phosphorus speeds up the growth of roots and helps fruit to ripen.
- Potassium is for healthy leaves and flowers.

fertility: how able a female is to produce offspring. There are now drugs to help women who haven't been able to conceive (fertility drugs) and also drugs to prevent women conceiving (birth control drugs).
- Human female fertility is mainly controlled by two *hormones*: *FSH* produced by the pituitary gland at the base of the brain and *oestrogen* produced by the ovaries.
- FSH stimulates eggs in the ovaries to mature and stimulates the production of oestrogen.
- Oestrogen inhibits the production of FSH (see *feedback*).
- If insufficient FSH is produced, eggs will not be released and the woman is infertile – FSH (fertility drug) injections may enable such a woman to release eggs However, if the FSH dose is too high, many eggs may be released resulting in a multiple pregnancy.
- Many birth control pills contain oestrogen – this inhibits FSH production so that the woman does not produce eggs and cannot therefore become pregnant.

- Uncontrolled use of 'the pill' may lead to promiscuity and the spread of sexually-transmitted diseases.

fibre optics: a means by which we can see into human organs (e.g. the stomach) without the need for surgery. Fibre optics uses flexible glass fibres to transmit light.

Its uses include:
- looking inside the human body (endoscope)
- transmitting information via communication networks.

In fibre optic transmission:
- all the light stays inside the fibre because of *total internal reflection*
- the angle at which the light rays strike the glass is greater than the *critical angle*, so all the light is reflected within the fibre.

fibrin and fibrinogen: substances in the blood that help to stop bleeding from a cut.
- They are proteins in the blood that are involved in the formation of clots.
- Fibrinogen is a protein molecule which is curled up, rather like a ball of wool.
- When the body is wounded an enzyme called *thrombin* converts fibrinogen to fibrin, which has long, thread-like molecules.
- These thread-like molecules form a mesh which traps blood cells and forms the clot.

filtration: a means of separating a suspended solid from a liquid, for example separating sand from water.
- Filter paper allows small particles to pass through, but not large ones.
- The liquid which passes through the filter paper is called the filtrate.
- The solid left in the filter paper is called the residue.

fish: a group of animals which have backbones and which live mainly in water. Typical fish:
- are covered by scales
- have fins to help them during swimming
- have gills for extracting oxygen from water
- have eggs without shells.

fission (biology): division of a cell into two or more parts – for simple organisms it is the most common way of reproducing.

- It is the way in which bacteria and many single-celled organisms multiply.
- The genetic material is replicated before the organism divides.
- Each offspring receives an identical copy of the genetic information.
- All the offspring are therefore identical to each other and to the parent cell.
- It is a method of *asexual reproduction*.

fission (nuclear) is the splitting of the *nucleus* of an unstable atom; this is how radioactive substances produce *radiation*. It forms the basis of how a *nuclear reactor* works.
- When a nucleus splits up, a different atom with a different number of *protons* is formed.
- In a nuclear reactor a *chain reaction* occurs – nuclei split when they are bombarded with *neutrons*.
- The energy transferred when nuclei split is much greater than the energy transferred when chemical bonds are formed or broken.

flaccid means limp and flabby.
- The leaf of a plant that has not been watered becomes flaccid.
- The leaves and young parts of plants are supported mainly by the fluid in the *vacuoles* of their cells.
- Water enters the vacuoles by *osmosis*.
- This increases the pressure inside the cells.
- The cell walls are strong enough to withstand this pressure, known as *turgor pressure*, and help keep the plant rigid.

Fleming, Alexander: a British scientist who lived 1871–1955.
- Fleming discovered penicillin.
- He noticed that a fungus which had contaminated a bacterial culture was destroying the bacteria.
- He found that this was because the fungus was creating a chemical (*antibiotic*) which killed bacteria.
- He realised that these chemicals could be used to kill disease microbes in the human body.
- Scientists have now isolated many antibiotics from a range of microbes and as a result millions of lives have been saved.

foetus: an unborn or unhatched animal.
- In humans, the developing baby is referred to as an embryo for the first eight weeks, then a foetus until it is born.
- A human foetus receives nutrients and oxygen from its mother's blood.

- These materials diffuse from the mother's blood into the blood of the foetus where the two sets of vessels run close together in the *placenta*.

---

follicle stimulating hormone (FSH): a *hormone* which stimulates eggs to mature in the ovary of a female mammal.
- FSH is produced by the *pituitary gland* at the base of the brain.
- In humans it causes one egg to mature each month.
- FSH also stimulates the ovaries to produce the hormone *oestrogen*.
- FSH is also known as the 'fertility drug'. It is given to women who cannot become pregnant because they are not making enough FSH.
- Too high a dose of FSH can result in multiple births since it may cause several eggs to mature at once.

---

food chain: shows the feeding relationships between organisms in a habitat (e.g. grass $\longrightarrow$ antelope $\longrightarrow$ lion).
- The food chain X $\longrightarrow$ Y $\longrightarrow$ Z means that Y eats X and Z eats Y.
- Food chains usually begin with plants (*producers*) which provide food for the other organisms (*consumers*).
- There are two ways of naming the organisms in food chains:
  producer $\longrightarrow$ primary consumer $\longrightarrow$ secondary consumer
  producer $\longrightarrow$ *herbivore* $\longrightarrow$ *carnivore*
- Food chains are usually interconnected to form *food webs*.
- Food chains and food webs show the transfer of materials and of energy from one type of organism to another.

---

food tests: you may need to know the tests for starch, reducing sugar, protein and fat.

Food	Name of test	Positive result
starch	*iodine*	blue-black colour
reducing sugar	Benedict's	brick-red precipitate
protein	biuret	lilac coloration
fat	alcohol emulsion	white emulsion

---

food, types of: see *carbohydrate, protein, fat, minerals, vitamins, fibre.*

---

food web: a set of interconnected *food chains*; it usually includes most of the organisms that live in a particular *habitat*.
A food web for a stream is shown on the next page.

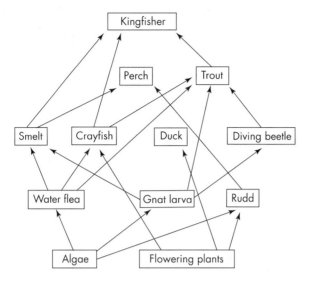

One food chain in this food web is:

algae $\longrightarrow$ water fleas $\longrightarrow$ smelt $\longrightarrow$ perch

You should be able to say which organisms are:

- *producers* – algae and flowering plants
- *herbivores* (primary *consumers*) – rudd, duck, gnat larvae, water fleas
- *carnivores* (secondary consumers) – e.g. smelt, diving beetles
- *omnivores* – crayfish.

---

force: a push or pull on an object. For example, when you are sitting on a chair you are exerting a force on the chair and the chair is exerting a force on you.

For an object resting on a surface:

- if the forces acting on an object do not balance each other out, an unbalanced force will act on the object
- a stationary object will begin to move in the direction of the unbalanced force

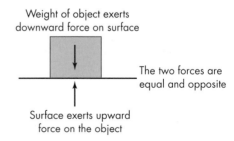

- an object moving in the direction of the unbalanced force will speed up
- an object moving in the opposite direction to the force will slow down
- the greater the unbalanced force acting on an object the greater the *acceleration* in the direction of the force
- the greater the mass of the object the greater the force needed to give it a particular acceleration.
- The unit of force is the newton (N).

- A force of 1 N will give a mass of 1 kg an acceleration of 1 m/s^2.
- Force, mass and acceleration are related as follows:

$$\begin{array}{ccccc}
\text{force} & = & \text{mass} & \times & \text{acceleration} \\
\text{(newtons, N)} & & \text{(kilograms, kg)} & & \text{(metres/second}^2\text{, m/s}^2\text{)}
\end{array}$$

formula mass: see *relative formula mass*.

fossil: the remains of an organism that died thousands of millions of years ago which have not decayed and disappeared. Fossils have given us much information on how organisms have changed since life began on Earth. They also give us information about animals that became extinct millions of years ago, e.g. dinosaurs. Fossils are formed:
- from hard parts of organisms that do not decay easily
- from parts of organisms that have not decayed because one or more conditions for decay are absent (e.g. lack of oxygen or of water)
- when part of the organism is replaced by another material.

Much of the evidence for the theory of *evolution* by *natural selection* has come from the study of fossils.

fossil fuels: examples are coal, oil and natural gas; most of our energy comes from burning these fuels.
- Fossil fuels were formed from the remains of organisms which lived millions of years ago (see *coal*, *oil*, *natural gas*).
- Fossil fuels are *non-renewable* – once they are used up they cannot be replaced.
- The burning of fossil fuels releases carbon dioxide into the atmosphere.
- Increasing levels of carbon dioxide from the burning of fossil fuels are partly responsible for the *greenhouse effect*.

fovea: the part of the eye which gives us most acute vision. The fovea is:
- part of the retina of the eye (see *eye, structure*)
- made up mainly of *cones* – receptor cells which are sensitive to colour
- where an object is focused when the light is bright.

fractional distillation is how we get petrol from crude oil.
It consists of separating the materials in crude oil (fractions) by:
- first *evaporating* the mixture
- then allowing it to *condense* at different temperatures.

(See also *crude oil, fractional distillation of*.)

free electron: an electron that can move around within a metal and does not stay in an energy level around a nucleus (see *bonding*).
Free electrons are important in conduction of:
- electricity
- thermal energy (heat).

freezing: changing a liquid into a solid (e.g. water into ice). See also *changes of state*.
- As a liquid is cooled down energy is transferred from the particles.
- The particles slow down.
- Strong forces are formed between the particles and they cease to move about – they can only vibrate.

frequency is the number of wave crests that pass a given point in one second. For sound waves, the greater the number of waves per second (the greater the frequency) the higher the note sounds.
- The unit of frequency is the hertz (Hz).
- The wave illustrated has a frequency of 3 Hz.
- For *electromagnetic waves* the higher the frequency the shorter the *wavelength*.

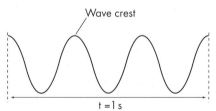

Wave crest

$t = 1\,s$

friction: the force that opposes one surface from sliding over another surface. Smooth surfaces (like ice) have a lower frictional force than rough objects (like sandpaper).

Direction of movement of object

Direction of force of friction ⟶

- Friction acts when an object moves through any liquid or gas (for example water or air).
- Friction acts when solid surfaces slide over each other.
- Friction causes objects to heat up and wear away.
- Friction is a major reason why machines with moving parts are less than 100% efficient.
- The faster an object moves through a gas or a liquid the greater the force of friction on it.
- This is why objects moving through a gas or a liquid have a *terminal velocity*.

fruits are the parts of a plant that contain seeds, for example apples, oranges and nuts.

- Fruits are formed by flowers after *fertilisation* has occurred.
- Fruit formation can be controlled artificially by using plant *hormones*.

FSH: see *follicle stimulating hormone*.

fuels: materials like *coal* that we burn to release energy.
- Fossil fuels such as coal, oil and gas are non-renewable fuels – once used they can never be replaced.
- Wood is a renewable fuel – we can grow more wood to replace that which we use.

fungi are organisms such as moulds and mushrooms.
- Fungi do not contain chlorophyll so they cannot produce their own food.
- They are very important in the *decay* process by which materials from dead and waste matter are recycled.
- Some fungi, e.g. *Penicillium*, produce antibiotics.
- Some are grown in fermenters to produce mycoprotein which is used as a meat substitute in some foods.

fuse (electrical): a safety device in an electric circuit.
- A fuse usually contains a strip of metal which becomes hot and melts if too high a current flows through it.
- The value of a fuse should be slightly higher than the maximum current expected to flow through the circuit in normal use.

fusion of gametes: the joining of two sex cells, e.g. a *sperm* and an *egg*.
- The resulting cell is called the zygote.
- It contains a mixture of genetic material from the two sex cells.
- The zygote divides repeatedly to form a new organism.
- The organism will be similar to both parents but identical to neither.

fusion (nuclear): the joining of two atomic nuclei; it is what happens in the Sun to release energy.
- When two small nuclei fuse, great amounts of energy are released. For example, two isotopes of hydrogen (deuterium and tritium) can be made to fuse to form helium:
$$^2_1H + {}^3_1H \longrightarrow {}^4_2He + {}^1_0n$$
- Reactions similar to this inside the Sun are responsible for much of the energy that reaches Earth.

galaxy: a group of stars held together by gravitational forces.
- Our own Sun is a member of the galaxy called the Milky Way.
- Besides suns, galaxies may contain planets and hydrogen gas.

Galileo: an Italian scientist who lived 1564–1642.
- Galileo discovered the laws that govern the acceleration of falling bodies and the path taken by projectiles – until Galileo it was thought that heavy objects fell faster than light objects.
- He used telescopes to examine the planets in our solar system, discovering mountains on the Moon and satellites moving around Venus.
- These observations supported the views of *Copernicus*, that the Earth was not the centre of the universe.

---

gall bladder: a part of the liver that stores *bile*.
- Bile is made by the liver and stored in the gall bladder until food enters the small intestine.
- The gall bladder then contracts, forcing bile down the bile duct into the small intestine.

(See also *digestion* and *bile*.)

---

galvanise: one way of preventing iron from rusting.
- Zinc is used to coat iron and so prevent corrosion.
- The iron is cleaned then dipped in a bath of molten zinc.
- The thin layer of zinc prevents oxygen and water reaching the iron.
- Without water and oxygen iron does not rust.
- Iron does not rust even if the zinc coat is scratched. This is because zinc is more reactive than iron – so water and oxygen react with zinc rather than iron.

---

gamete: a sex cell such as an *egg* or a *sperm*. An egg and a sperm between them contain all the genetic information needed for the development of a human.
- In humans, sperm are small and have a tail so that they can swim; eggs are larger, because they contain food reserves, and are non-motile.

- In humans and flowering plants, gametes are formed by a process of cell division called *meiosis*.
- This means that a gamete contains only half the number of chromosomes of a body cell.
- Male and female gametes fuse (join) in a process called *fertilisation*.
- The fertilised egg is called a zygote – this then divides continually by *mitosis* to form the new organism.

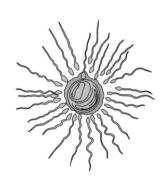

gamma radiation: the most penetrating of the three kinds of radiation (*alpha, beta* and gamma rays).

- Gamma rays (γ-rays) are released by the unstable nuclei of some radioactive substances.
- They consist of very short wavelength *electromagnetic radiation*.
- They are very penetrating – they can pass through several centimetres of lead.
- They are therefore very dangerous to the body.

USES OF GAMMA RAYS

- sterilising surgical instruments
- examining welds in metal for faults

gas: a substance that spreads out to take up all the space available to it (see *changes of state*). You have to know the differences between gases, *liquids* and *solids*.

- The particles in a gas are well spread out.
- This is why gases can be compressed easily.
- They move quickly in all directions.
- This is why they *diffuse* rapidly and mix completely with other gases.

Geiger–Müller tube: a device that detects particles emitted by radioactive sources – usually called a 'Geiger counter'.

- The instrument detects particles which are charged and which therefore cause ionisation.
- The ions that they cause to be formed allow an electric current to flow through the tube.
- It is this current which is detected.

gender is the sex of a person, that is whether they are male or female.
- In humans gender is determined by *genes* carried on the *sex chromosomes*.
- In females both sex chromosomes are the same – XX.
- In males the sex chromosomes are different – XY.
- All eggs carry a single X chromosome.
- Sperm also carry one chromosome, either an X chromosome or a Y chromosome.
- There is a 50% chance of an X-carrying sperm fertilising the egg and producing a female.
- There is a 50% chance of a Y-carrying sperm fertilising the egg and producing a male.

---

gene: a unit of information that controls a particular characteristic of the body such as eye colour.
- A gene is actually a section of a *DNA* molecule.
- It contains coded information that determines the order in which amino acids are assembled to make a protein.
- Genes can be cut out of chromosomes and transferred to other organisms (see *genetic engineering*).

---

generator: a device which produces our supplies of mains electricity.

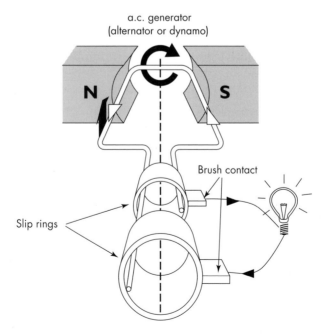

a.c. generator
(alternator or dynamo)

- A machine that produces electricity by spinning a magnet inside a coil (most bike dynamos work like this) or spinning a coil in a magnetic field.
- When the coil of wire cuts through a magnetic field a voltage is produced between the ends of the wire – it is this induced voltage that causes a current to flow if the wire is part of a complete circuit.
- This type of generator produces an *alternating current*.

The size of the induced *voltage* can be increased by:
- increasing the speed of rotation of the coil
- increasing the strength of the magnets
- increasing the number of turns on the coil.

genetic means concerned with inheritance. Genetic influence is why you are similar in appearance to both your parents, but identical to neither. Differences between individuals depend on:
- the *genes* they inherit from their parents
- the conditions in which they develop – environmental causes
- the interaction of genes and the environment, or both.

genotype: all the genetic information in your cells.
- The genotype of an individual consists of all the *alleles* which are found on their chromosomes.
- This is different from *phenotype*, which is all the observable characteristics – these are affected both by *genes* and by the *environment*.

geo-stationary: a satellite that stays above the same point on the Earth's surface is geo-stationary.
- Used for communication satellites (e.g. for satellite TV) so that home receiver dishes do not have to be moved.
- Such a satellite stays above the same place on the Earth because it moves at the same rate at which the Earth spins.

geothermal: energy that is obtained from the Earth's interior. The hot water from geothermal sites can be used directly in district heating schemes or geothermal steam can be used to drive turbines in power stations.
- The energy is transferred mainly by *radioactive decay* in the *crust* and the upper *mantle*.
- This energy is distributed by convection currents in the magma of the mantle and by convection in water in the crust.

geotropism is why plant roots grow downwards.
- It is the movement of plant organs in response to gravity.

- Most plant roots grow in the direction of the force of gravity.
- Most plant stems grow against the force of gravity.
- These responses are brought about by unequal distribution of hormones in the plant organs.
- This causes unequal growth at the tip of the root or the stem.

germination: the initial growth of a plant from a seed. The conditions needed for germination include:
- moisture
- warmth
- oxygen.

giant structure: see *covalent giant structure*, *ionic giant structure* and *metal giant structure*.

gill: an organ which animals such as fish use for breathing.
- Aquatic animals use gills to exchange oxygen and carbon dioxide with the surrounding water.

Gills have:
- a large surface area
- a good blood supply.

As water passes over a gill:
- oxygen diffuses from the water into the blood capillaries
- carbon dioxide diffuses from the blood capillaries into the water.

Because water is continually passing over the gills and blood is continually flowing over the capillaries, there is always a diffusion gradient between the blood and the water for oxygen and carbon dioxide.

glands produce substances that the organism uses. For example, your salivary glands produce *saliva* for digestion and your pancreas produces *insulin* to control blood sugar.

There are two kinds of glands:
- glands whose secretions pass out of the gland via a duct (tube) (examples of this type of gland include sweat glands in the skin and glands which produce digestive *enzymes*, e.g. the pancreas)
- glands whose secretions pass directly into the blood capillaries (an example of this type of gland is the ovary which passes oestrogen directly into its blood supply).

glass: a hard, brittle translucent substance. Glass is:
- made by heating a mixture of limestone, sand and soda

- translucent, which is why it is used to make windows
- unreactive, which is why it is used to make laboratory apparatus.

global warming is an increase in the mean temperature of the Earth's atmosphere brought about mainly by burning fossil fuels and deforestation. Its immediate cause is the *greenhouse effect*.

CAUSES

- Burning fossil fuels releases carbon dioxide into the atmosphere.
- Deforestation increases the carbon dioxide content of the atmosphere if the trees are burned.
- Deforestation decreases the rate at which carbon dioxide is removed from the atmosphere because the felled trees no longer photosynthesise (see *photosynthesis*).
- Increases in the numbers of cattle and of rice fields has increased the amount of methane in the atmosphere.

EFFECTS

- Carbon dioxide and methane reduce the amount of energy radiated from the Earth.
- This keeps the Earth warmer than it would otherwise be by enhancing the *greenhouse effect*.

glucagon is produced by your body when your blood sugar level begins to fall, due to exercise for example.
- Glucagon is a *hormone* which raises the amount of blood sugar in humans.
- It is produced by the *pancreas* when blood sugar levels fall.
- It stimulates the liver to convert *glycogen* into glucose and and thus raise blood sugar levels.
- It has the opposite effect to *insulin*.

glucose is a sugar with the formula $C_6H_{12}O_6$. It is where most of your body's energy comes from.
- Glucose is made by plants in *photosynthesis*.
- It is converted into starch by plants for storage.
- It is the form into which most of the *carbohydrates* that we eat is digested.
- It is converted into glycogen for storage.
- It is used in *respiration* to release energy.

glycerol: part of a fat molecule.

glycogen is an energy storage molecule in animals. You call on your glycogen stores when, for example, you are playing tennis or soccer.
- Glycogen is a *carbohydrate*.
- It is a polymer made up of glucose molecules.
- It is stored in the liver and muscles of mammals when blood sugar levels rise.
- It is converted back to glucose when blood sugar levels are low (see *insulin* and *glucagon*).

gold (Au): gold is a soft, dense metal used mainly to make jewellery. This is because it is:
- relatively unreactive (low down in the reactivity series)
- malleable (very easily worked)
- attractive.
Silver or zinc is often added to gold to make it harder.

gradient (of a graph): how steeply the line on a graph rises or falls. You may be asked to calculate the gradient of a graph to find, for example, the acceleration of a car.
- Sometimes the gradient is called the 'slope' of the line on the graph.
- The greater the gradient the steeper the slope.

EXAMPLE

In this graph the velocity rises from 5 m/s to 30 m/s in 10 s.

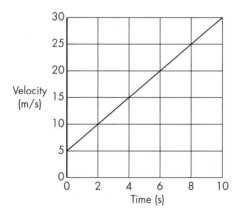

the gradient of the graph is: $\dfrac{30 - 5 \text{ m/s}}{10 \text{ s}}$

$= 2.5 \text{ m/s}^2$

- The gradient of a velocity/time graph is the *acceleration*.

graphite is a soft, black form of carbon. It is used as the 'lead' in pencils. Another form of graphite is used as a lubricant. These different forms of graphite have different structures.
- Each carbon atom forms 3 covalent bonds with neighbouring carbon atoms.
- These atoms form layers which can slide over each other (for diagram see *covalent giant structures*).
- Graphite has *free electrons* so it can conduct electricity.

gravitational force: an attractive force that exists between all objects. It is why things fall when we drop them.
- The force of gravity pulls objects in the direction of the centre of the Earth.
- If an object is allowed to fall, the force of gravity causes it to accelerate.
- If friction due to air resistance is ignored the acceleration produced is about 10 m/s².

gravitational potential energy: the amount of *potential energy* you have gained when, for example, you have climbed up to a diving board.
- It is the energy stored in an object because of the height that the object has been lifted against the force of gravity.
- The Earth is surrounded by a gravitational field; the strength of this field on Earth is about 10 N/kg (a force of 10 N acts on each 1 kg of an object's mass).
- The *weight* of an object is calculated by:

$$\text{weight} = \text{mass} \times \text{gravitational field strength}$$
$$\text{(newtons, N)} \quad \text{(kilograms, kg)} \quad \text{(newtons/kilogram, N/kg)}$$

- Weight and mass are not the same – weight is a force measured in newtons.
- When an object is lifted against the force of gravity the change in its gravitational potential energy can be calculated by:

$$\text{change in gravitational potential energy} = \text{weight} \times \text{change in vertical height}$$
$$\text{(joules, J)} \quad \text{(newtons, N)} \quad \text{(metres, m)}$$

- Because this is a change in energy, it is measured in joules.

greenhouse effect: the reason why the Earth's atmosphere is getting warmer. It is also know as 'global warming'.
- The atmosphere plays a role in helping warm the Earth's surface.
- The atmosphere allows shortwave radiation from the Sun to pass through.
- Some of this radiation warms the Earth's surface.
- Much of this radiation is then re-emitted at longer wavelengths.
- This radiation is reflected back by 'greenhouse' gases such as carbon dioxide

and methane. The greater the amount of these gases in the atmosphere, the greater the degree of global warming.

grid, national: the name given to the network of circuits which delivers electricity from power stations to homes and industry throughout the UK. You see it as pylons, power lines and substations.
- Electricity is transmitted at very high voltages (up to 440 000 V) and low current to reduce energy losses due to the heating effects of the current.
- Transformers are used to 'step up' the voltage at the power stations and step it down for safe use in homes.

group: a vertical column in the *periodic table*. You need to be able to explain why elements in the same group have similar chemical properties.
- This is because they have the same number of electrons in the highest occupied *energy level*.
- The higher this energy level the more easily are electrons lost and the less easily are they gained.
- In Group I, the further down the group an element is, the <u>more</u> reactive the element and the <u>lower</u> its melting point and boiling point.
- in Group VII, the further down the group an element is, the <u>less</u> reactive the element and the <u>higher</u> its melting point and boiling point.

growth: an increase in the size of an organism by cell division.
- A balanced supply of *nutrients* is needed for healthy growth.
- The maximum size of an organism usually depends on its *genes*.

guard cells: cells that surround each tiny hole in the surface of a leaf (*stoma*). They prevent the plant from losing too much water.
- Two guard cells surround each stoma.
- They control the width of the stomata.
- Stomata are normally open during the day (to allow the entry of carbon dioxide for *photosynthesis*) but closed at night to conserve water vapour.
- Stomata open when guard cells take in water by *osmosis*.

gypsum: mineral from which we get plaster of Paris.
- It consists mainly of calcium sulphate, $CaSO_4.2H_2O$.
- When heated it loses water and becomes plaster of Paris.
- When water is added to plaster of Paris it sets quickly to form a solid mass.
- As it sets it expands to fill even very small cavities, which is why plaster of Paris is often used to make moulds and moulded items.

Haber process: an industrial process for making ammonia from nitrogen and hydrogen. Most artificial *fertilisers* are made from ammonia produced by the Haber process. At a higher level you will may be asked about equilibrium in the reaction.

- The reaction is a *reversible reaction*:

$$N_2(g) + 3H_2(g) \rightleftharpoons 2NH_3(g)$$

- The mixture of nitrogen and hydrogen is heated at 450°C and pressurised to 200 atmospheres.
- The equilibrium mixture contains only about 15% ammonia.
- Higher temperatures make the reaction go faster, but reduce the percentage of ammonia in the equilibrium mixture.

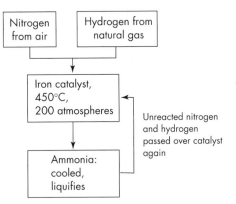

- Higher pressures would increase the percentage of ammonia in the mixture, but the improvement would not be economic because of the cost of plant needed to withstand higher pressures.
- An iron catalyst speeds up the attainment of equilibrium but it does <u>not</u> increase the percentage of ammonia in the equilibrium mixture.

---

habitat is the place where an organism lives. For example, a woodpecker's habitat is a woodland. Most organisms have specific habitats which provide them with some or all of:

- nutrients
- shelter
- a place to breed.

---

haematite is iron(III) oxide (Fe_2O_3) from which we get most of our iron.
- It is the principal iron-containing ore.
- Iron is produced in the *blast furnace* by using carbon monoxide to *reduce* haematite.

---

haemoglobin is the red pigment found in *red blood cells*. It carries most of the oxygen to your muscles. Haemoglobin:

- has a high affinity for oxygen
- combines with oxygen as red cells pass through the lung capillaries:

    haemoglobin + oxygen $\longrightarrow$ oxyhaemoglobin

- gives up its oxygen as red cells pass through the other organs:

    oxyhaemoglobin $\longrightarrow$ haemoglobin + oxygen

---

haemophilia is an inherited disease in which the blood does not clot as readily as in healthy people, so even a minor cut can lead to severe blood loss.

- It is caused by a *mutation* of the gene H that produces a protein called factor VIII – haemophiliacs do not produce this protein.
- The mutant allele h is *recessive*.
- The alleles of the gene are found on the X chromosome, so males inherit the disease from a carrier mother of genotype $X^H X^h$.
- Carriers show no symptoms of the disease.

Genotype	Description
$X^H X^H$	healthy female
$X^H X^h$	carrier female
$X^H Y$	healthy male
$X^h Y$	haemophiliac male

- When a healthy father and a carrier mother have children there is a 1 in 2 chance that a son will be a haemophiliac and a 1 in 2 chance that a daughter will be a carrier.

		Father	
		X^H	Y
Mother	X^H	$X^H X^H$	$X^H Y$
	X^h	$X^H X^h$	$X^h Y$

---

half-life: a property of radioactive materials which can be used to find the age of an object.

- The half-life is the average time taken for the number of parent nuclei present in a radioactive substance to decay.

- It is also the time taken for the count rate of a radioactive substance to fall by half. For example, if a substance has a half-life of eight days and an original count rate of 160:

Time (days)	Corrected count rate
0	160
8	80
16	40
24	20
32	10

- You might also be given a graph and asked to calculate half-life from the data in it.

EXAMPLE

Find from the graph how long it takes the count rate to fall by half.

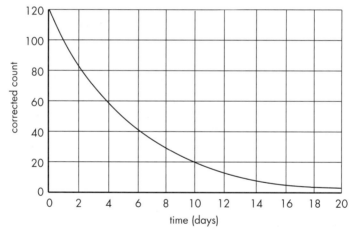

It takes 4 days to fall from 120 to 60 or it takes 4 days to fall from 40 to 20, so the half-life is 4 days.

(Always remember to subtract background count rate from total count)

halogens: the group of elements which includes chlorine, bromine and iodine. You will probably be asked why elements in this group have similar chemical properties but different physical properties. Halogens:

- are elements in Group VII of the *periodic table*.
- are non-metals
- have coloured vapours
- consist of molecules made up of pairs of atoms

- form *ionic salts* in which the halide ion (chloride, bromide or iodide) carries a 1– charge
- form molecular compounds with other non-metallic elements.

halogens, reactivity: all the halogens have seven electrons in their highest energy level, but reactivity decreases down the group.

- The decrease in activity is because the lower down the group is the element, the less easily electrons are gained into the highest energy level.

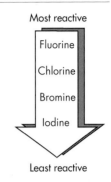

Most reactive

Fluorine

Chlorine

Bromine

Iodine

Least reactive

halogens, uses

Halogen	Uses
fluorine	toothpaste non-stick pans (as, for example, Teflon)
chlorine	bleach disinfectant antiseptic
bromine	pesticides photographic film
iodine	antiseptic

hard water is water that does not easily form a lather with soap; compared with soft water which does.

- Hard water contains dissolved calcium or magnesium compounds.
- It forms when natural water flows over rocks containing magnesium or calcium compounds
- In hard water areas, more soap is needed to make a lather and scale forms in kettles and central heating systems.

Hard water can be softened by:

- passing it through ion-exchange columns which replace the calcium and magnesium ions
- adding sodium carbonate solution to precipitate out calcium compounds as calcium carbonate and magnesium compounds as magnesium carbonate.

hazard symbols: you should be able to recognise the following symbols:

Oxidising
These substances provide oxygen which allows other materials to burn more fiercely.

Highly flammable
These substances easily catch fire.

Toxic
These substances can cause death. They may have their effects when swallowed or breathed in or absorbed through the skin

Corrosive
These substances attack and destroy living tissues, including eyes and skin.

Harmful
These substances are similar to toxic substances but less dangerous

Irritant
These substances are not corrosive but can cause reddening or blistering of the skin.

heart, disease: caused by blocking of the supply of blood to the heart muscle, causing heart pain (angina) or heart attack.

Heart disease is caused by:

- unbalanced diet – a diet containing too much fat or carbohydrate may result in 'furring up' of the coronary arteries (arteries supplying blood to the heart muscles) by fat deposits; a blood clot might then block one of these narrower vessels causing part of the heart muscle to die; this is a heart attack.
- smoking – smoking increases the risk of heart attack because chemicals in the smoke make blood clot more easily, so there is a greater risk of a coronary artery becoming blocked.

heart, structure: you need to be able to label the heart and to describe the function of each of its parts.

- *Atria* receive blood from veins.
- *Ventricles* pump blood out via arteries.
- *Valves* prevent backflow of blood.
- Blood flowing through the right side of the heart and the pulmonary artery is deoxygenated (low oxygen, high carbon dioxide).
- Blood flowing through the left side of the heart and the pulmonary veins is oxygenated (high oxygen, low carbon dioxide).

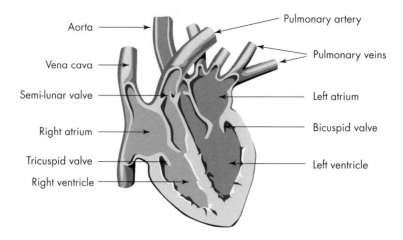

heartbeat: the pulse in the arteries felt when the heart muscles contract.
- The atria contract, forcing blood into the ventricles.
- The ventricles then contract forcing blood out through the arteries.
- Backflow of blood from the ventricles into the atria is prevented by the bicuspid and tricuspid valves.
- Backflow of blood from the arteries into the ventricles is prevented by the semi-lunar valves.

heat: the transferred energy (see *energy, thermal*) between two substances which are at different temperatures. You have to know the difference between heat and *temperature*.
- Heat can be transferred by *conduction, convection* and *radiation*.
- The unit for heat is the joule (J).
- Heat is not the same as temperature – temperature is a measure of the kinetic energy of the particles which make up a substance.

heating effect of current is what makes an electric fire and an electric light bulb work.
- When an electric current passes through a conductor (e.g. a metal wire) the temperature of the conductor increases.
- This is because current is the flow of electrons, and as the electrons flow they transfer some of their energy to the particles of the conductor.
- The rate of energy transfer is given by the following equations:

Equation 1:
$$\underset{\text{(watts, W)}}{\text{power}} = \underset{\text{(volts, V)}}{\text{potential difference}} \times \underset{\text{(amperes, A)}}{\text{current}}$$

Equation 2:
$$\underset{\text{(kilowatt-hours, kWh)}}{\text{energy transferred}} = \underset{\text{(kilowatts, kW)}}{\text{power}} \times \underset{\text{(hours, h)}}{\text{time}}$$

● Always convert power to kilowatts and time to hours when using equation 2.

Equation 3: energy transferred = power × time
            (joules, J)   (watts, W) (seconds, s)

---

helium (He): An inert, colourless, odourless gas. It does not burn and is therefore used in lighter-than-air balloons rather than hydrogen.
● Helium is in Group 0 of the *periodic table*.
● It exists as individual atoms rather than molecules, unlike most other gaseous elements.
● It is inert because its single electron shell is complete.

---

hepatitis is a group of infectious liver diseases caused by viruses. They can cause serious damage to the liver.
● Hepatitis A is mainly spread via infected food and water.
● Other forms of hepatitis (B, C and E) are common amongst drug addicts due to transfer via infected syringes.

---

herbivore: an animal that eats principally plant material, for example rabbits and cows). They are also called primary *consumers*.
Mammalian herbivores often have:
● teeth specially adapted for grinding plant material
● digestive systems modified to contain large numbers of bacteria which digest the cellulose in the plant material.
Population size of herbivores depends mainly on:
● the amount of plant material available as food
● the numbers of animals (predators) that prey on them.

---

hertz (Hz): the unit for *frequency* of a wave:
  1 hertz = 1 wave front passes in 1 second

---

heterozygous: genes exist in two or more different forms, called *alleles*. An individual who receives different alleles of a gene from each parent is said to be heterozygous. Humans who are heterozygous for the *cystic fibrosis* gene, for example, can pass on the disease without suffering from it themselves; they are said to be carriers. You need to know the difference between *homozygous* and heterozygous.

---

homeostasis: the maintenance of relatively constant conditions inside the body (the internal environment). This is achieved via a number of different processes:

- Cell membranes control the movement of substances into and out of cells.
- The *pancreas* and *liver* work together to control the level of blood sugar (via the hormones *insulin* and *glucagon*).
- The *skin* is largely responsible for *temperature regulation* via *sweating*, *vasodilation* and *vasoconstriction*.
- The *kidneys* are responsible for controlling the water and ion content of the body (see also *ADH*).
- Many homeostatic process involve *receptors* and negative *feedback*.

homozygous: genes exist in two or more different forms called *alleles*. An individual who has received the same allele of a gene from each parent is said to be homozygous. You need to know the difference between homozygous and *heterozygous*.

Hooke's law states that the greater the stretching force applied to, for example, a wire or a spring, the greater the stretch (extension) it produces.

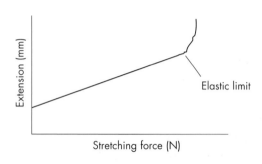

- Remember – it is the extension of the spring which is directly proportional to force – <u>not</u> the length of the spring.
- Hooke's law only applies if the *elastic limit* is not exceeded.

hormone (animal): a substance that regulates a body process, for example *insulin* and *glucagon* regulate the amount of sugar in your blood.

Gland	Main hormones produced	Main function of hormone
pituitary	ADH	control of water content of body
	FSH	stimulates eggs to mature in ovaries; stimulates ovaries to produce oestrogen
thyroid	thyroxin	controls physical and mental development
adrenal	adrenaline	'fight or flight' hormone
pancreas	insulin and glucagon	control of blood sugar levels
ovary	oestrogen progesterone	control of *menstrual cycle*; production of secondary sexual characteristics
testis	testosterone	production of secondary sexual characteristics

- In mammals, hormones are produced by ductless (endocrine) *glands* and are transported to their target tissues or organs via the bloodstream.
- The diagram shows the positions of some of the glands that produce hormones.

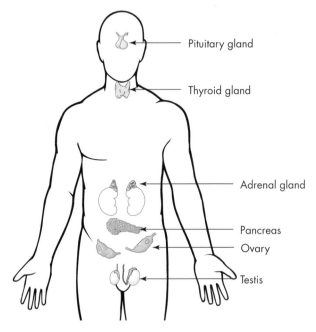

Pituitary gland

Thyroid gland

Adrenal gland

Pancreas

Ovary

Testis

hormone (plant): a substance that regulates a process in a plant, for example the production of flowers.
- Hormones are produced mainly at the root and stem tips.
- Tropisms (growth responses) in plants are brought about by unequal distribution of hormones in stems and roots.

Humans use plant hormones to:
- produce large numbers of plants quickly by stimulating the growth of roots in cuttings
- regulate the ripening of fruits
- kill weeds.

Hubble, Edwin: an American astronomer who lived 1889–1953.
He was the first scientist to propose that:
- the further away from us galaxies are, the further their light is shifted to the red end of the spectrum (red shift)
- the universe is expanding and might have started from one place with a huge explosion or *big bang*.

A telescope launched into space in 1990 is named after him.

humus is decaying animal and plant matter in the soil. It is a major constituent of soil, the other being rock particles.
- Humus contains mineral ions that are recycled as it decays.
- It contributes to the water-holding ability and drainage of the soil.

Huntington's disease is an inherited disease whose symptoms include involuntary spasms (muscular contractions). The symptoms do not usually appear until middle age.
- It is caused by a dominant *allele* H.
- People with the condition are usually *heterozygous*, Hh (it would be very unusual for two people with Huntington's disease to have children).
- If a person with the Huntington's allele (Hh) marries a healthy person (hh) there is a 50% chance that any child they produce will inherit the disease.
- Punnett square:

gametes	H	h
h	Hh	hh
h	Hh	hh

hydraulics: A method of transmitting pressure using liquids. It is how garage car-hoists work.
- A force is applied to a liquid using a master piston.
- This puts the liquid under pressure.
- This liquid presses on a slave piston which exerts a force where it is needed (see *brake, hydraulic*).
- If the area of the slave piston is greater than that of the master piston then it exerts a greater force as given by the equation:

$$\frac{\text{force on master piston}}{\text{area of master piston}} = \frac{\text{force on slave piston}}{\text{area of slave piston}}$$

EXAMPLE
You are usually asked to calculate the force on a slave piston.
A master piston has an area of 5 cm^3 and a slave piston has an area of 10 cm^3. Calculate the force exerted on the slave piston when a force of 1000 N is exerted on the master piston.
Rearrange the equation:

$$\text{force on slave piston} = \frac{\text{force on master piston} \times \text{area of slave piston}}{\text{area of master piston}}$$

$$= \frac{1000 \, N \times 10 \, cm^3}{5 \, cm^3}$$

$$= 2000 \, N$$

hydrocarbon, saturated: a compound containing only carbon and hydrogen, with only single carbon–carbon bonds, e.g. *methane* (see *alkanes*).

hydrocarbon, unsaturated: a compound containing only carbon and hydrogen, but with some carbon–carbon double bonds, e.g. *ethene* (see *alkenes*).

hydrochloric acid is the acid formed when hydrogen chloride (HCl) dissolves in water.
● In solution the hydrogen chloride dissociates into hydrogen ions and chloride ions (H^+ and Cl^-).
● Hydrochloric acid reacts with many metals forming metal chlorides and hydrogen gas.
● It also reacts with salts of weak acids, forming chlorides and the weak acids (see *acids and alkalis*).

hydroelectric: powered by electricity generated using water from a fast-moving river or from a dam or reservoir. This type of energy source will have to be developed if fossil fuels run out.
● The kinetic energy of moving water is transferred to turbines.
● The turbines then drive generators.
● The main advantage of hydroelectric power is that it is a *renewable energy resource*.
● Disadvantages include the fact that the dams used to collect the water may take up large areas of countryside.

hydrogen (H) is a colourless, odourless, reactive gas. Substances are acids if they contain aqueous hydrogen ions, H^+ (see *acids and alkalis*).
● Hydrogen molecules contain two hydrogen atoms, H_2.
● Hydrogen burns with a 'squeaky pop' if a lighted splint is applied – this is the usual test for hydrogen.

hydrogen, manufacture is mostly by the electrolysis of brine (see *brine, electrolysis of*).

hydrogen, reactions: hydrogen is reactive since it contains only one electron in its energy shell. In its reactions, hydrogen:

- combines with nitrogen in the presence of a *catalyst* to form ammonia (see *Haber process*)
- combines with sulphur to form hydrogen sulphide
- combines with chlorine to form hydrogen chloride
- combines with oxygen when it burns, or in the presence of a platinum catalyst, to form water
- combines with some metals, such as sodium, to form hydrides
- can reduce metal oxides, such as copper oxide, to the metal.

hydrogen, uses: hydrogen is used mainly:
- to solidify vegetable oils to make margarine
- as a fuel for space rockets
- in fuel cells on space craft.

hydrogen chloride (HCl) is a colourless, reactive gas which dissolves in water to form *hydrochloric acid*.

hydrogen ions are the ions, H^+(aq), that make solutions acid (see *acids and alkalis*).

hydrogen peroxide: chemical that can be used to bleach hair. It is a compound of hydrogen and oxygen, formula H_2O_2.
- It easily decomposes into water and oxygen:
$$2H_2O_2(aq) \longrightarrow 2H_2O(aq) + O_2(g)$$
- It is sold as a weak aqueous solution for use in the home as a bleach for delicate materials (e.g. human hair) and an antiseptic.
- It is used as a source of oxygen for space rockets.

hydrogencarbonate (HCO_3^-): an ion formed when only one of the hydrogens from carbonic acid (H_2CO_3) is replaced. It is one of the main ingredients in baking powder.
- Only the alkali metals (e.g. sodium and potassium) produce stable hydrogen carbonates.
- Baking powder contains sodium hydrogencarbonate and a weak acid which react to form carbon dioxide. This makes dough rise – soda bread and cakes are made in this way.
$$\text{acid} + \text{hydrogencarbonate} \longrightarrow \text{carbon dioxide} + \text{water} + \text{a salt}$$

hydroponics is the growing of crops such as tomatoes in a nutrient solution rather than in soil. It is environmentally friendly since excess nutrients are recycled instead of being leached into rivers.

- The plants are grown in trays of gravel.
- The gravel is flooded at regular intervals with nutrient solution.
- The nutrient solution drains off and can be used again when the nutrients have been replenished.

hydroxide ions (OH⁻) are produced when alkalis dissolve in water (see *acids and alkalis*).

- Hydroxides are formed by the alkali metals and also by metals such as calcium and barium.
- They feel slippery and will neutralise acids.
- They are important in the manufacture of soap, paper and cellophane.

hyphae are the tiny tubular structures that make up the body of fungi such as mushrooms and moulds. Together they look like fine cotton wool.

- The walls of hyphae consist of a substance similar to cellulose.
- Inside the wall is cytoplasm in which are embedded many nuclei.
- Hyphae do not contain chloroplasts.
- To feed, hyphae produce enzymes which pass out onto the food source.
- The food is digested outside the hyphae and the soluble food absorbed back into the hyphae.

hypothermia is a drastic fall in body temperature brought about by over-exposure to cold. Hikers who are ill-equipped to walk in mountain areas run the risk of hypothermia.

- Elderly people are more susceptible to hypothermia than younger people.
- Treatment involves slowly raising the body temperature using blankets, warm drinks and warm baths. Never follow the traditional practice of administering alcohol.

identical twins are twins who look alike because they have identical genetic information. Compare with non-identical twins, who can even be of different *gender*.

- Identical twins are formed when a fertilised egg divides into two cells that separate completely.
- The fertilised egg divides by *mitosis*, so each of the two cells receives identical genetic information.
- Each of the two cells continues to divide to produce two individuals.
- Although the twins have identical genetic information they may show some variation (e.g. in mass due to different diet or amount of exercise).

igneous: rock formed when molten rock (*magma*) cools (e.g. *basalt* and *granite*). You need to know why igneous rocks produced from volcanoes are different from those formed in the crust of the Earth.

- As magma cools it forms crystals.
- When magma is forced out of a volcano it cools very quickly, forming small crystals (e.g. basalt). This type of igneous rock is said to be *extrusive*.
- If magma cools deep in the Earth's crust it forms large crystals (e.g. granite). This type of igneous rock is said to be *intrusive*.

images, real and virtual: you need to know the difference between images produced by lenses and those produced by mirrors.

- A *real* image can be formed on a screen, for example the image on a cinema screen or the image focused on the film in a camera.

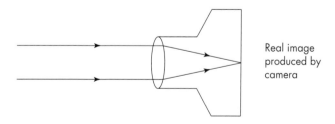

Real image produced by camera

- A *virtual* image cannot be formed on a screen, for example the image of your face you see in a mirror appears to be behind the mirror, but the image cannot be focused on a screen held behind the mirror.

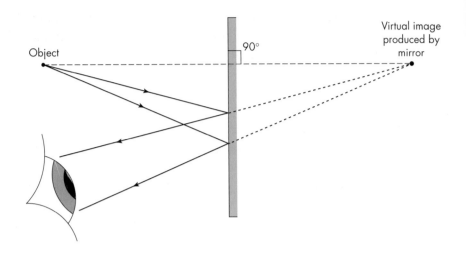

immunisation: a treatment that prevents a person from catching an infectious disease.

- A mild or dead form of the infecting organism (e.g. bacterium or virus) is introduced into the body.
- The *white blood cells* respond by producing *antibodies* which kill the infecting organism.
- If the person is subsequently infected by the organism, white cells can quickly produce antibodies to kill it. The person is then said to be immune from the disease.

immunity is the reason you don't catch some infectious diseases, even when you come into contact with them.

- Immunity means having substances in the body that prevent infectious organisms from causing disease.
- In active immunity, the person produces *antibodies* to the infection, either as a result of being infected or through *immunisation*.
- In passive immunity, antibodies or *antitoxins* are injected to help to defend the body against the infective microbes. This is usually done to protect doctors and nurses who have to treat people who are already infected.

impermeable: not allowing liquids or gases to pass through.

- Impermeable rocks trap natural gas and *crude oil*.
- The epidermis (outer skin) of most terrestrial organisms is impermeable to water, preventing excessive moisture loss.

impulse: the form in which information is carried by the nervous system. Always use the word impulse, <u>never</u> say signal or message.

- Nerve cells (neurones) carry information in the form of electrical impulses.
- Information is carried across *synapses* (connections between neurones) by chemicals which diffuse across them.

in vitro fertilisation: fertilisation of an egg outside the body; it is how 'test-tube babies' are produced.
- in vitro fertilisation is a technique used in both humans and animals.
- *FSH* (a hormone) is given to the female to cause her to produce several eggs at the same time.
- These eggs are removed from the woman's body (they are located by using ultrasound techniques).
- The eggs are then incubated with sperm in a nutrient medium for about 18 hours.
- Those eggs which are fertilised successfully will begin to divide to form embryos.
- One or more of these embryos are placed in the female's womb where it may develop into a foetus. The chance of this occurring is about 20%.
- The rest of the embryos are preserved in case the foetus does not develop.

inclined plane: a slope used to raise an object; one of the simplest types of *machine*.
- A slope is used to reduce the force needed to raise an object.
- It is thought that the ancient Egyptians used inclined planes to raise the large stone blocks used to build the pyramids.

Smaller force needed to raise block (load) ...

... but load moved through a greater distance – so work done is the same, or greater because of increased friction

indicators are chemicals used to find out whether a substance is acid or alkaline by the way their colour changes (see *acids and alkalis*).
- Litmus turns red in acid solution and blue in alkaline solution.
- Universal indicator has a range of colours in solutions with different *pHs*.

induction, electromagnetic: see *electromagnetic induction*.

induction of charge: if you rub a balloon on your sleeve then hold the balloon against a wall, the balloon will 'stick' to the wall. This is an example of induced charge.
- Rubbing the balloon on your sleeve moves electrons from your sleeve onto the balloon.

- The balloon is then negatively charged.
- When the balloon is brought near to a wall, the negative charges in the wall are repelled leaving positive charges near to the surface.
- The negative charges on the balloon and the positive charges on the wall attract each other and the balloon 'sticks' to the wall.

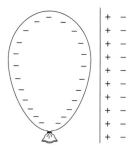

inert: will not react easily, for example helium or neon. Group 0 elements (the *noble gases*) do not react easily. This is because their highest occupied energy level is full, so the atom has no tendency to accept or donate electrons.

infection: a disease produced by microbes.
Disease-producing microbes may enter the body:
- through the air we breathe in
- in food or drink
- via cuts
- by direct contact (e.g. sexual intercourse).
If the body's defence mechanisms (e.g. *white blood cells*) do not destroy the microbes, the microbes multiply and produce poisonous waste products (toxins) that make us feel ill.

influenza: commonly called flu.
- Flu is an infectious disease caused by a virus which attacks the breathing organs.
- It is spread when infected people breathe out the virus and other people breathe it in.
- It is more likely to spread in poorly ventilated conditions.
- The influenza virus mutates fairly frequently to produce new forms.
- The white cells do not recognise these new forms so we are no longer immune to them.

infra-red radiation: waves given off by, for example, grills and toasters.
Infra-red waves are:
- *electromagnetic waves*
- just beyond the red end of the visible *spectrum*
- longer than visible light waves but shorter than radio waves
- mainly used (in addition to toasters etc.) in TV and other remote controllers, optical fibre communication and 'night vision' binoculars.

inherited characteristics are characteristics that you inherit from your parents (e.g. blue eyes), as opposed to those which depend on environmental factors (e.g. mass, which depends on the amount of food we eat and the amount of exercise we take).
- Inherited characteristics are determined by the *genes* carried on the *chromosomes* present in the sex cells (*egg* and *sperm*) that your parents produce.

inhibitor: a substance which slows down or stops a chemical reaction.
- An inhibitor often works by preventing an *enzyme* or other type of *catalyst* from working.
- An inhibitor often has the same shape as the molecule that normally fits into the *active site* of the enzyme.
- The inhibitor attaches itself to the active site and prevents the reacting molecule from reaching it.

injuries in sport: injuries caused by sudden, severe stress on muscles and joints (e.g. sprained muscle).
- Warm-up exercises help to avoid sports injuries.
- Sprains occur when ligaments or muscles are torn.
- Dislocations occur when a bone is forced out of a joint.

inner core: the material at the centre of the Earth (see also *mantle* and *core*). The inner core:
- has a radius of about 500 km
- is solid
- consists largely of iron with some nickel
- is at a temperature of about 6500°C
- has a relative density of about 13.

insecticide: a chemical used to kill insect pests.
- They are used mainly by farmers and gardeners to reduce damage to crops and animals, though they are also in the home, often in the form of aerosols, to kill flies, ants etc.
- Although they protect our food supplies, insecticides may kill other insects such as bees which are not pests.
- Organochlorine insecticides such as DDT are now banned in most countries because they are not broken down in the environment (they are non-*biodegradable*) and accumulate in *food chains*, killing animals such as birds at the tops of the food chains.

- Ideal insecticides should only kill pests and should decompose on contact with soil.

insects: the group of *invertebrate* animals that includes bees, flies and butterflies.

Characteristics include:

- three pairs of jointed limbs
- one pair of antennae
- one pair of compound eyes
- an exoskeleton (tough outer skin)

insemination: introduction of sperm into the body of a female.

- Insemination is done artificially, particularly in the breeding of cattle. Sperm from a bull is frozen for storage and then introduced into many different cows.
- Artificial insemination is possible in humans, but there are moral issues surrounding it.

insoluble: does not normally dissolve (e.g. sand is insoluble in water – it only ever forms a *mixture* with it).

- Most *ionic compounds* dissolve in water.
- Many *covalent compounds* do not dissolve in water.

insulator (electrical): a material which does allow an electric current to pass through it (e.g. plastic).

- This is why most electrical wiring is covered by plastic.
- Most metals conduct electricity because they have many *free electrons*.
- Insulators do not have these free electrons so they do not conduct electricity.

insulator (heat): a material that reduces the transfer of thermal energy (heat) from a hot region to a cold region (e.g. the plastic handle on a teapot).

- Glass wool is used to make jackets to reduce heat loss from hot water tanks.
- Woollen clothes are good insulators for the human body.
- Most metals conduct thermal energy well because they have many *free electrons*.
- Insulators do not have these free electrons so they do not conduct thermal energy well.
- Gases are very poor conductors of heat – this is why there is an air gap between the two layers of glass in *double glazing*.

insulin is a *hormone* involved in the control of blood sugar levels. If the body produces insufficient insulin, the person may develop the disease *diabetes*.

- Insulin is produced by the *pancreas*.
- High blood sugar levels stimulate the liver to convert glucose into glycogen for storage.
- This reduces the blood sugar level.
- Insulin has the opposite effect to *glucagon*.

---

intercostal muscles are the muscles between the ribs that you use to breathe.

- To breathe in the intercostal muscles contract, pulling the ribs upwards and outwards.
- This movement of the ribs, together with the downward movement of the *diaphragm*, increases the volume of the chest cavity (*thorax*).
- This increase in volume results in a decrease in pressure and air enters the lungs from the atmosphere via the windpipe (*trachea*).

---

intestine: the place where most digestion of food occurs in your body.

- The intestine is the part of the *digestive system* between the stomach and the anus.
- It is a long, tubular structure.
- It has a muscular wall to move food along by *peristalsis* (rhythmic muscular contractions).

The intestine is divided into two distinct parts:

THE SMALL INTESTINE

- produces *digestive enzymes* to complete the digestion of *carbohydrates*, *fats* and *proteins*
- contains *villi* to absorb the soluble, digested food into the bloodstream

THE LARGE INTESTINE

- absorbs most of the water from the indigestible food
- produces *faeces* which are stored until passed out of the body via the anus

---

intrusive rock is molten rock which has cooled slowly, deep in the Earth's *crust* (e.g. granite). You need to know the difference between intrusive and *extrusive* rocks.

Intrusive rocks:

- are *igneous* rocks since they are formed by the cooling of *magma*
- cool slowly, therefore they contain large crystals.

---

invertebrates: animals that do not have a backbone; mainly 'soft-bodied' animals (see also *vertebrates*). Examples are worms, insects, starfish, as opposed to vertebrates such as fish, birds and mammals.

iodide: a compound formed when a metal reacts with iodine (e.g. sodium iodide, NaI). Iodides give a yellow precipitate when tested with silver nitrate solution.

iodine (I): a blue-black, solid, reactive element. You may be asked to compare the properties of iodine with those of *chlorine* and *bromine*.
- Iodine is a *halogen*.
- It is in Group VII of the *periodic table*.
- Iodine is less reactive than bromine and chlorine and has a higher melting point because it is lower down the group.
- This is because it has electrons in higher energy levels and therefore gains electrons less easily.

iodine in the diet is needed to make *thyroxin* (a *hormone*). If iodine is lacking in the diet the thyroid gland swells, producing a condition called goitre.
- Thyroxin contains iodine.
- It is made by the thyroid gland found in the neck.
- Thyroxin controls mental and physical development.
- Some children are born with the inability to make sufficient thyroxin – such children grow up mentally retarded if they are not given thyroxin.

ion: a charged particle formed when an atom gains or loses an electron. Examples are Na^+ and Cl^-, the ions that make up table salt. *Ionic compounds* are composed of ions.
- If an atom loses an electron it becomes a positively charged ion called a *cation* (e.g. a sodium atom forms a sodium ion Na^+).
- If an atom gains an electron it becomes a negatively charged ion called an *anion* (e.g. a chlorine atom forms the chloride ion Cl^-).
(For diagrams see *bonding, ionic*.)
- Atoms can be converted to ions by radiation – such radiation is called ionising radiation.

ion exchange: removing unwanted ions from, for example, *hard water*.
- Hard water contains unwanted calcium and magnesium ions.

- If hard water is passed through a column containing a compound such as zeolite that has sodium ions, these sodium ions are exchanged for the calcium and magnesium ions.
- The water coming out of the column contains sodium ions rather than calcium and magnesium ions, and so it is 'softer'.

ionic bonding: see *bonding, ionic*.

ionic compound: a compound such as sodium chloride crystals, held together by strong ionic bonds (see *bonding, ionic*). You need to know the differences between ionic bonding and *covalent bonding*.

- Ionic compounds are giant structures made out of *ions*.
- They are held together by strong forces of attraction between the oppositely charged ions forming giant ionic lattices (see *giant structures, ionic*).
- Because of this they have high melting and boiling points.
- They conduct electricity when molten or in solution because the ions are then free to move.

ionic equation: an equation which shows only the *ions* that are deposited (in *electrolysis*) or precipitated.

- You will be asked questions similar to the following:
  Aluminium can be produced by the electrolysis of aluminium oxide (Al_2O_3). Complete the ionic half-equation for the formation of aluminium at the cathode:
  $$Al^{3+} + ...e^- \longrightarrow ...$$
- Remember, you need to give the number of electrons, which must equal the number of positive charges on the aluminium. You must also give the symbol for the aluminium atom (which is electrically neutral). Thus:
  $$Al^{3+} + 3e^- \longrightarrow Al$$

ionic giant structure: a structure such as a sodium chloride crystal.
- It is held together by strong forces between the oppositely charged *ions* (see *bonding*).
- Because of this, giant ionic structures have high melting points.
- When giant ionic compounds are melted or dissolved they can conduct electricity because the ions are then free to move.

ionisation: the formation of *ions* from atoms (see *bonding, ionic*).

ions, charges on: the table below shows the charges on some common ions.

| Positive ions | | Negative ions | |
Name	Formula	Name	Formula
Hydrogen	H^+	Chloride	Cl^-
Sodium	Na^+	Bromide	Br^-
Silver	Ag^+	Fluoride	F^-
Potassium	K^+	Iodide	I^-
Lithium	Li^+	Hydroxide	OH^-
Ammonium	NH_4^+	Nitrate	NO_3^-
Barium	Ba^{2+}	Oxide	O^{2-}
Calcium	Ca^{2+}	Sulphide	S_2^-
Copper(II)	Cu^{2+}	Sulphate	SO_4^{2-}
Magnesium	Mg^{2+}	Carbonate	CO_3^{2-}
Zinc	Zn^{2+}		
Lead	Pb^{2+}		
Iron(II)	Fe^{2+}		
Iron(III)	Fe^{3+}		
Aluminium	Al^{3+}		

iris: the coloured part of your eye – usually brown or blue.
- The iris controls the amount of light which enters the eye by making the pupil (gap in the iris) narrower or wider.
- In dim light radial muscles in the iris contract to make the pupil wider.
- In bright light circular muscles in the iris contract to make the pupil narrower.

iron (Fe): a metallic, magnetic element which has been used widely in manufacturing since prehistoric times. This is because:
- it is easily extracted from its ores
- it is *malleable*
- it is *ductile*
- it can be converted into a harder form called *steel*.

iron extraction: carbon monoxide is used to reduce the iron oxide from its ore *haematite* (see *blast furnace*).

iron, reactions of: iron is a fairly reactive metal.
- It displaces hydrogen from dilute acids.
- It rusts when exposed to damp air.
- It is a *transition metal*.
- It has a high melting point.
- It forms coloured compounds.
- It can be used as a *catalyst* in many reactions.

iron in the diet: iron is needed for the production of *haemoglobin* which makes up the bulk of red blood cells.
- Insufficient iron in the diet results in *anaemia* where the person becomes pale and listless.
- Women need more iron than men because iron is lost from the body during *menstruation*.
- Pregnant women need extra iron to meet the needs of the developing foetus.

isotopes are different forms of the same element. Radioactive isotopes have many uses, for example as tracers to investigate disease.
- Isotopes have the same number of *protons*.
- Isotopes therefore have the same number of *electrons*.

Isotopes have different numbers of *neutrons* and therefore different nucleon numbers. For example, ^{238}U and ^{235}U are both isotopes of uranium:
- they both have 92 protons
- ^{238}U has 146 neutrons
- ^{235}U has 143 neutrons.

Jenner, Edward: a British doctor who lived 1749–1823.

● He discovered the first vaccine – inoculation for smallpox.
● He noticed that farming workers who had been infected with a disease called cowpox did not catch smallpox when there was an epidemic.
● He inoculated a six-year-old boy with cowpox, then, six weeks later he injected the boy with smallpox.
● The boy did not develop smallpox.
● The procedure was published and doctors all over the world soon began to use the technique. The number of cases of smallpox fell rapidly.

joints, structure of: you may be asked to label a joint and describe the functions of its parts.

● The drawing shows a section through the hip joint.
● The bones at a joint are held in place by strong fibres called *ligaments*.
● The surfaces of the bone which rub together at the joint are covered with a slippery layer of *cartilage*.

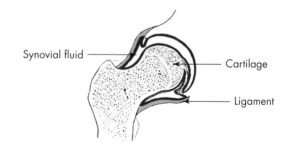

Synovial fluid

Cartilage

Ligament

● The synovial membrane in the joint produces an oily fluid to lubricate the joint.

joints, types: different joints allow different degrees of movement.

● Hinge joints (e.g. elbow and knee) allow movement in one plane – just like the hinge on a door.
● Ball-and-socket joints (e.g. shoulder and hip) allow movement in all directions.
● Pivot joints (e.g. neck) allow nodding and turning.

joule (J): the unit of both energy and work. The amount of energy transferred is measured in joules (see also *power*).

- When a force moves an object, energy is transferred and work is done.

  work done = energy transferred

- The amount of work done is related to the force applied and distance:

  work done = force applied × distance moved in direction of force
  (joules, J)   (newtons, N)   (metres, m)

- Joules are also used to measure energy transfer in electrical appliances:

  energy transferred = power   ×   time
  (joules, J)   (watts, W)   (seconds, s)

  energy transferred = potential difference ×   charge
  (joules, J)   (volts, V)   (coulombs, C)

kelvin (K): the unit of absolute temperature. You may have to convert °C to K and vice versa:

- 0 K = −273°C
- 1°C = 273 K
- To convert K to °C subtract 273 (e.g. 10 K = (10 − 273) = −263°C)
- To convert °C to K add 273 (e.g. 10°C = (10 + 273) = 283 K

---

kerosene is a liquid fuel used in domestic heaters and jet engines.

- It is obtained by the *fractional distillation* of *crude oil*.
- Kerosene has longer chain *hydrocarbons* than petrol and so it has a lower boiling point than petrol, is more difficult to ignite and is more viscous than petrol.
- About 7% of crude oil consists of kerosene.

---

kidney: the organ which gets rid of waste materials and controls the amount of water in your body. If your kidneys stop working, your life expectancy is only a few days unless you are put on a *kidney machine* or have a *kidney transplant*.

- The kidney is made up of thousands of kidney tubules, as shown in the diagram on the next page.

HOW THE KIDNEYS WORK

Ultrafiltration

- Blood enters the glomerulus (a knot of capillaries) from a branch of the renal artery.
- High pressure of blood forces water, glucose, salts and urea, but <u>not</u> blood cells or proteins, into Bowman's capsule.

Selective reabsorption

- As the filtered liquid passes through the first convoluted tubules all the glucose and most of the salts and water are reabsorbed into surrounding capillaries.
- Most of this absorption is against a *concentration gradient* – so *active transport* is involved which needs energy from *respiration*.

Concentration

- The rest of the kidney tubules are concerned with adjusting the concentration of water and salts in the blood; just sufficient is reabsorbed to keep the blood at the correct concentration.
- The reabsorption of water is controlled by the hormone *ADH*.

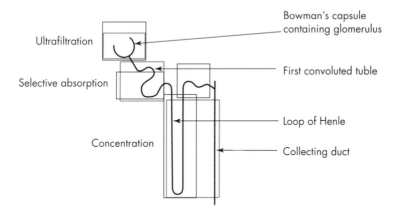

Urine is the liquid which is left after all reabsorption has taken place. It consists of:

- *urea*
- excess water
- excess salts.

---

kidney, artificial: a machine which removes waste products from a patient's blood and restores to normal levels concentrations of dissolved substances in the blood; also called a dialysis machine.

- It is used to <u>treat</u> patients whose kidneys have failed, but does not cure them.
- In the machine the patient's blood is separated from a fluid called dialysis fluid by a *partially permeable membrane* (a membrane that allows small molecules to pass through but not large ones) made out of cellophane.
- The concentration of dissolved substances in the dialysis fluid supplied to the machine is the same as the concentration of these substances in blood leaving a healthy kidney.
- Substances which are of higher concentration in the patient's blood than in the dialysis fluid (e.g. urea, excess salts, excess water) diffuse from the patient's blood into the dialysis fluid.
- The treatment takes several hours and is done twice a week.

---

kidney transplant: replacing a failed kidney with a healthy kidney from another person.
- If successful, a kidney transplant is a permanent cure (see *kidney, artificial*).
- There is a danger that the transplanted kidney will be rejected by the body. To minimise the risk of rejection:
- the donor organ should have a 'tissue type' as similar as possible to that of the patient
- the white blood cell-producing areas of the body are irradiated to inhibit white cell production
- the recipient is kept in sterile conditions for some time after the operation
- the patient is given drugs which suppress the immune system.

kilowatt (kW): a measure of the *power* of an electrical appliance and therefore how much it costs to run the appliance.
- 1 kilowatt = 1000 watts
- You will sometimes be given the power of an appliance in watts (e.g. the power of a light bulb given as 200 W); always convert this to kilowatts for calculations (200 W = 0.2 kW).

kilowatt-hour (kWh): a measure of the amount of *energy* transferred from the mains to an electrical appliance.

$$\begin{array}{ccccc} \text{energy transferred} & = & \text{power} & \times & \text{time} \\ \text{(kilowatt-hours, kWh)} & & \text{(kilowatts, kW)} & & \text{(hours, h)} \end{array}$$

Before using this equation always convert:
- power given in watts into kilowatts
- time given in minutes or seconds into hours.

kinetic energy is the energy you and a vehicle has when you are riding in/on it, by virtue of its motion.
- It is the energy possessed by an object because of its motion and is measured in joules (J).
- An object has more kinetic energy the greater its mass and the greater its speed.
- Kinetic energy, mass and speed are related by the equation:

$$\begin{array}{ccccc} \text{kinetic energy} & = & \dfrac{1}{2} \times & \text{mass} & \times & \text{(speed)}^2 \\ \text{(joules, J)} & & & \text{(kilograms, kg)} & & \text{([metres/second]}^2, \text{[m/s]}^2) \end{array}$$

- Do not confuse (speed)^2 ([m/s]^2) with acceleration (m/s^2).

EXAMPLE

Calculate the kinetic energy of a car of mass 900 kg travelling at 10 m/s.

$$
\begin{aligned}
\text{kinetic energy (J)} \; &= \; 900 \text{ kg} \times (10 \text{ m/s})^2 \\
&= \; 900 \text{ kg} \times 100 \text{ m/s} \\
&= \; 90\,000 \text{ J}
\end{aligned}
$$

kinetic theory of gases: theory concerning the relationships between the temperature, pressure and volume of a gas. To use this theory you have to be able to explain volume and pressure changes in a gas in terms of particles.

- The particles in a gas move around very quickly in all directions.
- The kinetic theory of gases helps to explain volume changes in gases (when the pressure on a gas increases and its temperature remains the same its volume decreases – because the particles of gas are closer together).
- It also helps to explain pressure changes in gases (if the temperature rises, energy is transferred to the gas particles and they move faster – if the volume of the gas is kept constant the particles hit the sides of the container both more often and harder causing the pressure to rise).

lactic acid is a weak acid found both in yoghurt and in your muscles when they are beginning to tire during exercise.

- Lactic acid is produced by the action of bacteria on the sugar lactose in milk when yoghurt is made – an example of *fermentation*.
- Lactic acid is produced by *anaerobic respiration* (respiration without oxygen) in muscles when the supply of oxygen to the muscles is insufficient to provide all the energy by *aerobic respiration*.
- Lactic acid build-up in muscles is partly responsible for muscle cramp and muscle fatigue.
- The amount of oxygen needed to get rid of the lactic acid produced during exercise is know as the *oxygen debt*.

Lamarck: a French scientist who lived 1744–1829.

He produced a theory of evolution based on the inheritance of acquired characteristics. He proposed the following mechanism.

- As the environment changes new influences affect organisms.
- These new influences trigger new needs.
- As a result, new structures arise or old structures are modified.
- These modified structures (acquired characteristics) are passed on to the next generation and are therefore inherited.

His theory would explain the long neck of the giraffe in this way:

- As conditions became drier there was increased competition amongst animals for food.
- Giraffes stretched their necks and were able to obtain food from higher up the trees.
- The stretched necks were inherited by the next generation.

His theory is now largely discredited because we now know that changes in the characteristics of an organism in response to environmental change cannot alter the *genes* in the *gametes* (sex cells), and so cannot be inherited by subsequent generations.

large intestine: the last part of the *digestive system*, ending at the anus.

- Its main function is to absorb most of the water from indigestible food.
- What remains is known as *faeces*.

- The large intestine has muscles in its walls that enable it to force the faeces out of the body via the anus.

larynx: the voice box or Adam's apple. The larynx:
- is at the top of the *trachea* (windpipe)
- is made mainly from *cartilage*
- contains elastic threads called vocal cords which can be made to vibrate to produce sound.

lattice: a regular arrangement of particles that gives a crystalline solid (solid made out of crystals) a particular shape.
- Lattices are found in *giant structures, covalent giant structures, ionic giant structures* and metals.
- Lattices are held together by strong chemical bonds between the atoms, ions or molecules.

lava: molten rock which flows up to the surface of the Earth through cracks, particularly from volcanoes.
- Larva solidifies to form *igneous* rocks such as basalt.
- These igneous rocks contain small crystals because the lava cools quickly.

Lavoisier, Antoine: a French scientist who lived from 1743 to 1794.
- He developed the idea of the *element*.
- He was the first to understand the nature of *combustion* – that when an element burns it combines with oxygen in air.
- Although Joseph Priestley had demonstrated that heating mercuric oxygen released a gas, Lavoisier was the first to realise the nature of this gas – that it was oxygen.

leaching is the washing of nutrient ions, including fertilisers, from farmland into rivers and lakes. It can lead to serious damage to freshwater environments.
- Leaching happens if too much nitrate or phosphate is used as fertiliser, or if there is more rainfall than usual.
- This may lead to *eutrophication* – excessive growth of water plants.

lead (Pb): a soft, bluish-grey metal. It was one of the earliest metals to be used by humans.

USES

- storage batteries
- sheaths for electric cables

- paint manufacture
- protective sheathing in X-ray departments and in the nuclear industry

PROPERTIES

- It reacts only slowly with water.
- It does not react with dilute acids except nitric acid.
- It is low down in the reactivity series.

leaf: the part of a plant whose main function is to produce food. Most of the food on Earth comes originally from plant leaves.

- Most leaves are green because they contain chlorophyll which is needed for *photosynthesis* (the process which plants use to make food).
- Leaves are usually broad and thin.
- This shape gives them a large surface area for absorption of light for photosynthesis.
- It reduces the distance that carbon dioxide has to travel from the air to the cells that photosynthesise.

INTERNAL STRUCTURE OF THE LEAF

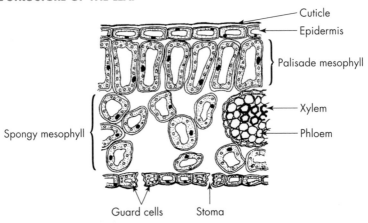

Part of leaf	Main function
cuticle	prevents excess water loss
epidermis	transparent to allow light to pass through
palisade mesophyll	closely packed cells to absorb maximum light for photosynthesis
spongy mesophyll	large air spaces to allow carbon dioxide to diffuse rapidly to palisade cells
stoma (plural stomata)	allow gases, particularly carbon dioxide, to enter
guard cells	control the width of the stomata

legumes: the family of plants that includes peas, beans and clover. Many of them can replace nitrogen compounds in the soil, thus reducing the need for artificial fertilisers. For this reason they are often grown on organic farms.

- Many of the plants in this family have *nitrogen-fixing* bacteria in their roots.
- These bacteria can 'fix' nitrogen from the air, converting it to compounds such as nitrates.
- The legumes can use these nitrates to make the proteins they need for growth, therefore they do not need as much fertiliser as other crops.
- In some types of crop rotation, clover is grown one year then ploughed into the soil. This increases the nitrogen content of the soil without having to use fertilisers.

lens: a transparent object used to focus or disperse light; a lens is found in your eyes and in a camera.

CONVEX LENSES

A convex lens will focus parallel rays of light at a point which is called the principal focus of the lens.

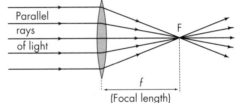

- The distance between the principal focus (F) and the lens is known as the focal length of the lens (*f*).
- This image is a real image (see *image, real*).

CONCAVE LENSES

A concave lens will diverge parallel rays of light.

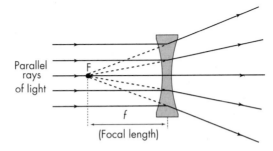

- The diverged rays of light appear to come from a point known as the principal focus (F) of the lens.
- The distance between the principal focus and the lens is known as the focal length of the lens (*f*).

Remember that:
- the thicker the lens, the less its focal length
- the bending of light waves by lenses is due to refraction
- convex lenses are used to treat long-sightedness

- concave lenses are used to treat short-sightedness
- the shape of the lens in the human eye can be varied to focus on near or distant objects (see *eye, focusing*).

leucocyte: a type of *white blood cell* that helps to protect us from disease microbes. Leucocytes:
- are made mainly by the bone marrow
- have a lobed nucleus
- protect the body from infection, mainly by engulfing invading microbes.

LH: a *hormone* which causes the monthly release of an egg from the human ovaries.
- LH is produced by the *pituitary gland* at the base of the brain.
- LH production is stimulated by the hormone oestrogen which is produced by the ovaries.
- LH production rises to a peak in the middle of the *menstrual cycle* and it is this high level that causes the egg to be released.

light: light waves that can be detected by eyes. They are *electromagnetic waves.*
- Light waves have a shorter wavelength than infra-red waves but a longer wavelength than X-rays.
- White light can be *dispersed* by a prism into the colours of the *spectrum*: red, orange, yellow, green, blue, indigo, violet.
- Red light has the longest *wavelength* and ultraviolet the shortest.
- When light strikes an object some wavelengths are absorbed and some are reflected.
- The colour of an object depends on which wavelengths are reflected. For example, a red object appears red because it reflects red light but absorbs light of all other wavelengths.
- Light waves are *transverse waves* and can travel through a *vacuum.*
- Light waves can undergo *reflection*, *refraction* and *diffraction.*

lime: a white solid containing mainly calcium oxide (CaO). It is used to make cement and slaked lime (calcium hydroxide). Lime is made by heating limestone (calcium carbonate) in a *lime kiln.*

lime kiln: used to make *lime* from limestone.
- The breakdown of calcium carbonate is an example of *thermal decomposition*:

  calcium carbonate $\longrightarrow$ calcium oxide + carbon dioxide

  $CaCO_3(s) \longrightarrow CaO(s) + CO_2(g)$
- The hot air provides oxygen for the reaction. It also speeds up the reaction.

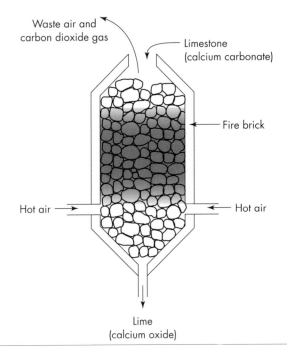

Waste air and carbon dioxide gas

Limestone (calcium carbonate)

Fire brick

Hot air → ← Hot air

Lime (calcium oxide)

limestone is a common rock which is usually white or whitish.
- Limestone contains mainly calcium carbonate ($CaCO_3$).
- It is a *sedimentary rock*.
- Most limestones are made from the shells of organisms that lived millions of years ago.
- These remains were cemented together by a combination of great pressure and the crystallising out of salts.
- Limestone is used as a building material and to make *lime*.

limewater is a liquid used to test for carbon dioxide (CO_2).
- A saturated solution of calcium hydroxide, $Ca(OH)_2$, turns milky when carbon dioxide is passed through it. This is because insoluble calcium carbonate is formed.

limit of elasticity: see *elastic limit*.

limit of proportionality: how far you can stretch an object such as a spring without permanently changing its shape. It can also be thought of in terms of force:
- It is the maximum force that can be applied to an object (such as a wire or a spring) and the extension still be proportional to the applied force (see *elastic behaviour*).

limiting factor: a factor that limits how fast a process proceeds (e.g. light intensity limits how fast photosynthesis proceeds). Farmers who grow crops in greenhouses need to know whether light, temperature or the carbon dioxide content of the air is limiting how fast the crops are growing – and therefore whether to switch on lights or heaters.

- At noon on a warm summer's day, carbon dioxide concentration may limit the rate of photosynthesis.
- In the evening of a warm summer's day, light intensity may limit the rate of photosynthesis.
- At noon on a cold, sunny winter's day, low temperature may limit the rate of photosynthesis.

lines of force: a magnet is surrounded by a *magnetic field* which exerts forces on other magnetic materials; the strength and direction of these forces can be represented by lines of force.
These lines of force can be plotted by:

- using a compass
- placing a sheet of paper over the magnet and dusting the paper with iron filings.

A coil of wire with a current passing through it produces similar lines of force (see *electric motor*).

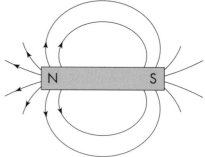

lipase: an *enzyme* that digests fats (see *digestion*).

- Lipases digest fats into fatty acids and glycerol.
- They are produced by the *pancreas* and the *small intestine*.
- Their action is aided by *bile* which emulsifies fats, giving them a larger surface area for the lipase to act upon.

liquid: a substance that can be poured, and takes the shape of its container. You have to know the similarities and differences between *solids*, liquids and *gases* (see *change of state*).

- Liquid particles are close together.
- A liquid has a definite volume.
- The particles can move around each other.
- Heating a liquid makes the particles move around more quickly.
- Particles which have enough energy are able to escape attractive forces and become a gas – this is *evaporation*.

lithium (Li): is a silvery-white metal.

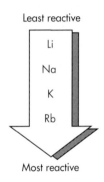

Least reactive

Li

Na

K

Rb

Most reactive

- Lithium is an *alkali metal*.
- It is an element in Group I of the *periodic table*.
- It reacts with water, releasing hydrogen and forming an alkaline hydroxide solution.
- It is the least reactive of the alkali metals.
- It is least reactive because its outer electron energy level is at a lower level than that of the other elements in the group, therefore it finds it less easy to lose an electron.

---

live (electricity): the wire that carries the electricity supply to an appliance. You must know what the colours of the wires mean to connect a plug correctly and safely.

The live wire is:

- covered with <u>brown</u> plastic insulator
- attached to the fuse in a *three-pin plug*.

---

liver: a large organ found in the upper right-hand side of the *abdomen*. The liver is the 'chemical factory' of the body – all the food you eat is processed by the liver after it has been digested in the *digestive system*. The liver:

- produces *bile* which *emulsifies* fats during digestion
- stores *glycogen* – an insoluble carbohydrate that can be converted to glucose when blood sugar level is low (see *glucagon* and *insulin*)
- breaks down *(deaminates)* excess *amino acids*, forming *urea*
- breaks down poisonous substances (toxins) including alcohol and solvents.

---

longitudinal wave: a 'push-pull' wave – the vibration is along the length of the wave. You must know the difference between longitudinal waves (e.g. sound waves) and *transverse* waves (e.g. light waves).

- A longitudinal wave consists of *compressions* and *rarefactions*.
- Its vibrations are parallel to the direction of the wave.
- Examples are *sound waves* and *P-waves*.

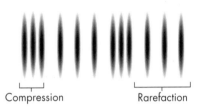

Compression   Rarefaction

---

loudness: the harder air molecules hit the eardrum, the louder the sound seems. Very loud sounds, such as those produced by some industrial machinery or in discos, can damage our hearing.

- Loudness is a measure of the *amplitude* of a sound wave.
- It depends on how much the air molecules in a sound wave vibrate.

lubricating oil is the least runny liquid produced during the *fractional distillation* of *crude oil*. It is important in reducing the wear caused by *friction* in car engines and machinery.
- Lubricating oil has a boiling point of over 350°C.
- It consists of *hydrocarbons* with chains containing between 20 and 30 carbon atoms, which is why it has a high boiling point and a high *viscosity*.

lungs are the breathing organs in the chest (*thorax*) of animals such as mammals.

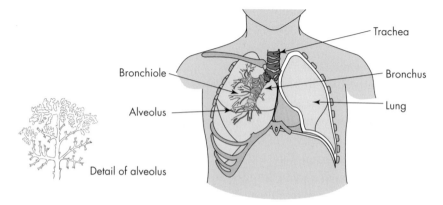

Detail of alveolus

- The lungs are where oxygen passes from the air into the blood system, and carbon dioxide is passed from the blood system into the air.
- They are made up largely of air sacs called *alveoli*.
- Alveoli are supplied with air via the *trachea*, *bronchi* and *bronchioles*.
- The lungs are ventilated by movements of the *intercostal muscles* and the *diaphragm*.

lymphocyte: a type of *white blood cell* important in protecting us from disease.
- Lymphocytes help to defend the body by producing *antibodies* which kill disease microbes.
- They are produced mainly in the lymph glands (which are found mainly in the neck, armpits and groin).

machine: a device that enables a person to exert a greater force than by using only muscles. Machines are designed to make tasks easier for us. Examples of machines include:

- levers
- pulleys
- inclined planes
- wheels and axles.
- Most machines make an applied force larger – the resultant force is larger than the applied force. They do this by making the applied force move further than the resultant force:

$$\text{applied force} \times \text{distance moved in direction of applied force} = \text{resultant force} \times \text{distance moved in direction of resultant force}$$

- The efficiency of most machines is less than 1 because some energy is transferred as heat due to friction.

---

magma: molten rock from just under the *crust* of the Earth. We can see magma flowing out of an erupting volcano.

- Magma is formed from rocks in the lower part of the crust and the upper part of the *mantle*.
- The energy to melt rock to form magma is transferred from *radioactive decay* of, for example, uranium.
- In volcanoes, magma is sometimes forced out of the crust as *lava*. This rock cools rapidly forming igneous rocks which contain small crystals (*extrusive igneous rocks*).
- Magma is sometimes forced into the crust where it cools slowly forming igneous rocks which contain large crystals (*intrusive igneous rocks*).

---

magnesium (Mg) is a silvery-white metallic element. You will probably have seen magnesium ribbon burning fiercely in your laboratory.

- Magnesium is in Group II of the *periodic table*.
- It is an alkaline earth metal – these metals are less reactive than the *alkali metals*.
- It is the sixth most abundant element in the Earth's crust.

● It occurs mainly as minerals such as dolerite and as magnesium chloride in seawater.

magnesium, reactions of:
● Magnesium does not react with oxygen or with water at room temperature.
● It burns fiercely in oxygen if heated to 800°C.
● It reacts with dilute acids forming hydrogen and a salt, for example:

magnesium + dilute hydrochloric acid $\longrightarrow$ hydrogen + magnesium chloride

$$Mg(s) \quad + \quad 2HCl(aq) \quad \longrightarrow \quad H_2(g) \quad + \quad MgCl_2(aq)$$

magnesium, uses of: magnesium is used to form *alloys*, typically with copper or aluminium.
● Because it has a very low density it is used in alloys which need to be light (e.g. for sports car engines).
● These alloys usually have a high tensile strength and are used in, for example, aircraft manufacture.

magnet: an object which will attract metals such as iron, steel and nickel. Without magnets there would be no mains electricity or electric motors.
● If a magnet is free to move it will come to rest in a north–south direction: the end of the magnet which points north is called the north pole, the end of the magnet which points south is called the south pole.
● Like poles repel each other.
● Unlike poles attract each other.
● Iron magnets are 'soft' magnets because they lose their magnetism easily – that is why iron is used to make *electromagnets*.

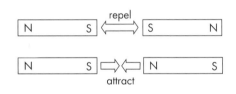

● Steel magnets are called 'hard' magnets because they do not lose their magnetism easily, which is why steel is used to make permanent magnets.

magnetic effect of current: a coil of wire acts like a bar magnet when an electric current passes through it. The magnetic field is just like that around a bar magnet.
● One end of the coil becomes a north-seeking pole, the other a south-seeking pole.
● Such an arrangement is called an *electromagnet*.

magnetic field: the region around a magnet where it exerts a force on other magnetic materials. It is this force that enables us to build electric generators and motors.

- The lines shown on a magnetic field are called magnetic flux lines.
- You should be able draw the magnetic fields shown here.

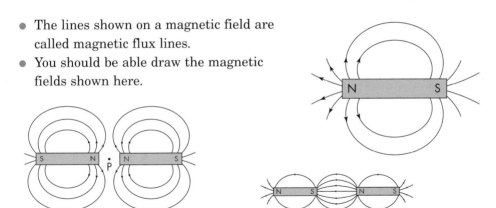

magnetic induction: making a piece of iron or steel magnetic by holding a strong magnet next to it. Most objects made out of steel are slightly magnetised by the Earth's magnetic field (see *magnetism, Earth's*).

magnetism, Earth's: the Earth acts as if it has a bar magnet running through the middle of it. This is why a magnetic compass works.
- The magnetic north pole of the Earth is about 1300 km south of the geographical North Pole, and it is moving west at about 20 km per year.
- The Earth's magnetism is thought to be caused by liquid iron in the *core*.
- Because the north pole of a bar magnet is attracted to it, the magnetic north pole of the Earth acts like the south pole of a bar magnet.

mains electricity is the 230 V electricity that is supplied to our homes and provides power for most of our daily needs.
- Mains electricity can kill if it is not used correctly.
- It is an *alternating current* with a *frequency* of 50 *hertz*.
- Most appliances are connected to the mains supply using cable and a *three-pin plug*.
- Mains electric circuits are protected by *fuses* or by *circuit breakers* – these switch off the current if a fault develops.
- Electrical appliances should be connected to an earth, so that if a fault develops a very large current flows to earth, causing the fuse to melt.
A mains cable has:
- three wires made out of copper, which is a good electrical *conductor*
- plastic insulation around each wire
- brown coloured insulation on the *live* wire
- blue coloured insulation on the *neutral* wire
- yellow and green striped insulation on the *earth* wire.

malleable: able to be hammered easily or pressed into a shape. It is a useful property of most common metals – non-metals are usually brittle and therefore break if hammered or pressed.

maltose is a sugar formed when starch is digested.
- During digestion starch is broken down by *carbohydrase* (specifically *amylase*) enzymes into maltose.
- Maltose consists of two glucose molecules.
- During *brewing*, enzymes in barley grains digest the starch in the barley into maltose.

mammals are animals that produce milk to feed their young. It includes animals as diverse as anteaters, elephants, cats, dogs and humans. Milk is produced by *mammary glands*.

Other characteristics of most mammals include:
- they are *vertebrates* (have a backbone)
- the body is covered by hair (for *insulation*)
- they have a high, constant body temperature
- the young develop in the *uterus* (womb) of the mother
- whilst in the womb the young receive food and oxygen from an organ called the *placenta*
- they have a *diaphragm* which separates the thorax from the *abdomen*.

mammary glands are the structures that produce milk in female mammals, such as humans and cows. The milk is produced to feed the young.
- The human mammary glands (breasts) enlarge when the woman becomes sexually mature during *adolescence*.
- The maturation is controlled by females *hormones* including *oestrogen*.

mantle: the part of the Earth between the *crust* and the *core* (see *Earth, structure of*). The continents float on the molten rock that makes up the mantle.
- The mantle consists of molten rock extending almost halfway to the centre of the Earth.
- It is extremely viscous (non-runny).
- *Convection* currents in the mantle cause movements of the plates which make up the crust.

marble is a rock used for making statues and for facing buildings.
- Marble is a form of *limestone*.
- It is mainly calcium carbonate. $CaCO_3$.

- It is a *metamorphic* rock containing many crystals.
- It is formed by the action of high pressures and high temperatures on chalk, deep in the Earth's *crust*.

Marconi, Guglielmo: an Italian engineer who lived 1874–1937.
- In the 1890s he was the first person to both transmit and receive radio waves over several kilometres.
- His equipment was called the 'wireless' because messages were transmitted through the air – a wire was not needed, as in the telegraph.

margarine is a manufactured food consisting mainly of fats and oils. It is claimed that it is more healthy to eat margarine than butter.
- It is made mainly from vegetable oils such as sunflower oil.
- The oils are made more solid by reacting them with hydrogen in the presence of a nickel *catalyst*.
- Margarine consists mainly of unsaturated fats which many claim to be more healthy than the saturated fats found in animal products.

mass is the amount of matter in an object. Mass and weight are related, but they are <u>not</u> the same – make sure that you understand the difference.
- Mass is measured in kilograms (kg).
- Do not confuse mass with weight – weight is the mass of an object multiplied by the gravitational field strength.
- The mass of an object is the <u>same</u> on the Moon as it is on Earth.
- The weight of the object is <u>less</u> on the Moon because the gravitational field strength of the Moon is smaller than that on Earth.

mass number is the number of particles in the nucleus of an atom (also called *nucleon number*). Make sure that you know the difference between mass number and *proton number*.
- In the symbol of the uranium atom, $^{238}_{92}U$, the mass number is 238.
- This means that the total number of *protons* and *neutrons* is 238.
- Because the number of protons is given by the *proton number* (92) the number of neutrons is (238 − 92) = 146.
- Uranium-235 has the symbol $^{235}_{92}U$.
- ^{238}U and ^{235}U are the same element because they have the same number of protons (92).
- They are called *isotopes* of uranium because they have different numbers of neutrons.

matter, states of: see *states of matter*.

meiosis is the type of cell division which takes place during the formation of *gametes* (sex cells) in most organisms. Meiosis, along with *fertilisation*, is the reason why we all look different.
- Do not confuse meiosis with *mitosis*.

During the formation of a gamete (e.g. a sperm):
- the *chromosomes* are first copied
- then the cell divides twice to form four cells.
- Each of these cells contains a single set of chromosomes
- and therefore one of each pair of *genes*.
- During the formation of these cells, parts of chromosomes within pairs are exchanged, resulting in genetic variation.
- when the gametes fuse (join together) during fertilisation, a single body cell with new pairs of chromosomes is formed.
- This cell then divides repeatedly by mitosis.

melamine is a plastic used to make cups and plates, and also to give a pleasant surface to furniture such as tables.

melanin is a dark-coloured pigment found in the skin of many animals. The amount of melanin in your skin determines how dark you look.
- A recessive allele results in an animal lacking melanin pigment in the skin; such an animal is said to be an albino.
- Melanin pigment (or lack of it) is often useful in camouflage.

In the peppered moth, for example:
- individuals with melanin are camouflaged against trees which have been blackened by soot.
- individuals without melanin are camouflaged against trees with pale bark or which have light-coloured lichens growing on them.

melting: changing of a solid into a liquid, e.g. when ice changes to water.
When energy is transferred to a solid:
- its particles vibrate more violently
- and they begin to separate from each other.
- With sufficient energy they can move freely.
- The solid has now turned into a liquid.

membrane: see *cell membrane*.

Mendel, Gregor: an Austrian monk who lived 1822–1884.
- He investigated the inheritance of characteristics in pea plants.
- In a scientific paper published in 1866 he proposed two laws of inheritance:
  1 There are hereditary units (which we now call *genes*) which control the inheritance of characteristics and these often occur in two forms – *dominant* and *recessive*.
  2 These genes remain unchanged from generation to generation.
- The importance of Mendel's work was not recognised until 1900.
- His work laid the foundations for the study of genetics.

Mendeleyev, Dmitri: a Russian scientist who lived 1834–1907.
- In 1871 he published what became known as the *periodic table* of the elements.
- He placed the elements in order of their atomic mass, like Rowlands had once, but in addition elements were arranged in the table so that elements with similar properties were in the same vertical columns (*groups*).
- Where there was no known element that would fit a particular place in the table he left a gap.
- Elements discovered later filled these gaps, strongly supporting his ideas.

menstrual cycle: a monthly series of changes that prepare a woman's body for pregnancy. Each month, hormones in the woman's body cause:
- an egg to mature and be released from an ovary
- the lining of her uterus (womb) to change in order to receive a fertilised egg.
- If the egg is not fertilised the inner lining of the womb breaks down and leaves the body of the woman as the menstrual flow (see *menstruation*).

The following are some of the hormones involved in the control of the menstrual cycle:

FOLLICLE STIMULATING HORMONE

FSH is secreted by the *pituitary gland* and causes:
- an egg to mature in one of the ovaries
- oestrogen to be produced by the cells of the ovary.

OESTROGEN

The effects of *oestrogen* are:
- to inhibit the production of FSH by the pituitary gland (this is an example of negative *feedback*)
- to cause the inner lining of the womb to become thicker to receive a fertilised egg
- to stimulate the pituitary gland to produce *LH*.

LH

The effect of LH is to cause the mature egg to be released from the ovary.

menstruation is the loss of cells and blood from the lining of the womb of a woman. Menstruation:
- occurs approximately once per month
- lasts for approximately three to seven days
- begins during adolescence and ends when a woman is about 50 years old.
- Menstruation does not occur when a woman is pregnant – if a woman does not menstruate at the normal time in the month, it is often the first sign that she is pregnant (see *menstrual cycle*).

mercury (Hg) is a silver-coloured metal that is liquid at room temperature.
- Mercury is used to make thermometers because it expands in a very regular way when heated.
- It is a *transition metal*.
- Its vapour is very poisonous – it causes damage to the brain, liver and kidneys.

metal giant structure is the reason why metals are so good at conducting both electricity and heat.
- They have a structure in which the outer electrons of the metal atoms are free to move.
- These *free electrons* hold the metal ions together in a regular structure and allow the metal to conduct heat and electricity.

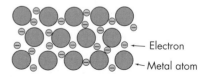

metal oxides are compounds formed when metals react with oxygen or water.
- All metal oxides are bases (see *acids and alkalis*).
- Some metal oxides dissolve in water to form *alkalis*:

sodium oxide + water $\longrightarrow$ sodium hydroxide solution

$Na_2O(s)$ $+ H_2O(l) \longrightarrow$ $2NaOH(aq)$

- Other metal oxides (e.g. copper oxide) do not dissolve in water but do react with dilute acids.

metalloid: an *element* with some of the properties of a metal and some of a non-metal. They have properties that make them ideal for making integrated circuits ('chips') for computers.

- Examples of metalloids include silicon and germanium.
- Silicon is like a metal because it is shiny and like a non-metal because it is very brittle.
- It is used to make chips because its electrical conductivity is between that of a metal and a non-metal.

***

metals are elements with properties that have made them useful to humans for thousands of years.

All metals have most of the following properties:
- solid at room temperature (except mercury)
- high melting point
- shiny (when freshly cut)
- good conductor of both heat and electricity
- mostly tough, strong and *malleable* (except metals such as sodium and potassium)
- form *alloys* (mixtures with other metals).

***

metals, reactions with acids: most metals react with dilute acids to form hydrogen and a *salt*. For example:

magnesium + dilute hydrochloric acid $\longrightarrow$ hydrogen + magnesium chloride

$Mg(s)$ + $2HCl(aq)$ $\longrightarrow$ $H_2(g)$ + $MgCl_2$

- The table shows how vigorously different metals react with dilute acid.

Metal	Reaction with dilute acid
potassium sodium calcium	violent reaction, giving off hydrogen
magnesium aluminium zinc iron	react more slowly, giving off hydrogen
lead	only gives off hydrogen if the acid is warmed
copper silver gold	do not react with dilute acids

(see also *reactivity series*.)

***

metals, reactions with oxygen: most metals react with oxygen to form *metal oxides*. For example:

copper + oxygen $\longrightarrow$ copper oxide

$2Cu(s) + O_2(g) \longrightarrow 2CuO(s)$

The table shows how vigorously metals react with oxygen (see also *reactivity series*):

Metal	Reaction with oxygen
potassium sodium calcium magnesium aluminium zinc iron	burn in air forming an oxide
lead copper	do not burn in air – only form an oxide if heated strongly in air
silver gold	do not react with oxygen

metals, reactions with water: some metals react with water to produce hydrogen, others will only react with steam and the rest do not react at all with water. For example:

sodium + water $\longrightarrow$ hydrogen + sodium hydroxide solution

$2Na(s) + 2H_2O(l) \longrightarrow H_2(g) + 2NaOH(aq)$

magnesium + steam $\longrightarrow$ hydrogen + magnesium oxide

$Mg(s) + H_2O(g) \longrightarrow H_2(g) + MgO(s)$

The table shows how metals react with water or steam:

Metal	Reaction with water or steam
potassium	reacts violently with cold water
sodium	reacts quickly with cold water
calcium	reacts slowly with cold water
magnesium	reacts slowly with cold water but violently with steam
aluminium	reacts very slowly with water (because it forms a layer of aluminium oxide), reacts slowly with steam
zinc	reacts fairly quickly with steam
iron	reacts slowly with steam
lead copper silver gold	do not react with water or steam (which is why pipes in plumbing systems are made from copper or lead)

(See also *reactivity series*.)

metals, structure of: metals form giant molecules (see *bonding of metals*). It is the bonding in metals that makes them so useful as conductors of both electricity and heat.

- In metal giant structures the outer electrons of the metal atoms are free to move.

The *free electrons*:

- hold the metal ions together in a regular structure
- allow the metal to conduct heat and electricity.

metamorphic rocks are rocks whose structure has been changed by the action of heat and pressure deep in the Earth's *crust*. You have to know the different ways in which *sedimentary*, *metamorphic* and *igneous rocks* are formed.

- Marble is a metamorphic rock formed by the action of pressure and heat on chalk or limestone.
- Many metamorphic rocks (e.g. schist) have crystals arranged in bands.
- Metamorphic rocks are found most commonly where mountain ranges have formed.

methane is a colourless, odourless gas, formula CH_4. It makes up most of the natural gas we burn in our homes.

- Methane is a *hydrocarbon*.
- It is an *alkane* with only one carbon atom.
- The proportion of methane in the atmosphere is rising due to increases in the number of cattle and of rice fields.
- Methane is partly responsible for the *greenhouse effect*.

microbes are microscopic organisms (see *bacteria, fungi, viruses*), most of which are important in the recycling of materials in the environment (see *carbon cycle, decay, biological; nitrogen cycle*).

- Some microbes are used in industry (see *baking, brewing, fermentation, yoghurt*).
- Some microbes produce *diseases*.

microwaves: waves used in communications and in cooking food.

- They are electromagnetic waves with a longer wavelength than infra-red waves but shorter than radio waves.
- They pass easily through the atmosphere, so they are used in *satellite communications* (including satellite TV).
- They are very strongly absorbed by water, so they are used in microwave cookers where they penetrate the food and cause the water molecules in

the food to vibrate rapidly. The energy from the vibrating water molecules is transferred to the rest of the food.

mineral: a naturally occurring solid compound of the Earth's *crust*. We obtain most of our industrial raw materials from minerals.
- Rocks are usually mixtures of minerals.
- Minerals containing useful quantities of *metals* are called *ores*.

mineral salts: elements needed in small quantities by both animals and plants for healthy growth and development.
- If insufficient amounts of an element are available, the organism will show symptoms called deficiency symptoms.

The tables show some of the elements needed by animals and plants:

Element	Needed by humans for	Effect of deficiency in humans
calcium	healthy bones and teeth	rickets, decayed teeth
iron	production of *haemoglobin* for red blood cells	*anaemia* (pale, listless)
iodine	*thyroxin* production by the thyroid gland	swollen neck (goitre)

Element	Needed in plants for	Effect of deficiency
nitrogen	production of proteins	stunted growth
iron magnesium	production of chlorophyll	yellow leaves
phosphorus	DNA production; photosynthesis and respiration	poor root growth; younger leaves purple
potassium	enzymes in photosynthesis and respiration	yellow leaves with dead spots

mitochondria are the part of a cell where *respiration* occurs. This is where most of the energy you use to move and to keep warm comes from.
- Mitochondria are found in large numbers in both animal and plant cells.
- Most of the reactions in *aerobic respiration* take place in the mitochondria.
- Most of the energy is transferred from sugars to uses such as growth, synthesis and movement.

mitosis is the type of cell division that occurs when body cells divide. It ensures that all your body cells contain the same genetic information. Do not confuse it with *meiosis*.

When body cells divide:
- a copy of each chromosome is made so that
- each body cell receives exactly the same genetic information and
- each body cell has the same number of chromosomes.
- Mitosis is the type of cell division that occurs in *asexual reproduction*, therefore all the offspring produced by asexual reproduction have identical genetic information.

---

mixture: a material that can be separated easily into different substances; you need to know methods of separating mixtures.
- Mixtures (unlike *compounds*) contain different substances that are not joined by chemical bonds.

Materials in mixtures can be separated by:
- *evaporation*
- *filtration*
- *distillation*
- *chromatography*.

Moh's scale: a scale that enables us to compare the hardness of materials.

Mineral	Hardness	Common example
diamond	10	
corundum	9	
topaz	8	
quartz	7	
feldspar	6	steel pin
apatite	5	
fluorite	4	copper coin
calcite	3	finger nail
gypsum	2	
talc	1	

- The hardness of a mineral can be found by trying to scratch it with a 'standard' mineral. A mineral can only be scratched by a harder mineral.

---

mole: the number of particles in the *relative atomic mass* (RAM) of an element. If you can understand moles, many chemical calculations become much easier.

- A mole is approximately 6×10^{23} particles.
- You should be able use the following formulae for an element:

$$\text{moles of atoms} = \frac{\text{mass}}{\text{RAM}}$$

$$\text{mass} = \text{moles} \times \text{RAM}$$

- Similar formulae can be used for molecules, this time using *relative formula mass* (RFM):

$$\text{moles of molecules} = \frac{\text{mass}}{\text{RFM}}$$

$$\text{mass} = \text{moles} \times \text{RFM}$$

---

molecular compounds are compounds which are gases or liquids at room temperature (or solids with low melting and boiling points) and which do not conduct electricity. You have to know the difference between molecular compounds and *ionic compounds*.

- The forces holding the *molecules* together in molecular compounds are weak.
- Molecules of these compounds do not carry an overall charge.

---

molecule: two or more *atoms* held together by sharing *electrons*. You have to know the difference between substances that form molecules and substances that consist of *ions*.

- The molecules of most gaseous elements consist of two atoms which share electrons. For example, chlorine gas consists of chlorine molecules (Cl_2) in which two chlorine atoms share a pair of electrons.

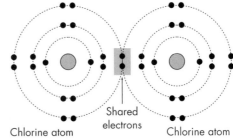

Chlorine atom   Shared electrons   Chlorine atom

- There are chemical bonds between the atoms in each molecule, but not between molecules (see *bonding, covalent*).
- Substances made from molecules are mainly liquids and gases; they have low melting and boiling points.

---

molluscs: animals that often have a shell, such as snails and mussels. Molluscs have the following characteristics:

- Many have a shell.
- Many have a large, muscular foot.
- Octopuses and squid have tentacles.

---

monomers are small *molecules* which can link together in chains to form very large molecules. The large molecules are called *polymers* – most of the plastics we use in everyday life are polymers.

- Glucose is the monomer for *starch* which consists of hundreds of glucose molecules joined end to end.
- *Ethene* is the monomer of *poly(ethene)* (see *addition polymer, condensation reaction*).

Moon: the natural *satellite* of Earth (when spelled with a capital letter, otherwise the satellite of any other planet).

- We can see the Moon when it reflects light from the Sun towards Earth.
- The Moon stays in orbit around the Earth because of its own speed and the gravitational pull of the Earth.
- The gravitational field strength of the Moon is about one sixth of that of Earth because the Earth has a much larger mass and much larger density than the Moon.
- The diameter of the Moon is about one quarter that of the Earth.

motor (electric): an appliance that transfers electrical energy into kinetic energy. Electric motors power most of our trains (including model trains!).

- In an electric motor a current is passed through a coil of wire called the armature which is between the poles of a powerful magnet.
- The magnetic field exerts a force on the coil, causing it to rotate.
- The size of the force on the coil can be increased by increasing the strength of the magnet or by increasing the size of the current.

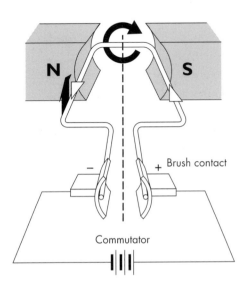

N   S

−   + Brush contact

Commutator

- The direction of the force on the coil is reversed if the direction of the current is reversed. (See also *armature, commutator.*)

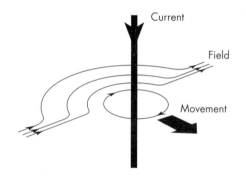

Current

Field

Movement

motor neurones are nerve cells which go to muscles or glands. Information passes down these to enable your muscles to contract.

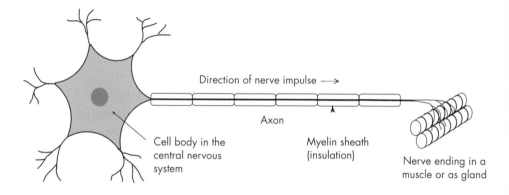

Direction of nerve impulse ⟶

Axon

Cell body in the central nervous system

Myelin sheath (insulation)

Nerve ending in a muscle or as gland

- They carry impulses from the central nervous system (*brain* or *spinal cord*) to a muscle or gland.
- Their axons are specialised structures for conducting electrical impulses.
- The myelin sheath acts as an insulator.
- In a *reflex action* the motor neurone carries impulses from the *coordinator* to the *effector*.

moulds are organisms which produce a mass of threads (*hyphae*) which look like cotton wool. The decay of dead material is usually started by moulds.
- Moulds are *fungi*.
- They grow on dead material.
- They are important in the decay process (see *decay, biological*).
- Moulds feed by passing *enzymes* out of the hyphae onto the food, where the enzymes digest the food. Soluble food is then absorbed into the hyphae.

mountain formation: mountains are formed where the plates in the Earth's *crust* which make up the continents collide.

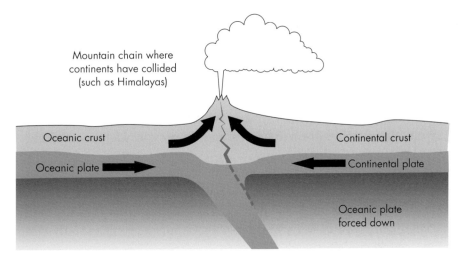

Mountain chain where continents have collided (such as Himalayas)

Oceanic crust

Continental crust

Oceanic plate

Continental plate

Oceanic plate forced down

- This occurs where *oceanic plates* and *continental plates* meet.
- The thinner, denser oceanic plate is forced under the thicker, less dense continental plate.
- When all of the oceanic plate has slipped under the continental plate, the two continental plates collide and rocks are forced upwards, forming mountains (see *destructive margin*).

mucus: a slimy substance produced in many parts of the body. It performs various, very important functions – mainly as protection and defence.
- Mucus is made by *glandular tissue*.
- In the breathing system mucus traps microbes.
- In the digestive system mucus prevents enzymes from digesting the organs in which they are produced and contained.

mudstone is a rock made out of clay.
- It is formed as a *sedimentary rock*.
- Clay is put under great pressure deep in the Earth's *crust*.
- Water is squeezed out and the clay particles cemented together.

muscle, antagonistic pairs: pairs of muscles which move a bone in opposite directions, like the muscles that bend and straighten your arms.
- Muscles work by contracting, thus pulling on bones.
- One muscle contracts to pull the bone in one direction.
- The other muscle contracts to pull the bone in the opposite direction.

- In the arm, the biceps muscle contracts to bend the arm at the elbow while the triceps muscle contracts to straighten the arm.

muscle, involuntary: muscle over which we have no conscious control – you cannot, for example, stop your 'tummy' rumbling.
Examples include:
- the muscles in the digestive organs which bring about the movement of food through the system (*peristalsis*)
- the muscles in the *iris* which control the size of the *pupil*
- the muscles which pull the hairs in the skin upright when we are cold
- *effectors* in many *reflex actions*.

muscle, voluntary: muscles over which we have conscious control – you can decide whether or not to move your arm. Most voluntary muscles are attached to bones which only contract when *impulses* arrive from the *brain* or *spinal cord* via *motor neurones*.

muscular tissue: cells that are able to contract and thus bring about movement (see *muscle, voluntary* and *muscle, involuntary*).
- The energy for contraction is transferred mainly from *aerobic respiration*.
- During strenuous exercise some energy for contraction is transferred from *anaerobic respiration*.

mutation: a random change in the genetic information of an organism. Without mutation there would be no *natural selection* and *evolution*.
- Mutations result in a new form of a *gene*.
- Mutations can occur naturally.
- The frequency of mutations is increased by exposure to radiation (ultraviolet light, X-rays and radiation from radioactive substances) and certain chemicals (e.g. mustard gas).
- Most mutations are harmful – they cause abnormal development.
- Mutations in body cells may cause them to multiply in an uncontrolled way, causing *cancer*.
- Some rare mutations may benefit the organism and increase the chances of survival of the organism and its offspring (see *evolution*).

naphtha is produced during the *fractional distillation* of *crude oil*.
- Naphtha has a boiling point of 90–150°C.
- It consists of *hydrocarbons* with chains containing 9 to 16 carbon atoms.
- It is used to make other *petrochemicals*.

---

natural fertiliser includes materials such as manure and compost. Farmers and gardeners can increase the yields of crops more cheaply and with less damage to the environment by using these rather than artificial fertilisers.
- Plants remove *mineral salts* from the soil for their growth.
- Fertilisers replace these mineral salts.
- Manure is mainly animal *faeces* and compost is dead plant material.
- Microbes in the soil help *decay* this dead and waste material, releasing the mineral salts for use by the plants.

(See also *nitrogen cycle* and *carbon cycle*.)

---

natural gas is gas which was formed at the same time as crude oil. Most of the power stations currently being built in the UK are powered by natural gas.
- It is a *non-renewable fuel*.
- It contains a mixture of *hydrocarbons*.
- Hydrocarbons with longer carbon chains, such as butane and propane, are removed and sold as bottled gas.
- The remaining gas, consisting mainly of *methane* and *ethane*, is used both for domestic gas supplies and as a raw material in the chemical industry.

---

natural polymers are long-chain molecules formed by living organisms. The proteins that form the basic building blocks of all living organisms are polymers.
- Proteins are built of long chains of amino acids.
- Starch, glycogen and cellulose are built of long chains of sugar molecules.

---

natural selection: the theory, commonly called 'survival of the fittest', proposed by *Darwin*. It is one of the most important theories in science since it gives an explanation for the origin of humans and is the 'driving force' behind *evolution*.

The main points of this theory are:

- Organisms show *variation*.
- Some variations make the organism better *adapted* (better fitted) to the environment.
- These organisms are more likely to survive to breed.
- Their offspring will tend to inherit these advantageous variations.

neon (Ne): a colourless, odourless gas. It is the main gas used in display tubes in advertising signs. Neon is:

- found in the atmosphere – about 18 parts per million
- inert (does not react) since it is one of the noble gases.

nephron: another name for kidney tubule (see *kidney*).

nerve cell: see *neurone*.

nerve impulse: the form in which information is transmitted in the nervous system (see *nerve*).

- Information is carried along *neurones* (nerve cells) as electrical *impulses*.
- There are junctions between neurones called *synapses*.
- Information is passed across these junctions by chemicals.

nervous system: enables the body to react to its surroundings and coordinates its behaviour. Without a nervous system we would not have any senses and we would not be able to move. It is made up mainly of cells called *neurones*. The nervous system consists of the following parts:

THE CENTRAL NERVOUS SYSTEM

- This is the *brain* and the *spinal cord*. These act as coordinators.

THE RECEPTORS

- These include the *ear* and the *eye*. These detect *stimuli* (changes in the environment).

THE NERVES

- These carry information between the receptors, central nervous system and the rest of the body.

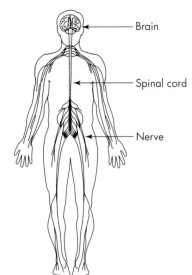

Brain

Spinal cord

Nerve

(See also *nerve, neurone, reflex action, receptors, eye, ear, brain.*)

nerves are structures which transfer information between the central nervous system (*brain* and *spinal cord*) and the rest of the body. If a part of the body loses its nerve supply (e.g. the legs if the spinal cord is injured) then that part of the body is paralysed and has no feeling. Nerves are made up of many *neurones* (nerve cells).

neurones are cells which make up most of the *nervous system*. Neurones are specialised for transmitting information. They consist of:
● a cell body which contains the nucleus
● dendrites which can both receive and transmit nerve *impulses.*
● an axon which conducts information as electrical impulses.
(For diagrams see *sensory neurone* and *motor neurone.*)

neutral (chemistry): neither acid nor alkaline (see *acids and alkalis*).

neutral (electrical): neither positive nor negative.

neutralisation: the reaction of an acid and a base to form a salt and water. It does not necessarily result in a *neutral* solution. (See *acids and alkalis.*)

neutron: a particle in the nuclei of all *atoms* except hydrogen. Neutrons, along with *electrons* and *protons*, are the basic building blocks of the atoms which form all matter, living and non-living.
● A neutron does not have an overall electrical charge.
● It has a relative mass of 1.
● *Isotopes* of an element have the same number of protons but different numbers of neutrons.
● The number of neutrons plus protons is the *mass number* of an element.
● In *nuclear reactors* free neutrons bring about *chain reactions.*

Newlands: a scientist who, in 1865, classified the elements by putting them in order of their *atomic masses.*
● He noted that for the elements with low atomic masses every eighth element had similar chemical properties.
● His 'rule' did not apply to many of the elements, so other scientists ignored his work.
(See also *Mendeleyev.*)

Newton, Isaac: a British scientist who lived 1742–1827.

- His early scientific work showed that white light was a mixture of rays of different colours.
- Later work led him to demonstrate how the motion of planets, satellites and comets could be explained in terms of gravitational forces.
- He also discovered 'laws of motion' which show us how forces affect the motion of an object.

newton (N): the unit of *force*. You are almost certain to have to use this unit in your examination, usually to calculate *pressure* or to calculate *work* done.

- One newton is the force required to give a mass of one kilogram an acceleration of one metre per second squared:

$$\begin{array}{ccccc} \text{force} & = & \text{mass} & \times & \text{acceleration} \\ \text{(newtons, N)} & & \text{(kilograms, kg)} & & \text{(metres/second}^2\text{, m/s}^2\text{)} \end{array}$$

- The formula for pressure also contains newtons:

$$\text{pressure (pascals, Pa)} = \frac{\text{force (newtons, N)}}{\text{area (metres}^2\text{, m}^2\text{)}}$$

- The formula for work done contains newtons:

$$\begin{array}{cccc} \text{work done} & = & \text{force applied} & \times \text{ distance moved in direction of force} \\ \text{(joules, J)} & & \text{(newtons, N)} & \text{(metres, m)} \end{array}$$

nickel (Ni) is a silvery-white metal. Nickel is:

- strongly magnetic
- used mainly in *alloys*
- used particularly with steel in alloys which are very strong and resist corrosion
- also used as an alloy with copper to make coins
- used as a *catalyst* in the chemical industry.

nitrate is formed when nitric acid is *neutralised* (see *acids and alkalis*).

- It is used as *artificial fertiliser*, mainly in *NPK fertilisers* (fertilisers that contain nitrogen, potassium and phosphorus).
- If nitrate fertilisers are leached into rivers or lakes they may cause *eutrophication*.

nitric acid: a strong acid, formula HNO_3. It is important in the chemical industry where it is used in the manufacture of most *artificial fertilisers*. It is made by the oxidation of ammonia.

- Ammonia gas reacts with oxygen in the presence of a platinum *catalyst* at 900°C to form nitrogen monoxide.
- The nitrogen monoxide is cooled then reacted with water and oxygen to make nitric acid.
- Most nitric acid is reacted with ammonia to make ammonium nitrate fertiliser.

(See also *ammonia*, *Haber process*.)

nitrifying bacteria are soil microbes that are important in recycling nitrogen compounds (see *nitrogen cycle*).

They convert ammonium compounds:

- first into nitrites
- then into nitrates.

nitrogen (N) is a colourless, odourless gas. Nitrogen is needed to make proteins, which are the basic building blocks of all living cells.

- Nitrogen makes up 80% of the atmosphere.
- It is obtained by the *fractional distillation* of liquid air.
- Most of this nitrogen is used to make *ammonia*, *nitric acid* and *fertilisers*.
- Plants need nitrogen as nitrate or ammonium compounds to make the proteins they need for growth.
- Some bacteria can 'fix' atmospheric nitrogen (see *nitrogen-fixing bacteria* and *nitrogen cycle*).

nitrogen cycle: the constant cycling of nitrogen between living organisms, dead organisms and the atmosphere. All animal waste and dead organisms are recycled in nature via the carbon and nitrogen cycles – imagine what the world would be like without these cycles!

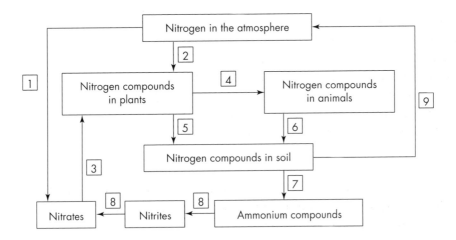

1 Nitrogen from the atmosphere is converted to nitrates during lightning storms.
2 *Nitrogen-fixing bacteria* also 'fix' atmospheric nitrogen.
3 Nitrates are absorbed from the soil by plants and converted into proteins.
4 Plants are eaten by animals and converted into animal proteins.
5 Dead plants enter the soil.
6 Excretory products and dead animals enter the soil.
7 Decay bacteria and fungi break down nitrogen compounds in the soil into ammonium compounds.
8 *Nitrifying bacteria* convert ammonium compounds first into nitrites then into nitrates.
9 In poorly drained soils, denitrifying bacteria convert nitrogen compounds back into nitrogen gas.

nitrogen oxides are the gases produced when *fossil fuels* such as petrol and oil are burned, causing oxygen and nitrogen to combine. They are partly responsible for the formation of *acid rain* – one of today's most serious environmental problems.
- Along with *sulphur dioxide* they dissolve in rain water to form *acid rain*.
- They can be removed from car exhaust fumes by devices called catalytic converters.

nitrogen-fixing bacteria convert nitrogen gas into nitrogen compounds (see *nitrogen cycle*).
- Some types live in the soil, others live in nodules of leguminous plants such as clover (see *legumes*).
- In some types of crop rotation, clover plants are grown then ploughed into the soil – the nitrogen compounds made by the bacteria then enter the soil nitrogen cycle.
- The use of such 'green manure' saves on the use of *artificial fertilisers*.

noble gases: a group of six unreactive gases. Because they are unreactive, they are used to fill electric light bulbs.
The noble gases are:
- helium, neon, argon, krypton, xenon and radon
- in Group 0 of the *periodic table*.
- present as individual atoms rather than diatomic molecules
- used as inert gases in filament lamps and discharge tubes
- unreactive because their highest energy level of electrons is full – they have no tendency to gain or lose electrons.

noise is unwanted sound.
- It consists of a mixture of frequencies.
- It may be just annoying or it may cause damage to the ears.

non-metals, properties of: you have to know the differences between the properties of *metals* and non-metals.
Typical non-metals:
- have low melting points and low boiling points (except carbon as diamond) therefore many are gases at room temperature
- are dull in appearance
- are brittle when solid
- are poor conductors of heat when solid
- are poor conductors of electricity when solid (an exception is carbon as graphite).

non-metals, reactions of: if non-metals burn they form oxides (e.g. *carbon dioxide, sulphur dioxide* and *nitrogen oxides*). For example:

sulphur + oxygen $\longrightarrow$ sulphur dioxide

$S(s) + O_2(g) \longrightarrow SO_2(g)$

- These gases contribute to two of today's great environmental problems – the *greenhouse effect* and *acid rain.*
- Most non-metal oxides are gases.
- Soluble non-metal oxides form acid solutions – they are basic. For example:

carbon dioxide + water $\longrightarrow$ carbonic acid

$CO_2(g) + H_2O(l) \longrightarrow H_2CO_3(aq)$

non-metals, uses: see *chlorine, uses; carbon.*

non-renewable energy resources cannot be replaced. One of the world's greatest problems is the 'energy crisis' – we are rapidly using up the Earth's *fossil fuels* and these cannot be replaced.
- Examples of non-renewable energy resources include coal, oil and gas.
- They were formed hundreds of millions of years ago, in the Earth's *crust*, by the action of heat and pressure on the remains of animals and plants.
- Economical use of these resources will make them last longer.
- Alternative energy sources will need to be developed as non-renewable energy sources run out.

(See also *renewable energy resources.*)

nose: the organ of smell. It contains *receptors* sensitive to chemicals in the air.

---

nuclear equation: an equation representing a change to an atomic nucleus. Most syllabuses do not require you to balance nuclear equations but you might be asked about changes in *nucleon number* and *proton number*.

- When a radioactive nucleus emits an alpha particle, ^4_2He, it loses two protons and two neutrons. For example, when radium decays to radon:

$$^{226}_{88}\text{Ra} \longrightarrow\ ^{222}_{86}\text{Rn} +\ ^4_2\text{He}$$

- Always reduce the nucleon number by four and the proton number by two for alpha decay.
- When a radioactive nucleus emits a beta particle, it loses an electron, $^0_{-1}\text{e}$, because a neutron changes into a proton. For example, when carbon decays to nitrogen

$$^{14}_6\text{C} \longrightarrow\ ^{14}_5\text{N} +\ ^0_{-1}\text{e}$$

- Always reduce the proton number by one but leave the nucleon number the same for beta decay.

---

nuclear fission: see *fission, nuclear*.

---

nuclear fusion: see *fusion, nuclear*.

---

nuclear reactor: used in nuclear power stations to transfer energy to steam, which then drives generators.

- A *chain reaction* involving uranium-238 is used as the energy source.
- Graphite rods are used as moderators – these absorb neutrons and so keep the reaction under control.
- The heat is carried away from the reactor by carbon dioxide.
- The hot carbon dioxide boils water and the steam produced drives the generator.
- The reactor is encased in steel and concrete to prevent radiation escaping.

---

nucleon: a particle in the nucleus of an atom (see *protons* and *neutrons*).

---

nucleon number is the number of particles in the nucleus of an *atom*. You are almost certain to be asked to interpret a symbol of the type $^{35}_{17}\text{Cl}$. The number of *protons* plus the number of *neutrons* in the nucleus gives the nucleon number. For example, for the chlorine nucleus, $^{35}_{17}\text{Cl}$:

- 35 is the nucleon number – the total number of protons + neutrons
- 17 is the proton number, so there are $(35-17) = 18$ neutrons in the nucleus.

---

nucleus of a cell: the part of the cell that controls cell activities. All the information needed for your development from a fertilised egg was contained in the nucleus of that cell.

- The nucleus contains *chromosomes*.
- Chromosomes carry *genes* that control the body's *characteristics*.
- Genes are sections of *DNA* molecules.

nucleus of an atom: the central part of an *atom*. Changes to the nucleus of an atom involve great energy changes, forming the basis of how nuclear power stations and nuclear weapons work.

- The nucleus consists of *protons* and *neutrons*.
- It contains almost all the mass of the atom.
- It is positively charged.
- The number of positive charges is equal to the number of protons (these positive charges are balanced by the negative charges on the electrons which make up the rest of the atom).

nutrient: an essential food material (e.g. *carbohydrate, vitamin*). Nutrients are what we need, along with oxygen, to keep us alive. A nutrient can be defined as a substance needed by a living organism for healthy growth and development (see *diet, balanced*).

nutrition: receiving food or *nutrients* (see *diet, balanced*; *digestion*).

nylon is an artificial fibre used to make clothing, ropes etc. It is:
- a *polymer*
- water resistant – so nylon fabrics dry quickly.

obesity: being very overweight. This can cause serious health problems. It is caused by taking in more energy in food than is expended, for example in exercise, usually by eating too much energy-rich food such as carbohydrate and fat. Obesity can be reduced by taking more exercise and controlling diet. Obesity leads to:
- increased stress on the heart
- increased stress on the joints
- increased chance of heart attack, stroke and diabetes.

---

oceanic plate: the part of the Earth's *crust* found under the oceans. It is movement of oceanic plates that cause most earthquakes. Most volcanoes occurs where oceanic plates and continental plates collide.
- Oceanic plates are thinner than *continental plates* but denser.
- Where an oceanic plate collides with a continental plate the oceanic plate is forced under the continental plate (*subduction*; see also *destructive boundary*).

---

oesophagus: the gullet where food goes immediately you swallow it. It takes food from the mouth to the stomach.
- The oesophagus wall consists mainly of muscular tissue.
- It contracts in waves bringing about *peristalsis* (see *digestive system*).

---

oestrogen is a *hormone* which helps in the control of reproduction in female mammals (see *menstrual cycle*). It is important both in controlling the monthly cycle in women and for its use in birth control pills.
- Oestrogen is produced by the *ovaries*.
- Its production is stimulated by the hormone *FSH* which is produced by the *pituitary gland*.

EFFECTS OF OESTROGEN

- causes the lining of the womb to prepare to receive a fertilised egg
- inhibits the production of FSH
- stimulates the production by the pituitary gland of the hormone *LH* which causes an egg to be released

Many birth control pills contain oestrogen because oestrogen inhibits the formation of FSH which is needed to make eggs mature in the ovaries.

ohm (Ω): the unit of electrical *resistance*. The resistance of an electrical appliance governs the *power* it takes to run the appliance. One ohm is the resistance between the two points in a *conductor* where a *potential difference* of one volt produces a *current* of one ampere.

Ohm's law states that the *current* flowing through a metal *conductor* is proportional to the *potential difference* across it (providing the temperature remains constant). You are almost certain to get an Ohm's law calculation in your examination, so you must learn the three forms of the equation:

$$\text{resistance (ohms, } \Omega) = \frac{\text{potential difference (volts, V)}}{\text{current (amperes, A)}}$$

$$\text{current} = \frac{\text{voltage}}{\text{resistance}}$$

$$\text{voltage} = \text{current} \times \text{resistance}$$

- You will usually be given two of the values then asked to calculate the third, so you should remember all three forms of the equation.
- Remember the correct units for potential difference, current and resistance.

oil is a naturally occurring substance formed deep in the Earth's *crust* (see *crude oil*).

omnivore: an animal that eats both plants and animals.
- In a *food web*, omnivores have at least two arrows coming into them, from different levels in the food web.
- Omnivores are both a primary and a secondary *consumers*.
- Humans are omnivores.
- Omnivores' teeth and digestive systems are not usually as highly specialised as those of *carnivores* or *herbivores*.

open cast: type of mining in which the mineral (e.g. coal) is just under the surface of the ground, so shafts do not need to be sunk.
- This kind of mining causes a lot of environmental damage, but the mining company is usually made to restore the countryside to its original condition when they have finished.

The usual procedure is that:
- the layers of soil over the mineral are moved to one side

- the mineral is extracted
- the soil is then replaced.

optic nerve: the nerve leading from the *brain* to the eye (see *eye, structure*). The optic nerve carries all the information received by your eyes to the brain. Damage to it can result in blindness.
- The optic nerve contains mainly sensory *neurones*.
- They carry *impulses* from the light receptors in the *retina* to the brain.
- It also carries *motor neurones* leading to, for example, the *iris* muscles.

orbit: the path of a body such as a planet through space. You need to know what keeps the Earth approximately the same distance from the Sun and what keeps television *satellites* in the same position above the Earth.
- The Moon orbits the Earth; the Earth orbits the Sun.
- A smaller body orbits a larger body because of a combination of the force of gravity between the two bodies and the higher speed of the smaller body.
- The orbits of the planets are ellipses (slightly squashed circles) with the Sun at the centre.
- The orbits of comets are highly elliptical – they are much closer to the Sun at some times than at others. We can see comets only when their orbits bring them close to the Sun.
- Artificial satellites have been placed in orbits around the Earth (see *satellite communication*; *satellite, monitoring*).

organ: a group of *tissues* with a common function, for example the *stomach*, *brain* or *heart*. Each of our organs has a specific function. For example, the function of the stomach is to churn and digest food. Its tissues include:
- *muscular tissue* to churn the food
- *glandular tissue* to produce *enzymes* to digest the food.

organ system: a group of organs with a common function, for example the blood system and the nervous system.
- The function of the nervous system is to enable the body to react to changes in the environment.
In this organ system:
- organs such as the *eye* contain *receptors* to detect changes
- the *brain* is an organ which coordinates responses.

organic compounds are compounds containing carbon. These are the basis of all living organisms – without organic compounds there would be no life.

- Originally 'organic' referred to carbon compounds produced by living organisms.
- Over the last 200 years many artificial organic compounds, such as drugs, have been created by chemists.

oscillate: to move to and fro or side to side between two points, like a swinging pendulum.
- Oscillation is the basis of *longitudinal waves* and *transverse waves*.
- Particle-transmitting sound waves oscillate (they move from side to side) but the energy is transmitted in the direction of the wave.

oscilloscope: an instrument used to 'see' waves. Waves such as sound waves are changed into electrical voltages which are displayed on a screen, rather like that of a television set.

osmosis is a type of *diffusion*. Osmosis is a process which occurs in every living cell. To understand why water moves in and out of cells you need to understand osmosis.

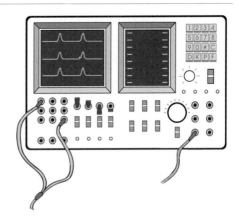

- Water diffuses from regions of high concentrations of water molecules to regions of low concentrations of water molecules.
- A solution contains a lower concentration of water molecules than pure water.

Partially permeable membrane

Water | Solution

Net movement of water molecules into solution greater than movement out

- A *partially permeable membrane* allows small molecules such as water molecules to pass through, but not larger molecules such as those of some *solutes*.
- If water is separated from a solution by a partially permeable membrane there will be a net diffusion of water molecules into the solution; this movement is called osmosis.

- Similarly, water moves by osmosis from a weak solution of solute to a concentrated solution of solute.
- Root hair cells absorb water from the soil solution by osmosis.

ovary: an organ in the female body that produces eggs and *hormones* (see *reproduction*).

- Besides producing eggs, human ovaries also produce hormones, including those that bring about changes to the body during *adolescence*.
- Human females have two ovaries situated in the abdomen.
- One egg is normally released each month.
- The ovaries produce *oestrogen*.

EFFECTS OF OESTROGEN

- causes development of secondary sexual characteristics, e.g. growth of the breasts (see *adolescence*)
- causes the lining of the womb to thicken
- inhibits the production of the hormone *FSH*
- stimulates the production of the hormone *LH*

(See also *menstrual cycle*.)

oviduct: a tube-shaped organ down which *eggs* travel from the *ovary* to the *womb*. Some women are unable to become pregnant because of blockages in their oviducts.

- The oviduct is where the egg is *fertilised* by a sperm.
- The cells lining the oviduct have tiny hairs (*cilia*) which move the egg down the tube.

ovulation is the release of an egg from an *ovary*. An egg has to be released for a woman to become pregnant – some types of birth control pill prevent the release of eggs (see *contraceptive*).

- In humans, ovulation occurs around the middle of the monthly *menstrual cycle*.
- The maturing of eggs in the ovary is stimulated by the hormone *FSH*.
- The actual release of the egg is stimulated by the hormone *LH*.

oxidation is a reaction in which a substance gains oxygen, for example when something burns.

- Most of the energy used to heat our homes, to propel motor vehicles and in our bodies themselves comes from oxidation reactions.

Oxidation is also when a substance:

- loses hydrogen or
- loses electrons.

Oxidation is the opposite of *reduction*. In the *blast furnace*, for example:

- iron oxide is reduced to iron because it loses oxygen
- carbon monoxide is oxidised to carbon dioxide because it gains oxygen:

iron oxide + carbon monoxide $\longrightarrow$ iron + carbon dioxide

$Fe_2O_3(s)$ + $3CO(g)$ $\longrightarrow$ $2Fe(l)$ + $3CO_2(g)$

---

oxide: a compound formed when an element reacts with oxygen.

- Many metals burn in air to form solid oxides:

magnesium + oxygen $\longrightarrow$ magnesium oxide

$2Mg(s)$ + $O_2(g)$ $\longrightarrow$ $2MgO(s)$

- These metal oxides dissolve in water to form *alkalis*:

sodium oxide + water $\longrightarrow$ sodium hydroxide

$Na_2O(s)$ + $H_2O(l)$ $\longrightarrow$ $2NaOH(aq)$

- Many non-metals burn in air to form oxides which are gases:

sulphur + oxygen $\longrightarrow$ sulphur dioxide

$S(s)$ + $O_2(g)$ $\longrightarrow$ $SO_2(g)$

- These non-metal oxides dissolve in water to produce acidic solutions:

carbon dioxide + water $\longrightarrow$ carbonic acid

$CO_2(g)$ + $H_2O(l)$ $\longrightarrow$ $H_2CO_3(aq)$

---

oxidise: to combine with oxygen (see *oxidation*). To oxidise is also to:

- lose hydrogen or
- lose electrons.

---

oxygen (O) is a colourless, odourless gas. Without oxygen there would be no life as we know it on Earth.

- About 20% of the atmosphere is oxygen.
- About 60% by mass of the Earth's *crust* is made up of oxygen-containing compounds such as *carbonates* and silicates.
- Most living organisms cannot survive without oxygen – they need oxygen for *aerobic respiration*.

---

oxygen, extraction of: oxygen is obtained by the *fractional distillation* of liquid air. The oxygen in cylinders used in hospitals and by welders comes from this process.

- Air is liquefied by cooling it down to about −200°C.
- Nitrogen has a lower boiling point than oxygen, so it evaporates off first, leaving mainly liquid oxygen.

oxygen, reactions of: oxygen is needed in order for substances to burn (see *oxidation*).
- When substances burn in oxygen they form *oxides*.
- Iron rusts if oxygen and water are present.
- Aluminium quickly forms a protective layer of aluminium oxide if it is exposed to air.

oxygen, test for: oxygen will relight a glowing splint.
- A wooden splint is lit, the flame is blown out.
- If the still-glowing splint is placed in a container of oxygen it will burst into flame.

oxygen, uses: oxygen is used mainly to oxidise (add oxygen) to substances (see *oxidation*).
- *Fossil fuels* such as oil and coal are oxidised to transfer energy when they are burned in power stations.
- Petrol is oxidised in car engines to transfer energy to propel the car.
- Foods such as glucose are oxidised in our bodies to transfer the energy we need.
- Oxygen is used in industry to make *steel*, *nitric acid* and *sulphuric acid*.

oxygen debt: the reason why you pant immediately after running fast.
- Most of the energy needed by your muscles is transferred from *aerobic respiration*.
- If there is insufficient oxygen to provide all the energy via aerobic respiration, there is an oxygen debt, and *anaerobic respiration* (respiration without oxygen) begins.
- Anaerobic respiration produces *lactic acid* as a waste product.
- To get rid of this lactic acid, the body has to *oxidise* it to carbon dioxide and water.
- You pant to take in extra oxygen to get rid of the lactic acid that has accumulated in this way.

oxyhaemoglobin is the form in which most oxygen is carried in our blood (see *haemoglobin*).

ozone layer: a layer in the atmosphere where oxygen has been converted into a form called ozone. This layer protects us from dangerous radiation, however pollution is causing the ozone layer to break down.

- Ozone molecules, O_3, contain three atoms of oxygen.
- The ozone in the ozone layer has been made over millions of years by the action of sunlight on oxygen.
- The ozone layer is important to us because it filters out much of the ultra-violet waves from the Sun (which can cause skin cancer).
- Substances called CFCs, which are used in aerosol cans, escape into the atmosphere and break down ozone in the ozone layer.
- This is why CFCs are now banned in most countries.

P

P-wave: a 'push-pull' shock wave produced by an earthquake – as compared with an *S-wave*.

- P-waves cause the surface of the Earth to move forwards and backwards.
- They are *longitudinal waves*.
- They travel through liquids as well as solids.
- They are refracted as the density of the material they pass through changes.
- The diagram shows that P-waves pass through the *core* of the Earth but S-waves do not.

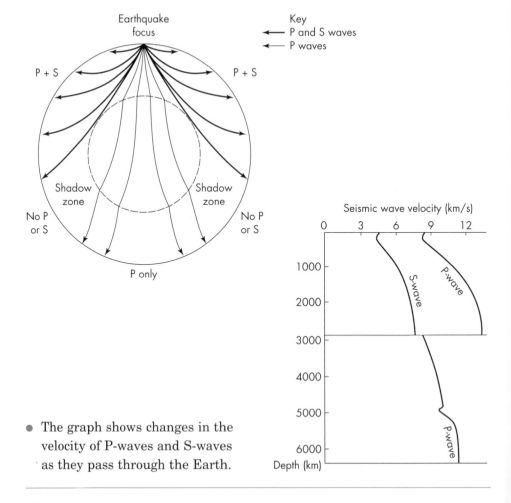

- The graph shows changes in the velocity of P-waves and S-waves as they pass through the Earth.

palisade mesophyll: the cells in a leaf that make most of the food.

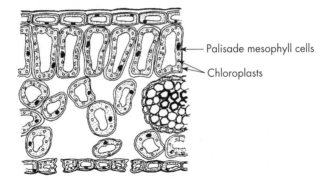

Palisade mesophyll cells

Chloroplasts

Palisade mesophyll cells:

- are situated just under the *epidermis* of the leaf, and
- are closely packed
- so that they can absorb maximum light for *photosynthesis*.
- They have many *chloroplasts* where photosynthesis takes place.

pancreas: a *gland*, near the stomach and liver, which is important both in digestion and in controlling blood sugar levels.
The pancreas produces three kinds of digestive *enzymes* which pass down a duct (tube) into the small intestine:

- *carbohydrase* (amylase) which breaks down starch to sugars
- *protease* which breaks down protein to amino acids
- *lipase* which breaks down fats to fatty acids and glycerol.

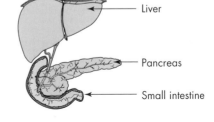

Liver

Pancreas

Small intestine

The pancreas also produces two *hormones* that control blood sugar levels, which pass into the blood flowing through the pancreas:

- *insulin* which stimulates the liver to store sugars as glycogen
- *glucagon* which stimulates the liver to break down glycogen into sugars.

Pangea: a super-continent that existed millions of years ago, and which split up to form the continents as they are now.

- In the diagram on the next page, X shows where Africa and South America were once joined together.
- Evidence of this comes from similarities in the rocks and fossils at the places where the join would have been.

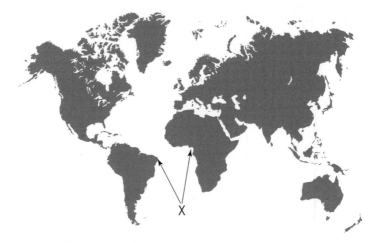

- The continents have moved apart as the *continental plates* have been shifted by convection currents in the *mantle*.

paraffin oil is a liquid fuel obtained from *crude oil*. It is used in portable heaters, lamps and stoves.
Paraffin oil:
- is obtained by *fractional distillation* of crude oil
- has a lower boiling point than petrol.

parallel circuit: see, *circuit, parallel*.

parasite: an organism that lives in or on another living organism (e.g. fleas living on a cat).
- The parasite benefits from living on its host – the flea gets its food by sucking the cat's blood.
- The host suffers – the cat loses blood.

partially permeable membrane: a layer that lets some things through but not others; it is how cells control what goes in and out (see *cell membrane*).

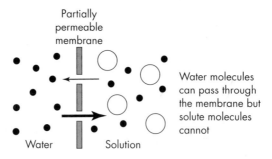

pascal (Pa): the unit of *pressure*. Always remember to convert the area to metres squared (m²) if you are asked to calculate pressure.
● A pressure of 1 Pa is exerted by a force of 1 N acting at right angles to an area of 1 m².

$$\text{pressure (pascals, Pa)} = \frac{\text{force (newtons, N)}}{\text{area (metres}^2, \text{m}^2)}$$

Pasteur, Louis: a French scientist who lived 1822–1895.
● He was the first scientist to prove that infectious diseases are caused by microbes getting into the body and multiplying there.
● He developed *vaccines* for two serious diseases – anthrax and rabies.
● He invented the process of *pasteurisation,* which prevents foods such as wines and milk going sour.

pasteurisation is a method of preventing milk and wine, for example, from going sour, without spoiling the taste.
● Milk is heated to 63°C for 30 minutes, then cooled to 10°C – the heating kills the bacteria which cause souring.
● Wine is heated to 70°C for 30 seconds then placed in *sterile* containers.

penicillin is a natural substance that kills *bacteria* (but not viruses). It has saved millions of lives since the 1940s.
● Penicillin was discovered by Alexander *Fleming* in 1928, but it took other scientists ten years to perfect ways of producing it in large quantities.
● It is an *antibiotic.*
● It kills many kinds of infectious bacteria but is particularly good at killing round bacteria (cocci).
● It is produced by growing selected strains of the mould *Penicillium* in fermenters.
● Many disease bacteria have become resistant to penicillin, but semi-synthetic penicillins have been developed to combat these.

penis: the male sexual organ.
● It contains a tube called the urethra which carries both urine and sperm.
● It contains erectile tissue which can make it firm enough to insert into the vagina of the female during sexual intercourse.

penumbra: the partial shadow created during an *eclipse* – the region of full shadow is called the *umbra*. The diagram shows the penumbra and the umbra during a solar eclipse.

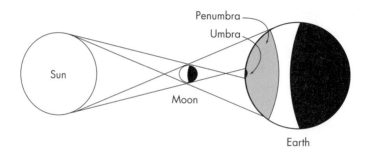

percentage composition: see *chemical calculations, percentage composition*.

period: a horizontal row in the *periodic table*. Compare this with a group, which is a vertical column in the periodic table.
- From left to right across each period a particular energy level is gradually filled up with electrons.
- The first five periods have 2, 8, 8, 18 and 18 elements respectively.

period (menstrual): the monthly loss of cells and blood from the lining of the womb of females of child-bearing age (see *menstrual cycle*).

periodic table: a table in which:
- the *elements* are arranged in order of their *proton (atomic) numbers*
- elements with similar chemical properties are arranged in vertical columns called *groups*
- the horizontal rows are called *periods*.

In the part of the periodic table shown below:
- the numbers are the *proton numbers* of the elements
- the unshaded elements are *metalloids*
- all the shaded elements to the left of the metalloids are *metals*

I	II											III	IV	V	VI	VII	0
						H 1											He 2
Li 3	Be 4											B 5	C 6	N 7	O 8	F 9	Ne 10
Na 11	Mg 12											Al 13	Si 14	P 15	S 16	Cl 17	Ar 18
K 19	Ca 20	Sc 21	Ti 22	V 23	Cr 24	Mn 25	Fe 26	Co 27	Ni 28	Cu 29	Zn 30	Ga 31	Ge 32	As 33	Se 34	Br 35	Kr 36
Rb 37	Sr 38	Y 39	Zr 40	Nb 41	Mo 42	Te 43	Ru 44	Rh 45	Pd 46	Ag 47	Cd 48	In 49	Sn 50	Sb 51	Te 52	I 53	Xe 54

- the lightly shaded metals are *transition metals*
- the heavily shaded elements to the right of the metalloids are *non-metals*
- hydrogen has unique properties
- elements in Group I are the *alkali metals*
- elements in Group II are *alkaline earth metals*
- elements in Group VII are *halogens*
- elements in Group 0 are *noble gases.*

(See entries for *metals, non-metals, transition metals, alkali metals, alkaline earth metals, halogens* and *noble gases.*)

peristalsis is the way that both food and *faeces* are moved through the gut.
- Muscular tissue in the wall of the gut contracts to force food through – rather like moving a marble through a piece of rubber tubing.
- Peristalsis is also responsible for churning the food in the stomach.

permanent hardness is water hardness that cannot be removed by boiling, as opposed to *temporary hardness* which can.
- It is caused by calcium salts such as calcium sulphate which are not decomposed by boiling; temporary hardness is caused by calcium hydrogencarbonate, which <u>is</u> broken down by boiling.
- Permanently hard water forms an unpleasant scum with soap and causes scale deposits to form in pipes and kettles.
- The calcium ions in permanently hard water can be removed by *ion exchange.*

Perspex is a transparent plastic used for making lenses and spectacles. It is a *polymer.*

pesticides are chemicals used to kill organisms which are harmful to domestic and farm animals and cultivated plants. It is estimated that 35% of crops are destroyed by pests whist growing and that a further 15% are lost to pests during storage. This is about half of the world's food supply.
- Fungi such as wheat rust are killed by fungicides.
- Weeds are killed by plant *hormones.*
- Animal pesticides include *insecticides.*

EFFECTS OF PESTICIDES ON THE ENVIRONMENT

- Pesticides often kill other species as well as the pests.
- *Food chains* are often disrupted.
- Pesticides may be concentrated in food chains so that the animals at the top of the food chains are poisoned (e.g. birds of prey).

- Because of this, some pesticides such as *DDT* are now banned in many countries.

petrochemicals are chemicals manufactured from *petroleum* or *natural gas* including *plastics*, fibres and *pesticides*.
- Many of these are obtained from *naphtha* – the mixture of hydrocarbons which have boiling points slightly higher than those of petrol.
- Many petrochemicals are broken down by *cracking* and then used to make *polymers*.

petrol is a liquid fuel used to power motor vehicles.
- It is obtained by the *fractional distillation* of *crude oil*.
- It is a *non-renewable energy resource*.
- It consists of a mixture of *hydrocarbons*.
- These hydrocarbons have boiling points between 40°C and 100°C and chains containing 4–12 carbon atoms.

petroleum is another term for *crude oil*.

pH: a scale measuring acidity and alkalinity (see *acids and alkalis*).

phagocyte: a type of blood cell that helps to defend us against disease microbes.
- A phagocyte is a type of *white blood cell*.
- It defends us by ingesting disease microbes.
- Phagocytes are formed in both the bone marrow and lymph nodes.

phenolphthalein: an indicator which tells us whether a substance is *acid* or *alkaline*. It is:
- colourless in acid solution
- pink in alkaline solution.

phenotype: all the observable characteristics of an organism (e.g. whether you have blue or brown eyes, how tall you are, what colour of hair you have). Your phenotype depends on:
- your *genotype* – the genetic information you inherited from your parents
- how the *environment* affects the genotype (although you inherit information for body-build, your mass will also depend on the amount of food you eat).

phloem: cells in plants that transport nutrients around the plant – compare with *xylem*, which transports mainly water up the plant. Sugars made in the leaves are transported by phloem both up to the growing parts of the plant and down to the roots.

phosphorus (P) is a reactive, solid, non-metallic element.
- Phosphorus is an important constituent of bones and teeth
- It is needed by all living organisms to produce *DNA* and for *respiration*.
- Plants also need phosphorus for *photosynthesis* and healthy growth; without sufficient phosphorus plants have poor root growth and purple younger leaves.
- *NPK fertiliser* contains phosphorus as phosphate.

phosphate: a compound containing the phosphate ion.
- The bulk of your bone is made up of calcium phosphate.
- *NPK fertilisers* contain phosphate for healthy plant growth.
- Phosphates from *fertilisers* and also from detergents may cause *eutrophication* if they are leached into lakes or rivers.

photosynthesis is the process in plants by which they manufacture their own food. Most of the world's food supply is therefore dependent upon photosynthesis.
- Green plants contain chlorophyll which can absorb light energy and transfer it to chemical energy.
- This energy is used to convert carbon dioxide and water into *glucose*.
- Oxygen is released as a waste product (this replenishes the atmospheric oxygen we use in respiration):

$$\text{carbon dioxide} + \text{oxygen} + \text{light energy} \longrightarrow \text{glucose} + \text{oxygen}$$
$$6CO_2 + 6H_2O + \text{light energy} \longrightarrow C_6H_{12}O_6 + 6O_2$$

FATE OF THE GLUCOSE

Glucose is:
- stored as insoluble *starch*
- used in *respiration*
- converted into *cellulose* to build cell walls
- combined with nitrogen compounds to make *amino acids* and *proteins*.

LIMITING FACTORS

The rate of photosynthesis may be limited by:
- low temperatures (e.g. on a cold summer's day)
- shortage of carbon dioxide (e.g. at noon in a well-stocked greenhouse)
- shortage of light (e.g. at dawn and dusk).

phototropism: if you leave a plant on a widow sill you will find that the stems grow towards the light. This response is an example of phototropism.
- Phototropism is the response of a plant organ to the stimulus of light.
- Plant stems are positively phototropic – they grow towards light.
- The advantage to the plant of this response is that it maximises light needed for *photosynthesis*.
- This response is caused by an unequal distribution of *hormones* in the stem.
- Hormones accumulate on the side of the stem opposite to the light.
- The higher concentration of hormones causes the cells on this side to grow faster and so the stem bends towards light.

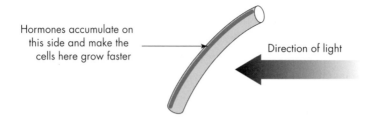

Hormones accumulate on this side and make the cells here grow faster

Direction of light

phytoplankton: microscopic plants that live near the surface of lakes and seas; a litre of lake water often contains hundreds of millions of these tiny organisms.
- Most of the *food chains* in lakes and seas begin with phytoplankton. They produce food by *photosynthesis* which is then used, directly or indirectly, by most of the other organisms.
- If *fertilisers* are leached into lakes, the phytoplankton population may increase rapidly causing *eutrophication*.

pitch, of sound: how high or low a note sounds.
- Pitch depends on the *frequency* of the sound wave – how many sound waves pass a given point in one second.
- The note 'middle A' has a frequency of 440 Hz.
- The A above this has a frequency of 880 Hz – so if we move up one octave we double the frequency.

placenta: the structure in the womb (*uterus*) which supplies the developing embryo with food and oxygen before it is born.
- The embryo is attached to the placenta by the umbilical cord which connects the embryo's blood vessels to the placenta.

- The blood vessels of the embryo and those of the mother run very close together in the placenta.
- Nutrients (e.g. glucose) and oxygen *diffuse* from the mother's blood into the embryo's blood.
- Waste materials such as carbon dioxide and urea diffuse from the embryo's blood into the mother's blood.
- The blood of the embryo and the mother do <u>not</u> mix.
- When the baby is born, the placenta is forced out of the womb as the after-birth.

planet: a large object that orbits a sun. Earth is one of nine planets that orbit our Sun.
- Planets look like stars to the naked eye, but stars are in fixed patterns called constellations, whereas planets appear to move across the constellations.
- Stars produce their own light, but we only see planets when they reflect light from the Sun towards us.
- The orbits of the planets are slight ellipses (slightly squashed circles).
- The further away from the Sun a planet is, the longer it takes to complete one orbit of the Sun (Earth takes one year to complete one orbit of the Sun).
- Planets stay in orbit around the Sun because of the force of gravity between the Sun and the planet, and the high speed of the planet.

plankton consists of microscopic organisms which live near the surface of lakes and seas. Many of the larger organisms (e.g. fish) depend on plankton for their food.
There are two types of plankton:
- *phytoplankton*, which can *photosynthesise* and therefore make their own food
- *zooplankton*, which eat either phytoplankton or each other.

plasma: see *blood, plasma*.

plasmolysis is what happens to plant cells when they lose a lot of water.
- It occurs when plants lose water by *transpiration* quicker than they can absorb it from the soil.
- It also happens when plant roots get flooded by seawater.
- As water leaves the cytoplasm by *osmosis*, the cytoplasm shrinks away from the cell walls, which are now said to be plasmolysed. (See diagram on next page.)
- The cell is also *flaccid* (limp) and does not support the plant.
- Plants may therefore wilt (droop) when their cells are plasmolysed.

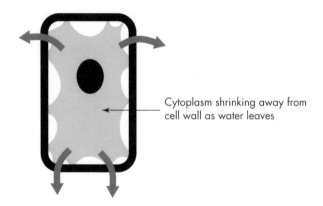

Cytoplasm shrinking away from cell wall as water leaves

plastics are synthetic chemicals with an almost unlimited range of uses. Examples are PVC, polythene, polystyrene, nylon and Teflon (PTFE).

- Plastics are *polymers* (see *addition polymer*).
- Many polymers are made from *hydrocarbons*; *poly(ethene)*, for example, is made from *ethene*.
- They have very long molecules in which atoms are joined by strong *covalent bonds* to form chains.
- There are two main kinds of plastic – *thermosetting* and *thermosoftening*.

plastics, thermosetting: plastics which cannot be remoulded.

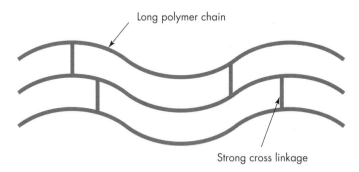

Long polymer chain

Strong cross linkage

- When a thermosetting plastic is heated (to mould it) strong cross-linkages form between the long polymer chains – these cannot be broken easily, so the plastic does not soften if it is reheated.

plastics, thermosoftening: plastics which can be remoulded.
- The cross-linkages between the polymer chains are weak so that the plastic softens when heated.

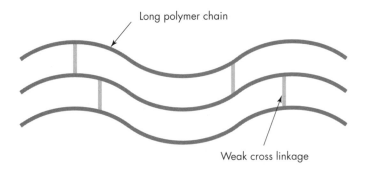

Long polymer chain

Weak cross linkage

plate boundaries are where two of the plates which make up the *crust* of the Earth meet. Earthquakes and volcanoes occur at these boundaries (see *constructive boundary* and *destructive boundary*).

plate tectonics is the theory that the Earth's *crust* is divided into several large pieces called plates that are moving at a rate of a few centimetres per year.
- The movement of these plates is caused by convection currents in the Earth's *mantle*.
- The energy for the movement comes from heat released by *radioactive decay*.
- Where plates slide past each other (e.g. in California) there are frequent earthquakes.
- Where plates collide there is a *destructive boundary*.
- Where plates are moving apart there is a *constructive boundary*.

platelets are tiny fragments of cells in our blood that help to stop bleeding from a cut (see *blood, cells* and *blood, clotting*).

platinum (Pt): a rare metal which is more valuable than gold.
- It is a *transition metal* and is often used as a *catalyst* in the chemical industry.
- It is fairly inert and therefore used to make jewellery and chemical apparatus.

pleura: a double skin that lines the inside of your thorax (chest) and covers the surface of your lungs. It produces a fluid that lubricates the surface of the lungs so that they do not irritate the chest wall as they expand and contract.

plug, three-pin: you need to be able to label the pins of the plug and to say which colour of wire is connected to each pin.

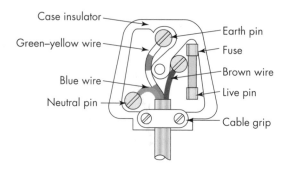

Case insulator
Green–yellow wire
Blue wire
Neutral pin
Earth pin
Fuse
Brown wire
Live pin
Cable grip

plumule: the tiny bud in a seed that grows into the shoot and is the first structure to appear above ground when some seeds germinate (see *germination*).

poles (magnetic): the two points on Earth which the needle on a compass points to (the north and south magnetic poles).

A compass needle is a magnet:
- its north-seeking end is the south pole of the magnet
- its south-seeking end is the north pole of a magnet.

The magnetic north pole is about 1300 km away from the geographical North Pole of the Earth and it moves a little each year.

pollen consists of tiny structures produced by flowers that contain the male sex cells of the plant.
- Pollen is produced by the *anthers* of the flower.
- The male sex cell in the pollen grain is produced by *meiosis*.
- The male cell therefore contains half the number of chromosomes of the cells in the rest of the plant.
- The pollen grains containing the male sex cells are usually transferred to the female parts of the flower by insects or by wind (see *pollination*).

pollination is the transfer of *pollen* grains from the male organs of a plant to the female organs; fertilisation then occurs, followed by the production of seeds and fruit.
- Pollen is transferred from the anthers (male organs) to the stigma (part of the female organs).
- It is usually transferred by insects or by wind.
- Transfer of pollen from an anther to the stigma of the same flower is called self-pollination.
- Transfer of pollen from an anther of one flower to the stigma of a different flower is called cross-pollination.

- Cross-pollination leads to more variation than self-pollination.
- During selective breeding of plants, breeders choose which plant to take pollen from, and which to pollinate – they also ensure that no other pollen reaches the stigma of the pollinated plant.

pollution, air: most air pollution is caused by burning *fossil fuels*. Some other substances (e.g. *CFCs*) also cause serious damage to the environment. The main pollutants produced by burning fossil fuels are:
- *carbon dioxide* from the oxidation of the carbon in the fuel; it is a gas partly responsible for the *greenhouse effect*
- *carbon monoxide* formed when there is insufficient oxygen to produce carbon dioxide – this often occurs in car engines
- *sulphur dioxide* from the oxidation of the sulphur in the fuels
- *nitrogen oxides* formed when high temperatures cause oxygen and nitrogen in air to combine (as they do naturally during lightning storms).

Acid rain is produced when sulphur dioxide and nitrogen oxides dissolve in rain water; acid rain damages trees and makes lakes and rivers too acid for living organisms.

pollution, freshwater: lakes and rivers are polluted mainly by *sewage* and by *fertilisers* and *pesticides*.
- Sewage provides food for microbes; these multiply rapidly and their *respiration* may deplete the oxygen in the water, causing animals such as fish to suffocate.
- Fertilisers cause aquatic plants to grow rapidly; this leads to *eutrophication* which has the same effect as sewage – it results in oxygen depletion.

pollution, sea: seas are polluted mainly by oil spillage and by the dumping of poisonous waste.
- Oil, for example, can kill seabirds by clogging their feathers. However, the *detergents* sprayed to disperse the oil probably kill more organisms than the oil, by poisoning them.
- Many heavy metals (e.g. mercury) have been dumped at sea; it is possible that these might become concentrated in organisms higher up in *food chains*, and poison them. Humans may be at risk through eating contaminated shellfish.

poly(ethene) is the chemical name for polythene – the plastic used to make plastic bags and clingfilm.
- It is manufactured from the *unsaturated hydrocarbon, ethene*.
- It is an *addition polymer*.

- The diagram shows how ethene molecules join to form poly(ethene).

poly(propene) is a firm plastic used for making plastic furniture and milk crates. It is a *polymer* made from the *alkene* propene.

poly(styrene) is a plastic used for making disposable cups and insulating materials. It is a *polymer* of the hydrocarbon phenylethene, which is related to *ethene*.

polymers are large molecules formed by joining many small molecules together. Most of the plastics we use every day are polymers, as are the *proteins* that make up much of solid content of our bodies.
- Many *addition polymers* such as *poly(ethene)* are made from *unsaturated hydrocarbons* such as *ethene*; no other molecules are formed in the reaction.
- Plastics such as nylon are formed by *condensation reactions*. Other small molecules are formed during the reaction; in the case of nylon the small molecule is hydrogen chloride.
- Natural polymers such as proteins, *starch* and *cellulose* are formed by condensation reactions; water is the small molecule formed in each case.

population: a group of organisms of the same species which live in the same habitat, for exampl, oak trees in a woodland or trout in a river. The size of a population is determined by:
- the amount of food (or nutrients in the case of plants) available
- how much *competition* there is for resources (e.g. food or nutrients)
- competition for light in the case of plants
- the amount of predation or grazing (see *predator–prey relationships*)
- disease.

positive: the resulting *charge* when something loses an electron.
- Remember than in an electric circuit, electrons flow from the negative electrode to the positive electrode.

potassium (K): a very soft, very reactive *metal*. You would not think of it as a metal to see it – but its reactions tell us that it is.

- It is in Group I of the *periodic table*.
- It is an *alkali metal*.
- It reacts violently with water to form hydrogen, so it is normally stored under oil.
- It reacts with non-metals to form ionic compounds in which the metal ion carries a +1 charge.
- It forms hydroxides which dissolve in water to give alkaline solutions.
- It is more reactive than sodium and lithium because its outer electrons are at a higher energy level and are therefore more easily lost.

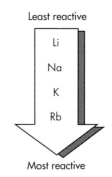

Least reactive

Li

Na

K

Rb

Most reactive

potential difference is the amount of energy available to make electricity flow round a *circuit*. It is measured in volts (V).

- A 12 V battery has twice as much energy to push electrons round a circuit as a 6 V battery.
- Two 6 V batteries connected in series have a total potential difference of 12 V. The bigger the potential difference, the greater the current which flows.
- The potential difference across a component in a circuit is measured by using a voltmeter connected across it in parallel, as shown in the diagram opposite.

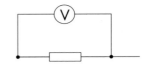

- The effect on the current of increasing the potential difference through different components is shown in the three graphs below.
- You should be able to recognise these graphs in the examination.
- The current through a *resistance* at constant temperature is proportional to the potential difference across the resistor.
- The shape of the curve for the filament is not a straight line because the resistance of the filament lamp increases as the filament gets hotter.

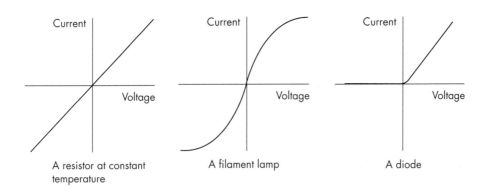

A resistor at constant temperature

A filament lamp

A diode

- The graph for the diode shows that the current flows through it in one direction only.
- The rate at which a component transfers energy (power) is given by:

$$\begin{array}{ccc} \text{power} & = & \text{potential difference} \times \text{current} \\ \text{(watts, W)} & & \text{(volts, V)} \qquad \text{(amperes, A)} \end{array}$$

- The higher the potential difference of the supply the greater the amount of energy transferred by the same amount of charge that flows, so:

$$\begin{array}{ccc} \text{energy transferred} & = & \text{potential difference} \times \text{charge} \\ \text{(joules, J)} & & \text{(volts, V)} \qquad \text{(coulombs, C)} \end{array}$$

---

potometer: a device for measuring the rate at which a plant shoot absorbs water – it is approximately the same as the rate at which the shoot loses water by evaporation (see *transpiration*).

The diagram shows one type of potometer, but they all work on the same principal.

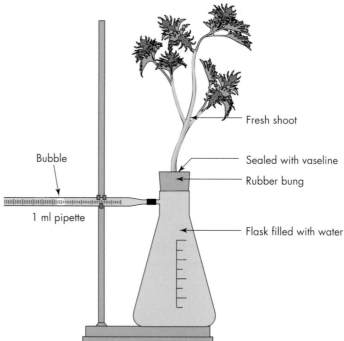

Fresh shoot

Bubble

Sealed with vaseline

Rubber bung

1 ml pipette

Flask filled with water

- Water evaporates from the leaves (transpiration).
- This causes water to be pulled up the *xylem*.
- This in turn takes in water from the flask
- which causes the bubble in the pipette to move to the right.
- The rate of transpiration is approximately equal to the rate at which water moves in the pipette (measured, for example, in cm^3 of water per hour).

---

power is a measure of how fast energy is transferred; its unit is the watt (W). The greater the power the more energy is transferred in a given time. You will meet power in both work done (see *work*) and *electricity* calculations.

WORK DONE CALCULATIONS

- When a force moves an object, energy is transferred, so work is done:

work done   =   force applied × distance moved in direction of force
(joules, J)   (newtons, N)   (metres, m)

- Power is the rate at which this work is done, so we divide work done by time – remember that time is measured in seconds:

$$\text{power (watts, W)} = \frac{\text{work done (joules, J)}}{\text{time taken (seconds, s)}}$$

So 1 watt is the transfer of 1 joule of energy in 1 second.

ELECTRICITY CALCULATIONS

- Remember that 1 watt is the transfer of 1 joule of energy in 1 second whether in work done or electricity:

power   =   potential difference ×   current
(watts, W)   (volts, V)   (amperes, A)

---

power station: building where *electricity* is generated. You need to know how both *non-renewable energy resources* (fuels) and *renewable energy resources* are used to generate electricity.

USING FUELS TO GENERATE ELECTRICITY

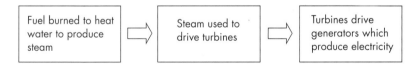

Fuel burned to heat water to produce steam ⇒ Steam used to drive turbines ⇒ Turbines drive generators which produce electricity

The main fuels used in British power stations are:
- coal
- oil
- natural gas
- nuclear fuels.

USING RENEWABLE ENERGY RESOURCES TO GENERATE ELECTRICITY

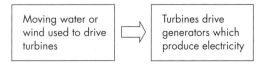

Moving water or wind used to drive turbines ⇒ Turbines drive generators which produce electricity

Water power

The energy in moving water can be used in power stations. Sources include:
- dams of hydroelectric schemes
- tidal barrages
- waves.

Wind energy

In wind stations, energy from the wind is used to turn huge propellers.

ENVIRONMENTAL DAMAGE

You may be asked to evaluate the environmental damage caused by power stations:
- for power stations burning fuels, the main effect is pollution, e.g. acid rain
- for power stations using renewable resources, the main impact may be visual – they often need to be sited in remote areas of countryside.

---

precipitate: an insoluble substance produced during a chemical reaction involving solutions. For example, the silver nitrate test for chlorides in which a white solid is produced if the test solution contains chloride ions.
- Precipitate refers to the process as well as the substances formed.

$$\text{sodium chloride} + \text{silver nitrate} \longrightarrow \text{silver chloride} + \text{sodium nitrate}$$
$$\text{(solution)} \qquad \text{(solution)} \qquad \text{(solid)} \qquad \text{(solution)}$$
$$NaCl(aq) \quad + \quad AgNO_3(aq) \longrightarrow \quad AgCl(s) \quad + \quad NaNO_3(aq)$$

The ionic equation for this is:
$$Ag^+(aq) + Cl^-(aq) \longrightarrow AgCl(s)$$

---

predator–prey relationships: a predator is an animal which eats another animal – the prey. A fox eats rabbits, so the fox is the predator and the rabbit the prey. You may be given data about the population sizes of predators and prey, either as graphs or as tables, as shown below.

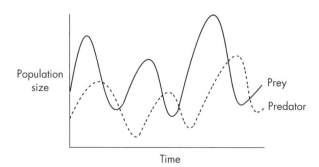

The graph shows:
- if the prey population increases, more food is available for the predators, so they increase in numbers
- if the predator population increases, more food is needed, so the prey population decreases
- if the prey population decreases, less food is available to the predators, so competition for food increases and the predator population decreases.

pregnancy starts when a *sperm* fertilises an *egg*, and ends when the young are born.
- The embryo develops in the *uterus* (womb) of the mother.
- It is supplied with nutrients and oxygen via the *placenta*.
- It is protected from physical damage by a water sac (amnion).
- Infertile women can be helped to become pregnant by using fertility drugs (see *FSH*).
- Pregnancy can be prevented by using *contraceptives*, including the birth control pills (see *oestrogen*).

pressure: *force* per unit area.
- The greater the force acting on a certain area, the greater the pressure; the greater the area the force acts on the less the pressure. For example, the stiletto heels of a small woman exert a greater pressure on the ground than the snow shoes of a large man.

$$\text{pressure (pascals, Pa)} = \frac{\text{force (newtons, N)}}{\text{area (metres}^2, \text{m}^2)}$$

- A pressure of 1 Pa is exerted by a force of 1 N acting at right angles to an area of 1 m^2.
- In pressure calculations, do not forget to convert the area to metre^2.

EXAMPLE
A brake pedal exerts a force of 500 N on the master piston of a braking system. The area of the master piston is 0.5 cm^2. Calculate the pressure on the master piston.
First convert 0.5 cm^2 to m^2 – divide by 10 000 (1 m^2 is 100 cm × 100 cm):

0.5 cm^2 = 0.00005 m^2

$$\text{pressure (pascals, Pa)} = \frac{\text{force (newtons, N)}}{\text{area (metres}^2, \text{m}^2)}$$

$$= \frac{500 \text{ N}}{0.00005 \text{ m}^2}$$

$$= 10\ 000\ 000 \text{ Pa}$$

Liquids can be used to transfer pressure (see *hydraulics*); pressure in a liquid varies with depth because pressure depends on the weight of water above:

- The greater the depth the greater the pressure, so submarines which need to descend deep into the oceans have to have very strong sides to withstand great pressure.
- The pressure of the atmosphere varies with altitude because pressure depends on the weight of air above.
- The pressure at the top of a mountain is far less than that at sea level.
- High flying aircraft have pressurised cabins to give us enough air to breathe (see *atmospheric pressure*).
- When the pressure on a gas increases and the temperature stays the same its volume decreases (see *Boyle's law*).

prey: see *predator–prey relationships*.

Priestley, Joseph: a British scientist who lived 1733–1804.

- He was the first scientist to isolate many gases, including oxygen, ammonia, carbon monoxide, nitrous oxide and sulphur dioxide.
- He was the first to describe the relationship between oxygen, respiration and burning.
- He did not, however, realise what oxygen was – he called it dephlogisicated air – and it was left to *Lavoisier* to establish that oxygen is an element.

primary (of a transformer): a *transformer* consists of an input coil, an output coil and an iron core – the primary is the input coil.

primary consumer: an animal that eats only plants; cows are primary consumers because they eat grass (see *herbivore*).

prism: a block made of glass or Perspex whose angles are either 60°, 60°, 60° or 90°, 45°, 45°.

- 60°, 60°, 60° prisms can be used to split up white light into a spectrum – this is called *dispersion*.

- Red light is bent (refracted) the least by a prism; violet the most, because violet light is slowed down much more than red light as it passes from air into the prism.

- 90°, 45°, 45° prisms are often used in periscopes and binoculars to turn light rays through 90°; the light is bent through 90° because of *total internal reflection*.

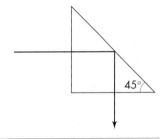

producer: an organism which produces its own food – most producers are plants. We get all our food directly or indirectly from producers.
- *Food chains* usually begin with producers:

  grass ⟶ antelope ⟶ cheetah

  producer ⟶ herbivore ⟶ carnivore

  primary producer ⟶ primary consumer ⟶ secondary consumer
- Producers use *photosynthesis* to make food.
- They contain a green pigment called *chlorophyll* that absorbs light energy and transfers it to chemical energy.

progesterone is a female sex *hormone*, commonly found in birth control pills and used in hormone replacement therapy (HRT).
- It is produced by the ovaries after an egg has been released.
- It causes the lining of the womb to prepare to receive a fertilised egg.
- Falling levels of progesterone towards the end of the *menstrual cycle* lead to the breakdown of the inner lining of the womb and *menstruation*.

propagation is the production of new plants from *cuttings*. It is used to produce crops and plants for houses and gardens.
- New plants grown from seed show more variation than those produced from cuttings (see *asexual reproduction*, *sexual reproduction*, *mitosis*, *meiosis*).

protease is an *enzyme* used to digest the *proteins* in our diet (see *digestion*). Proteases are produced by glands in the:
- *stomach*
- *pancreas*
- *small intestine*.
- Proteases break down *proteins* into soluble *amino acids* which can be absorbed into the blood.
- Biological washing powders contain proteases made by bacteria in fermenters – these proteases digest stains caused by proteins.

protein is needed in our *diet* for growth and repair.
- Protein molecules are long chains of *amino acids*.
- The order of amino acids in a protein is carried as a code by *DNA* molecules.
- Many proteins are denatured by high temperatures (e.g. the protein that makes up egg white turns solid when heated).
- All *enzymes* are proteins.
- Many *hormones* are proteins (e.g. *insulin*).

proton: one of the three particles that make up atoms (see *atom, neutron, electron*).
- Protons are the positively charged particles in the nucleus of an atom.
- They have a relative mass of 1 and a charge of +1.
- They are present in the nuclei of all atoms.
- All atoms of the same element have the same number of protons.
- The number of protons in an atom is called the *proton number* (atomic number).
- The number of electrons in an atom is equal to the number of protons so that the atom has no overall charge.

proton number: the number of protons in the nucleus of an *atom* – also called the atomic number.
In this way of representing a uranium atom, $^{238}_{92}U$:
- the proton number is 92
- the *mass number* is 238.
- This means that the total number of *protons* and *neutrons* is 238.
- Because the number of protons is given by the proton number (92), the number of neutrons is (238 – 92) = 146.

puberty is another word for adolescence – when you change from being a child into a man or woman (see *adolescence*).

pulmonary: to do with the *lungs*. The main blood vessel supplying the lungs is called the pulmonary artery, and infections of the lungs are called pulmonary infections, e.g. pulmonary tuberculosis.

pulse: regular surges of blood through the arteries, corresponding to beats of the heart (see *heart, beat*).
- You measure pulse rate to find how fast the heart is beating. You do this by pressing an artery against a bone (e.g. in the wrist or temple) then counting the number of pulses you can feel each minute.

- Each pulse corresponds to one heartbeat, caused by a contraction of the left ventricle of the heart forcing blood into arteries.
- Pulse rate varies from about 150 beats per minute in an embryo to about 60 in an elderly person.
- Your pulse rate increases when you exercise – this is because your heart beats faster to increase the rate of blood supply, and therefore of oxygen, to the muscles.

pupil: the 'black' part of the *eye*, in fact a hole in the *iris* that controls how much light enters the eye. You are dazzled when you leave a cinema during the day because your pupils have widened in the darkness of the cinema.
- The pupil is narrow in bright light and wide in dim light.
- The width of the pupils is controlled by a reflex action.

PVC: a common plastic. Its uses include the insulation on electric cables, pipes and gutters.
- PVC stands for polyvinyl chloride, but the chemical name is poly-chloroethene.
- It is a *polymer* based on the *unsaturated hydrocarbon* known as *ethene*.

pyramid of biomass: a diagram which shows the mass, drawn to scale, of living material (*biomass*) at each level in a *food chain* (see also *pyramid of numbers*).
- For the food chain
      producers ⟶ herbivores ⟶ carnivores
  a pyramid of biomass usually has the shape shown opposite, irrespective of the shape of the pyramid of numbers for the same food chain.

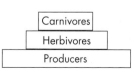

The biomass at each stage in the food chain is less than it was at the previous stage because:
- *herbivores* do not eat all the *producers* and *carnivores* do not eat all of the herbivores
- some materials are lost in the waste materials of the herbivores and carnivores
- when organisms respire, carbon dioxide is given off into the atmosphere.

pyramid of numbers: a diagram which shows the numbers, drawn to scale, of living organisms at each level in a *food chain* (see also *pyramid of biomass*).
- For the food chain
      producers ⟶ herbivores ⟶ carnivores

a pyramid of biomass often has the shape shown below:

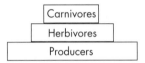

- Where the producers are very large (e.g. trees), there may not be many of them, and the pyramid of numbers will have this shape:

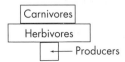

- Where the secondary consumers are very small, such as fleas living on an animal, they may be present in very large numbers. So the pyramid of numbers for the food chain

    leaves ⟶ earthworms ⟶ hedgehog ⟶ fleas

would look like this:

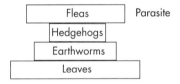

quartz is the most common mineral on Earth. It is:
- composed of silicon dioxide (SiO_2)
- found in rocks such as granite and sandstone.

---

quicklime is the main ingredient of the *cement* we use in building. It is:
- mainly calcium oxide (CaO)
- obtained by heating *limestone* (*thermal decomposition* of limestone) in lime kilns:

    calcium carbonate $\longrightarrow$ calcium oxide + carbon dioxide

    CaO(s) $\longrightarrow$ CaO(s)   + CO_2(g)
- treated with water to form *slaked lime* (*calcium hydroxide*) which is used to *neutralise* acid soils and in many industries (e.g. paper making).

---

radicle (seed): the tiny root in a seed that grows to form the main root of the plant.
- The appearance of the young root is the first sign of *germination*.
- This is an advantage, as the young root absorbs water and minerals from the soil for use by the growing plant.

radio waves are *electromagnetic* radiation used to transmit radio and TV programmes between different parts of the Earth's surface.
- They have the longest *wavelengths* in the electromagnetic spectrum and therefore the lowest *frequencies*.
- Radio waves with very long wavelengths are reflected from an electrically charged layer in the upper atmosphere – this means that they can be sent between distant parts of the Earth despite the curvature of the Earth's surface.
- *Diffraction* results in poor reception of TV and radio waves (see also *ripple tank*).

radioactive: a substance is radioactive if it gives out radiation all the time (see *alpha radiation, beta radiation, gamma radiation, background radiation*).
- Radioactivity occurs as a result of changes in the nuclei of *atoms*.
- When an unstable atom splits up it emits radiation and a different atom is formed.

radioactive decay: see *decay, radioactive*.

radiocarbon dating: see *dating*.

radioisotope: *isotopes* are *atoms* of the same *element* which have different numbers of *neutrons* (because they are the same element they have the same number of *protons*).
- Radioisotopes have unstable nuclei – they split up and emit radiation.
- Radioisotopes are produced by bombarding atoms with atomic particles in a *nuclear reactor*.
- Radioisotopes are now used extensively in medicine, industry and the home.

USE IN MEDICINE

Radioisotopes are used as tracers – they are injected into the blood and their circulation monitored outside the body. Technetium-90 is an example of a tracer.

- It emits *gamma rays* which can pass through body tissues, so its movement can be detected.
- It has a short *half-life* (about six hours) so that the amount of gamma radiation in the body declines rapidly.

USE IN INDUSTRY

- Radioisotopes are used in thickness detectors. For example, the thickness of aluminium being rolled into sheets can be controlled by measuring how much *beta radiation* from a radioisotope passes through the aluminium.
- Radioisotopes used for this purpose need to have a long half-life so that they do not have to be changed frequently.

USE IN THE HOME

- Most smoke detectors fitted in homes contain the radioisotope americum-241 – this emits *alpha radiation* which is so weak that the radiation does not pass out of the device to harm us.
- Americum-241 has a very long half-life, so it does not need to be changed.

---

radionuclide: another name for *radioisotope*.

RAM: see *chemistry calculations, relative atomic mass*.

---

rarefaction: part of a *longitudinal wave* (e.g. a sound wave) where the air particles are wide apart – like a 'slinky' where the coils are wide apart. (See also *compression*.)

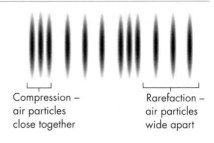

Compression – air particles close together

Rarefaction – air particles wide apart

---

rate of reaction, effect of catalyst on: *catalysts* speed up the rate of chemical reactions.

- This is important in industry because it reduces costs.

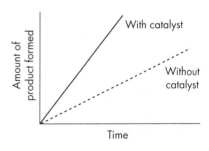

● It is also important in your body because *enzymes* speed up reactions and allow them to occur at body temperature.

rate of reaction, effect of concentration on:

increasing the concentration of reactants increases the rate of reaction.

● This is because reactions occur when particles collide, so when there is a higher concentration of reacting particles, the number of collisions between them is increased.

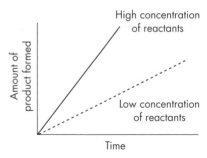

rate of reaction, effect of pressure on:

increasing the *pressure* in a reaction between gases increases the rate of reaction.

● This is because reactions occur when gas particles collide, and increasing the pressure increases the number of collisions between the reacting gas particles (see also *Haber process*).

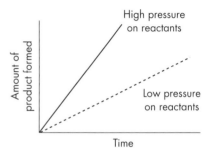

rate of reaction, effect of surface area on: marble chips react slowly
with hydrochloric acid, but if the chips are powdered the reaction goes much faster.

Marble lump   Marble powder

The powder has the same total volume as the lump – but a much greater surface is available for the acid to react with.

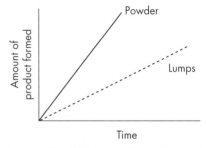

● This is because the total surface area of the powder is bigger than that of the chips, so there is a greater chance of reacting particles meeting and reacting.

rate of reaction, effect of temperature on: increasing the *temperature* of
a reaction increases the rate of reaction.

- This is because reactions occur when particles collide and increasing the temperature increases the speed of movement of the reacting particles, so they collide with each other more frequently and more energetically.

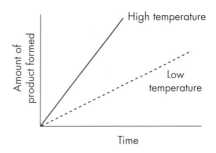

---

ray: a narrow beam of light. You have probably used a ray box to produce a light ray when you studied reflection from mirrors (see *angle of incidence and angle of reflection* and *angle of refraction*).

---

reactants are the starting materials in a chemical reaction.
- In the reaction:
    sodium + water ⟶ sodium hydroxide + hydrogen
    sodium and water are the reactants (sodium hydroxide and hydrogen are the *products* of the reaction).
- In any chemical reaction:
    reactants ⟶ products.

---

reaction time: the time it takes for you to react to an event, for example the time between seeing someone step into the road and your foot hitting the brake pedal of the car.

The stopping distance of a car depends on both:
- the reaction time of the driver
- the distance the vehicle travels under the force of the brakes.

---

reactivity series: metals listed in the order of how well they react with other substances.
- The table on the next page shows the trends (see also *metals, reactions with acids*; *metals, reactions with oxygen*; *metals, reactions with water*; *displacement reaction of metals*).
- You should be able to predict the reaction of a metal from its position in the reactivity series.

Metal	Reaction with dil. acids	Reaction with oxygen	Reaction with steam	Reaction with water	Displacement reactions
Potassium	react violently giving off hydrogen	burn in air forming an oxide	react explosively	react violently	metals higher in series displace
Sodium					
Calcium					
Magnesium					
Aluminium					
Zinc					
Iron					
Lead					
Copper					
Silver	do not react	do not react	do not react	do not react	metals lower in series
Gold					

- The reactivity series also tells us the best metal for a particular job. Copper is used for hot water tanks because it does not react with steam; iron (as steel) can only be used for cold water tanks since it does react with steam.

real image: see *images, real and virtual.*

receptor: a cell which is sensitive to a stimulus, for example cells in your eye that detect light.
- The table below gives the most common receptors in the body:

Organ	Contains receptors sensitive to
eye	light
ear	sound
ear	position
ear	balance
tongue	chemicals (of taste)
nose	chemicals (of smell)
skin	temperature change
skin	pressure (touch)

- Information from receptors passes as *nerve impulses* along nerve cells called *sensory neurones* to the *brain* and/or *spinal cord*.

recessive: an *allele* is recessive when it controls the development of a characteristic only when it is present on both chromosomes.
- The allele responsible for *cystic fibrosis* is recessive.
- Recessive is the opposite of *dominant* (an allele that controls development when it is present on only one chromosome, for example the allele responsible for *Huntington's disease*).

red blood cell: type of cell in your blood that carries oxygen to all your body cells (see *blood, cells*).

red giant: a stage in the life history of a star, as shown in the diagram.

Formation
Stars are formed when enough dust and gas is pulled together by gravitational forces

Main stage (yellow dwarf)
The energy from nuclear fusion reactions at the centre of the star, which use hydrogen and helium as fuel, tend to make the star expand. Very strong forces counteract the expansion. The star is stable. Our Sun is at this stage.

Red giant
As it uses up the fuels for nuclear fusion it cools and expands to become a red giant.

White dwarf
If it is a small star it eventually uses up all of its fuel and contracts further to become a white dwarf

Supernova
If the red giant is big enough it may contract and explode to become a supernova, throwing gas and dust into space

Black dwarf
As it cools further the white dwarf becomes a black dwarf

Neutron star
What remains after the explosion of a supernova is a neutron star, which is very dense. It may eventually become so dense that its gravity does not let light escape – it is then a black hole.

redox reactions are reactions in which one substance is *oxidised* and another is *reduced*, for instance the reaction in the *blast furnace* from which we get most of our iron:

iron(III) oxide + carbon monoxide $\longrightarrow$ iron + carbon dioxide

$Fe_2O_3(s)$ + $3CO(g)$ $\longrightarrow$ $2Fe(l)$ + $3CO_2(g)$

In this reaction:

- the iron(III) oxide is reduced – because it *loses* oxygen
- carbon monoxide is oxidised – because it *gains* oxygen
- because the carbon monoxide reduces the iron(III) oxide (takes oxygen away from it) it is known as a *reducing agent*.

Hydrogen can reduce heated copper oxide – the copper oxide is reduced and the hydrogen is oxidised:

copper oxide + hydrogen $\longrightarrow$ copper + water

$CuO(s)$ + $H_2(g)$ $\longrightarrow$ $Cu(s)$ + $H_2O(g)$

Aluminium oxide is reduced during *electrolysis*; the aluminium ions gain electrons so they are reduced:

$Al^{3+} + 3e^- \longrightarrow Al$

reducing agents are substances such as carbon monoxide and hydrogen which can take oxygen from a substance (see *redox reaction*).

reduction: a reaction in which a substance loses oxygen, for example when iron oxide loses oxygen in a *blast furnace*.

- Most metals occur as oxides, so to extract these metals we have to reduce the oxides (see also *redox reactions*).
- Reduction is also when a substance gains hydrogen.
- It is also when a substance gains electrons.
- It is the opposite to *oxidation*.

reflection is when a wave comes back from a surface rather than passing through it.

- You see yourself in a mirror because light is reflected from the back of it (see *ripple tank*).
- When a wave strikes a reflective surface it is usual for some of the energy of the wave to be absorbed and some reflected.

(See *angle of incidence* and *angle of reflection*.)

reflex action: an automatic response. Blinking is a reflex action in which the eyelids close and open automatically when an object approaches the eye rapidly.

You must remember the following terms in a reflex action:
- *stimulus* – the change that is detected
- *receptor* – the cell that detects the change
- *coordinator* – the *brain* or *spinal cord* where the action is coordinated
- *effector* – what brings about the response; usually a *muscle* or a *gland*
- *response* – what happens.

MECHANISM OF BLINKING REFLEX

stimulus ⇒	**receptor** ⇒	**coordinator** ⇒	**effector** ⇒	**response**
moving object	nerve cells in retina	brain	eyelid muscles	eyelid closes

You also have to know the path taken by the nerve impulses during a reflex action. These are shown on a diagram of a pain-withdrawal reflex (when you automatically pull your hand away if you touch something hot).

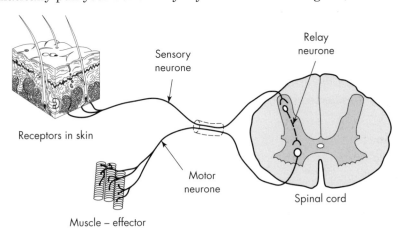

- Temperature receptors in the skin detect the large increase in temperature.
- *Sensory neurones* carry impulses from the temperature receptors to the spinal cord (the coordinator).
- The impulses pass across a *synapse* between the sensory neurone and the relay neurone (sometimes called connector neurone).
- The impulses pass across another synapse to the motor neurone.
- The motor neurone carries the impulses to the muscle.
- The muscle is the effector – it contracts to pull the arm away from the heat.

refraction: the change in direction of a wave when it crosses the boundary between two different substances (the reason that swimming pools look shallower than they are is that light waves bend as they pass from water into air).

- When a light wave passes from air into a plastic (or glass) block it bends *towards* the normal (unless it is travelling along the normal, in which case it does not bend). This is because light travels more slowly in glass than in air (see also *ripple tank*).
- When a light wave passes from a plastic (or glass) block into air it bends *away from* the normal. This is because light speeds up as it enters the air.

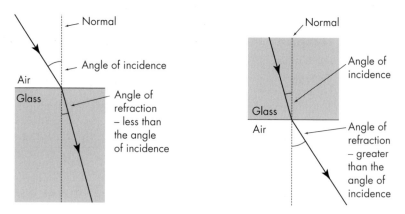

- If the *angle of incidence* is greater than a certain angle (the *critical angle*) all the light is reflected inside the glass. This is called *total internal reflection*.

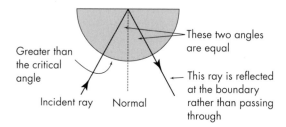

---

relative atomic mass (RAM): see *chemistry calculations, relative atomic mass*.

---

relative formula mass (RFM): see *chemistry calculations, relative formula mass*.

---

relative molecular mass (RMM): see *chemistry calculations, relative molecular mass*.

---

renal: to do with the kidney. The blood vessel supplying the kidney is called the renal artery.

---

renewable energy resources are energy sources that will not run out (compared with *non-renewable energy resources*, which will).

EXAMPLES

- Sunlight, which is transferred by plants during *photosynthesis*. We can use some plants (e.g. sugar cane) to produce *biofuels*. We can also transfer sunlight energy to electrical energy by using solar cells.
- Wood can be burnt as an energy resource; forests can be replanted.
- The wind can be used to generate electricity, by using it to drive turbines in power stations.
- Waves, running water and the tides can all be used to generate electricity by driving turbines in power stations.

rennin: an *enzyme* produced in the stomachs of young mammals (e.g. calves) to clot milk.
- The diet of young mammals consists entirely of milk.
- Although milk is a liquid food, the proteins in it still need to be digested (see *digestion*).
- Clotted milk moves more slowly through the gut, so it has more time to be digested.
- Rennin is used in *cheese* making to clot milk – the clots are the first stage in cheese formation.

reproduction: the production of new individuals from parent organisms. There are two main methods of reproduction:
- *asexual reproduction* – reproduction that does <u>not</u> involve the fusion (joining) of sex cells (*gametes*)
- *sexual reproduction* – reproduction that <u>does</u> involve the fusion of sex cells.

reptiles are animals such as snakes, lizards, crocodiles and tortoises. Reptiles:
- are *vertebrates* (have a backbone)
- have bodies covered by scales
- have lungs to breathe air
- lay eggs with a leathery skin, usually in the ground.

resistance is opposition to the flow of an electric *current*; its unit is the *ohm*, symbol Ω (see also *resistor*).
- The bigger the resistance, the smaller the current produced by a particular voltage.

- The bigger the resistance, the bigger the voltage needed to produce a particular current.

You are almost certain to be asked to calculate resistance, so remember the three forms of the equation which include resistance:

$$\text{resistance (ohms, } \Omega) = \frac{\text{potential difference (volts, V)}}{\text{current (amperes, A)}}$$

$$\text{potential difference (volts, V)} = \text{current (amperes, A)} \times \text{resistance (ohms, } \Omega)$$

$$\text{current (amperes, A)} = \frac{\text{potential difference (volts, V)}}{\text{resistance (ohms, } \Omega)}$$

EXAMPLE

Calculate the resistance of a 230 V light bulb when a current of 0.65 A flows through it.

$$\text{resistance } (\Omega) = \frac{\text{potential difference (V)}}{\text{current (A)}}$$

$$= \frac{230 \text{ V}}{0.65 \text{ A}}$$

$$= 353.8 \ \Omega$$

---

resistor: a component that opposes the flow of an electric *current*.

- The symbol for a resistor is: ⎯⎯⎯⎯▭⎯⎯⎯⎯
- The current through a resistor (at constant temperature) is proportional to the *voltage* across the resistor.
- The resistance of a filament lamp increases as the temperature of the filament increases.
- The resistance of a light-dependent resistor (LDR) <u>decreases</u> as light intensity <u>increases</u>.
- The resistance of a thermistor <u>decreases</u> as temperature <u>increases</u>.
- A diode has a very high resistance in one direction – this means the a current will flow through it only in the opposite direction.

---

respiration is the process that takes place in your body cells where energy is transferred from glucose – this is how, for example, you get the energy to run.

- Do not confuse respiration with breathing – they are not the same.
  Breathing is the moving of air in and out of the lungs.

There are two kinds of respiration:

- *aerobic respiration* which uses oxygen
- *anaerobic respiration* which does not use oxygen.

---

respire: break down sugars to release energy. Do not confuse respire with breathe, which is to move air in and out of the lungs.

response: the reaction of an organism to a *stimulus*, for example pulling your arm away from something hot (see *reflex action*).

retina: the inner layer of the *eye*. It contains cells which are sensitive to light (light *receptors*):
● *cones* are receptors used for colour vision
● *rods* are receptors used in dim light.

reversible reaction: a reaction in which the products can react to form the reactants. For example, in the production of ammonia, nitrogen and hydrogen react to form ammonia, but ammonia can split up to form nitrogen and hydrogen.
● For this type of reaction we use the symbol ⇌ rather than ⟶. So the reaction above is written as:
  nitrogen + hydrogen ⇌ ammonia
● In industry (*Haber process*) this reaction occurs in a closed system, so eventually the rates of the forward and backward reactions are the same.
● The reactions are now said to be in equilibrium (see *equilibrium reaction*).
● It is important to ensure that the equilibrium mixture contains as high a proportion of ammonia (rather than nitrogen and hydrogen) as possible.

rib and ribcage: the ribs form a ribcage surrounding the human *thorax* (chest).
● The ribcage protects the organs inside the thorax (*heart* and *lungs*).

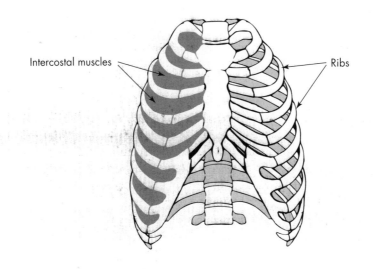

Intercostal muscles   Ribs

- The ribcage is important in breathing: to breathe in, the *intercostal muscles* contract, pulling the ribcage upwards and outwards. This, together with the downward movement of the *diaphragm*, increases the volume of the thorax, which decreases the pressure so that air enters the lungs.

ripple tank: a tray of water, illuminated to show how waves behave. The diagrams show some ways in which ripple tanks show wave behaviour:

- This diagram shows how a ripple tank shows *reflection* of waves:

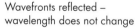

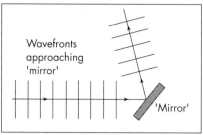

- This diagram shows how a ripple tank demonstrates *refraction* of waves:

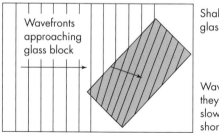

- This diagram shows how a ripple tank demonstrates *diffraction* of waves:

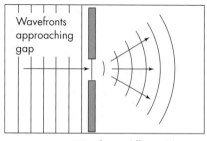

Wavefronts diffracted by gap

- This diagram shows how a ripple tank demonstrates 'shadows' produced by diffraction of waves (how, for example, hills interfere with radio and TV reception):

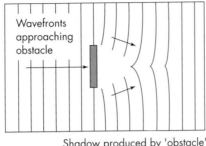

Shadow produced by 'obstacle'

rock cycle: this shows how rocks are formed and recycled.

You should be able to describe how each of the following rock types are formed:

- *sedimentary*
- *metamorphic*
- *intrusive igneous*
- *extrusive igneous.*

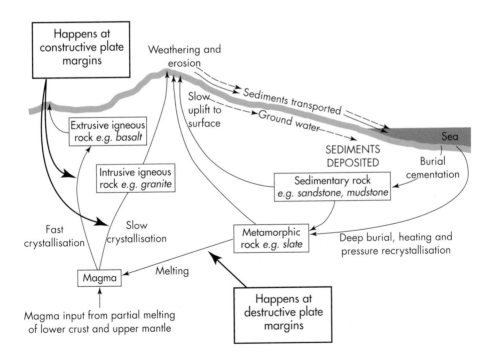

You should also be able to describe what happens at:

- *constructive plate margins*
- *destructive plate margins.*

rods are cells in the *eye* which help us to see at dawn and dusk.
- Rods are light *receptor* cells.
- They are found in the *retina* (inner layer of the eye).
- They work in low light intensities but only give us black-and-white vision (no colours).
- They are situated towards the edge of the retina, whilst *cones* (which give us colour vision) are found near the centre of the retina, especially at the fovea (yellow spot).

root: the part of the plant that:
- anchors it in the ground
- absorbs water from the soil
- absorbs mineral salts from the soil
- sometimes stores carbohydrate as *starch*.

root hairs are the tiny hair-like cells on young roots that absorb most of the water and mineral salts that the plant needs from the soil.
- Root hairs are found only near the ends of the youngest roots.
- Their hair-like shape gives them a large surface area for absorbing mineral salts.
- Water is absorbed from the soil, mainly by *osmosis*.
- Mineral salts are absorbed from the soil mainly by active uptake.

rooting powder is used to make stem *cuttings* form roots more quickly.
- It is used by gardeners and horticulturists who want to grow large numbers of plants that are identical to a particular parent plant.
- Stem cuttings have their cut ends dipped in rooting powder – this end is then pushed into soil and left in moist conditions.
- The powder contains plant hormones (*auxins*) which stimulate root growth.

rusting is the corrosion of iron.
- It is caused by a complex chemical reaction between iron, water and oxygen resulting in the formation of an oxide of iron.
- Rust is much weaker than iron; in the UK, damage to iron structures caused through rusting costs the country millions of pounds each year to put right.

rust prevention: there are three main methods of preventing rust:
- making *alloys* (e.g. stainless steel); in stainless steel, iron is alloyed with chromium and sometimes nickel

- *galvanising* the iron; this is coating the iron with zinc – zinc is more reactive than iron, so the zinc reacts with the oxygen and water in the air, rather than the iron reacting with them.
- painting the iron to prevent oxygen and water reaching it.

Rutherford, Ernest: a British scientist who lived 1871–1937.
- He discovered much of what we now know about the structure of the *atom*.
- Before Rutherford's experiments scientists thought that atoms were a solid mixture of different particles – rather like a 'plum-pudding'.
- Rutherford first identified the three types of radiation (*alpha, beta* and *gamma radiation*).
- After then bombarding gold leaf with alpha particles, he found that some particles went straight through the gold leaf, some were reflected and some were deflected.
- From these results he proposed the modern view of the atom – that there is a central *nucleus* around which *electrons* move.
- Later he bombarded nitrogen with alpha particles and found that some oxygen was formed; this led other scientists to study nuclear fission (see *fission, nuclear*), leading to nuclear power stations and atomic bombs.

S

S-wave: a 'side-to-side' shock wave produced by an earthquake (compared with a *P-wave*).

- S-waves are *transverse waves* (as are light waves).
- S-waves cause the surface of the Earth to move from side to side.
- They travel through solids but not through liquids.
- They are refracted as the density of the material they pass through changes.
- The diagram below shows that S-waves do not pass through the core of the Earth but P-waves do.

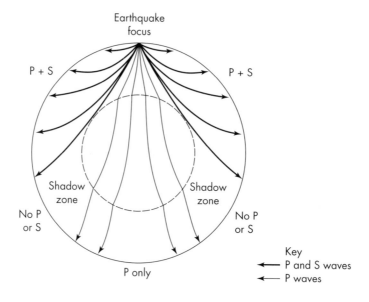

sacrificial protection means using one metal to protect another metal from corrosion or *rusting* (e.g. galvanising iron).

- In galvanising, iron is coated with a thin layer of zinc. In the presence of water and oxygen zinc reacts rather than the iron because zinc is the more reactive.
- Magnesium is much more reactive than iron. Large blocks of magnesium are sometimes bolted to the hulls of ships. The magnesium reacts with the seawater rather than the iron – it 'sacrifices' itself so the iron does not rust as quickly.

saliva: 'spit' – the liquid in your mouth when your mouth 'waters'.
- It is produced by the *salivary glands*.
- It contains an *enzyme* called *carbohydrase* or *amylase* that breaks down starch into sugars.
- It also contains *mucus* – a slimy substance that helps you to swallow food.

salivary glands: structures found near the mouth that produce the *saliva* which helps us to digest and swallow food.

salt: the substance formed when an acid reacts with an alkali (see *acids and alkalis*).

    acid + alkali $\longrightarrow$ salt + water
- The 'salt' we use in cooking and the most common 'salt' in seawater is sodium chloride.

    hydrochloric acid + sodium hydroxide $\longrightarrow$ sodium chloride + water
- Salts have *ionic bonding*.
- Salts conduct electricity when dissolved in water or when molten.

sand is produced when many kinds of rocks are broken down by *weathering* or *erosion*.
Sand:
- consists mainly of silica
- is an important part of soil – it helps soils to drain quickly
- is used to make glass and sandpaper.

sandstone is a rock formed when grains of sand are cemented together naturally. It is a *sedimentary* rock, formed when:
- layers of sand are laid down one on top of the other
- their weight squeezes out water
- and cements the particles together.

Crude oil is often found in sandstones.

saprophyte: an organism such as a mushroom that obtains its food by breaking down dead organisms – very important in recycling natural materials.
- The majority of saphrophytes are *fungi* such as mushrooms or moulds.
- Some *bacteria* are saprophytes.
- Both saprophytic bacteria and fungi are important in the breakdown of dead matter in the *carbon cycle* and the *nitrogen cycle*.
- Saphrophytes obtain their food by passing *enzymes* onto the dead matter; the enzymes break down the dead matter into soluble material which the saprophyte then absorbs.

- Saprophytes cannot make their own food by *photosynthesis*.

satellite: an object that orbits a planet or a star (e.g. the Earth is a satellite of the Sun; the Moon is a satellite of the Earth).
Satellites have been put into space:
- to act as communication devices – for example, to pass messages between places on opposite sides of the Earth (see *satellite communication*)
- to monitor global changes (e.g. the weather; see *satellite, monitoring*)
- to observe the universe without the interference of the atmosphere.
A satellite stays in orbit because of a combination of its high speed and the force of gravity.

satellite, monitoring: a satellite that can scan the whole of the Earth's surface in one day (e.g. weather satellites and spy satellites) These satellites are usually put into a low orbit around the poles so that the Earth spins beneath them (compare *satellite communication*).

satellite communication: modern communication satellites receive radio waves (for radio or TV) from one point on Earth and transmit them to another part.
- Most telephone calls between different countries now travel via communication satellites.
- TV programmes can also be transmitted between countries via these satellites.
- Most communication satellites are put into an orbit high above the equator so that they move around the Earth at exactly the same rate at which the Earth spins on its axis (compare *satellite, monitoring*). This means that they stay in the same position when viewed from Earth.
- Such an orbit is said to be geostationary or geosynchronous.
- The height of the orbit of a satellite above Earth is about 35 800 km.

saturated compounds are compounds such as *methane* (see *hydrocarbons*).
- All the carbon atoms are joined by single *covalent* bonds in a saturated compound.
- The *alkane* family are all saturated compounds.
- Saturated compounds are all relatively unreactive.
- Compare with the *alkene* family, e.g. ethylene, which are *unsaturated* because they have at least one covalent *double bond*.

saturated solution: a solution in which no more *solute* will dissolve, providing that the temperature does not change.

- If a saturated solution is cooled down some of the solute may crystallise out.
- If a saturated solution is heated more solute may dissolve.

sclera: the white outer coat of the eye (see *eye, structure of*). The sclera:
- is tough – to protect the eye from damage
- has a transparent region at the front called the *cornea*.

secondary (of transformer): a transformer consists of an input coil, an output coil and an iron core. The secondary is the output coil (see *transformer*).

sedimentary rock: rocks such as *sandstone* and *chalk* which are formed from layers of sediments. Sedimentary rocks are formed when:
- layers of sediment become buried
- their great weight squeezes water out of them
- the particles become cemented together when salts crystallise out of this water.
- The process takes millions of years.
- Sedimentary rocks often contain *fossils*.
- High temperatures are <u>not</u> involved in the formation of sedimentary rocks (compare *metamorphic rocks* and *igneous* rocks).

seed: a structure containing an embryo plant. We grow many types of plants from seeds.
- Seeds are formed as a result of *sexual reproduction* in flowering plants.
- Therefore plants grown from seed show more *variation* than plants produced by *asexual reproduction* (e.g. from *cuttings*).
- Seeds are formed after the egg (ovule) has been *fertilised*.
- In most cases seeds are formed inside a *fruit*.
Most seeds contain:
- an embryo shoot (*plumule*)
- an embryo root (*radicle*)
- a store of food.

seismic wave: the shock wave produced by an earthquake – it is these waves that cause most of the damage (see *P-waves* and *S-waves*).

seismometer: a device for recording shock waves (*seismic waves*) produced by earthquakes.
- They work by having a pendulum which touches a recording drum.
- When the Earth moves the drum also moves but the pendulum does not.

selective breeding: breeding method based on selecting organisms possessing desirable *characteristics*, for example breeding cows to produce more milk (see *artificial selection*).

- When breeding the next generation, farmers choose the cows with the largest milk yield as mothers.
- They repeat this in every generation.
- Over many generations there is a large increase in milk yield.

There are however, problems with selective breeding:

- the number of *alleles* in the population is reduced
- there is therefore less variation, and the species is less able to adapt to changing conditions (e.g. a new strain of disease).

semen is the fluid in which *sperm* leave the male body.

- Semen is produced mainly by the prostate gland, which is near the bladder.
- It provides nutrients for the sperm
- and a liquid in which they can swim.

sensitivity: the ability to react to the surroundings, for example blinking (see *reflex action*, *nervous system* and *tropism*).

Sensitivity usually involves the following:

- *receptors* which can detect a *stimulus* (e.g. cells in your eye can detect light)
- a *coordinator* – usually the *brain* or *spinal cord*
- an *effector* which brings about the response (e.g. the muscles which move your eyelid).

sensory neurone: a nerve cell which carries information to the *brain* or *spinal cord* (see *neurone*, *nervous system* and *reflex action*).

- The axon is specialised for conducting electrical impulses.
- The myelin sheath acts as an insulator.
- In a *reflex action* the sensory neurone carries impulses from the *receptor* to the *coordinator*.

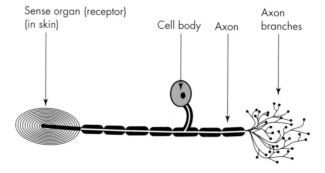

Sense organ (receptor) (in skin)   Cell body   Axon   Axon branches

series circuit: see *circuit, series*.

sewage is water-borne waste from homes and factories.
- Sewage from factories (e.g. sugar beet factories and paper factories) may contain materials which microbes can feed on.
- Sewage from homes contains human faeces which contain materials which microbes can feed on – it also contains large numbers of microbes.
- If untreated sewage flows into rivers, microbes feed on the materials in it and their population grows rapidly.
- The large population of microbes may use most of the oxygen in the water for their respiration causing other organisms (e.g. fish) to suffocate; this is called *eutrophication*.

sex chromosomes are the chromosomes which determine gender, that is, whether you are male or female.
- The sex chromosomes are called X and Y.
- A female has two X chromosomes.
- A male has one X and one Y chromosome.
- Many genes that are present on the X chromosome are missing on the Y.

sexual reproduction: reproduction that involves the fusion (joining) of sex cells (*gametes*), for example the joining of an *egg* with a *sperm* in humans.
- In sexual reproduction all the offspring are genetically different because they contain a <u>mixture</u> of genetic information from two parents.

Sexual reproduction gives rise to *variation* because:
- The gametes are produced by *meiosis*.
- When the gametes fuse, one of each pair of genes comes from each parent.
- The offspring therefore possess a different set of genes from either of their parents.

THE FEMALE REPRODUCTIVE ORGANS

- The ovaries produce the eggs.
- The vagina is where sperm are deposited during intercourse; it is also the birth canal.
- Fertilisation occurs in the oviduct.
- The embryo develops in the uterus.

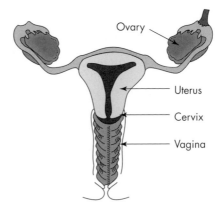

THE MALE REPRODUCTIVE ORGANS

- The testes produce sperm.
- The sperm ducts carry sperm to the urethra.
- The prostate gland produces *semen*.
- During sexual intercourse the penis is inserted into the female vagina; sperm is forced along the urethra into the vagina.

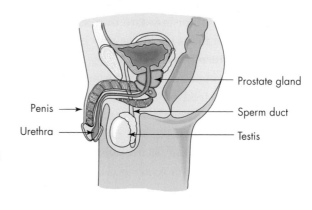

Penis →
Urethra
Prostate gland
Sperm duct
Testis

---

shale: a *sedimentary rock* made up of very fine mud or clay particles. In many parts of the world shales contain *crude oil*.

---

shell (atom): where *electrons* are found in an *atom*.
- It is better to describe electrons as occupying energy levels than shells.
- Each energy level can hold a maximum number of electrons (2, 8 or 18).
- An electron always occupies the lowest possible electron level.

---

sickle cell anaemia is an inherited disorder of the red blood cells.
- The *haemoglobin* of people with this condition has a different shape, causing the red blood cells to be deformed.
- It is caused by a *recessive allele*, h.
- Homozygous recessive people (hh) get painful swellings in parts of the body where blood capillaries get blocked by the deformed red blood cells.
- Heterozygous people are *carriers* (Hh); they have some deformed blood cells but they do not develop malaria as easily as healthy people, because the malaria microbe cannot reproduce inside the deformed red blood cells.
- It is therefore an advantage to be a carrier in areas of the world where malaria is common.

---

silicon (Si) is the second most abundant element on Earth.
- The great majority of *igneous* rocks contain silicon *minerals*.
- Silicon dioxide (silicon(IV) oxide) is the principal constituent of *sand*.
- Silicates are the principal constituents of clay.

---

silver (Ag) is a white metal used to make jewellery, ornaments and coins.
- It is very malleable and ductile which is why it is used to make jewellery.
- Also it is low in the *reactivity series* which means that it does not corrode with air or water.
- Silver is a *transition element*.
- Its salts (the *silver halides*) are used to make photographic films and paper.

silver halides: silver chloride, silver bromide and silver iodide are used to make photographic paper and photographic film; this is because they darken when exposed to light.

skeleton: gives support to many different kinds of animals.

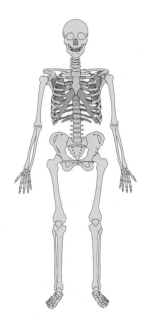

- *Vertebrates* (animals with a backbone) have an internal skeleton consisting mainly of bones (or of cartilage in fish such as sharks).
- *Invertebrates* (animals without a backbone) do not have bones, but many have a hard structure on the outside (exoskeleton) which gives them support (see *arthropods*).
- The bones in the human skeleton (see opposite) form joints which allow movement.
- Movement is brought about when muscles attached to the skeleton (skeletal muscles) contract to pull the bones.
- Some parts of the skeleton protect organs (e.g. the skull protects the brain and the ribs protect the heart and lungs).
- Some types of blood cells are made in the bone marrow.

skin is the outer covering of an organism.
- The outer layers of our skin consist of dead cells which protect the cells underneath against bruising.
- The dead cells also form a barrier against disease *microbes*.

The skin has receptor cells sensitive to:
- pressure
- temperature change
- pain.

The skin plays a vital part in *temperature regulation* via *sweating, vasodilation* and *vasoconstriction*.

slate is a rock often used to cover roofs. It is:
- a metamorphic rock
- formed by the action of heat and great pressure on clay or shale.

small intestine: the part of the intestine where the *digestion* of food is completed and most soluble food is absorbed.
Glands in the wall of the small intestine produce three types of *enzymes*:
- *carbohydrases* (such as amylase) which break down large carbohydrate molecules into sugars
- *proteases* which complete the breakdown of proteins into amino acids
- *lipase* which breaks down fats into fatty acids and glycerol.

The structure of the small intestine is specialised for absorbing soluble food.
- Its lining is folded to increase its surface area.
- The folds have tiny, finger-like projections called *villi* which in turn further increase the surface area.
- The villi have many blood capillaries to absorb the soluble food.

smell is one of our senses.
- Receptor cells in the nose are sensitive to chemicals in the air.
- If we cannot smell properly (e.g. when we have a cold) food often tastes different.

smoking: breathing in fumes from burning tobacco leaves.
Substances breathed in with the tobacco smoke can cause:
- lung cancer
- other lung diseases such as *emphysema*
- diseases of the heart and blood vessels.

Tobacco smoke contains drugs which change some chemical processes in the body, so that the person becomes dependent on cigarettes and suffers withdrawal symptoms if they try to stop smoking.

soap: a cleaning material made from fat. It is made by boiling animal or plant fats with alkalis such as sodium hydroxide solution.

sodium (Na): a very soft, very reactive metal; you would not think it was a metal by looking at it, but its reactions tell us that it is.
Sodium:
- is in Group I of the periodic table
- is an alkali metal
- reacts violently with water to form hydrogen, so it is normally stored under oil

- reacts with non-metals to form ionic compounds in which the metal ion carries a +1 charge
- forms hydroxides which dissolve in water to give alkaline solutions.

Sodium is less reactive than potassium because its outer electrons are at a lower energy level and are therefore less easily lost.

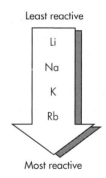

Least reactive

Li

Na

K

Rb

Most reactive

sodium, extraction: sodium is extracted by melting sodium chloride then electrolysing it:

- *ionic equation* at the anode

$$2Cl^- - 2e^- \longrightarrow Cl_2$$

- ionic equation at the cathode

$$Na^+ + e^- \longrightarrow Na$$

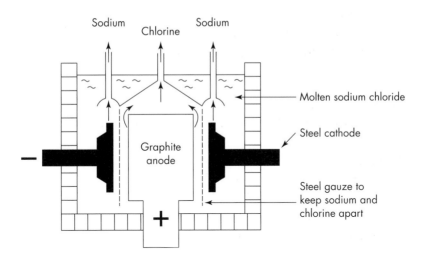

Sodium
Chlorine
Sodium

Molten sodium chloride

Steel cathode

Graphite anode

Steel gauze to keep sodium and chlorine apart

sodium, uses of: sodium vapour is used in street lamps (the ones that give out yellow light). Molten sodium metal is used as a heat exchanger in some nuclear reactors.

sodium carbonate is the chemical name for washing soda.

- Sodium carbonate is an *alkali*.
- It is used as a cleaning agent and to soften *hard water*.

sodium chloride is the chemical name for common salt (NaCl), the salt we put on our food and the most common salt in seawater.

sodium chloride, bonding: see *bonding, ionic*.

sodium chloride, electrolysis of brine: see *brine, electrolysis of*.

sodium chloride, electrolysis of molten: see *sodium extraction*.

sodium chloride, products from: see *brine, products from*.

sodium hydrogencarbonate: the chemical name for bicarbonate of soda ($NaHCO_3$). It is:
- a weak alkali
- used as a cleaning agent and in baking powder.

sodium hydroxide: a common *alkali* (NaOH) sometimes called caustic soda. It is:
- produced during the electrolysis of brine (see *brine, electrolysis*).
- used in the manufacture of *soap*, paper and ceramics.

soil: top layer of the Earth in which most higher plants grow.
It consists of inorganic matter such as gravel, sand and clay, and humus which is the decaying remains of plants and animals.
It provides plants with:
- support
- water
- mineral salts.

solar cell: a device that transfers light energy into electrical energy (such as in calculators that work without batteries).
- Solar cells are very efficient – around 30% of the light energy is transferred to electrical energy.
- They cost too much to produce to be used to provide electricity for the home.
- They are used to provide electricity for remote objects (e.g. buoys and space stations).

solar system: usually means our Sun with all the planets and comets that orbit it.

The ancient Greeks had the following model of the universe:
- the Earth was at the centre
- the stars were on the inside of a sphere which rotated around the Earth once every day
- the Sun and Moon also rotated around the Earth – the Moon once every day and the Sun once every year.

The modern model of the solar system was developed by *Copernicus*:
- the Sun is at the centre of the solar system
- the Earth and the other planets orbit the Sun (the Earth takes 365 days)
- the Moon orbits the Earth once every 28 days.

solder is a mixture (*alloy*) of metals that melts at a low temperature.
- It is used to join metals (e.g. joining wires to components in electric circuits.)
- It commonly contains lead and tin.

solenoid: a coil of insulated wire around a soft iron core, used in electric bells for example (see *magnetic effect of current*).

solid: has a definite shape (as opposed to *liquids* and *gases* which do not) because its particles:
- are very close together
- cannot move from place to place
- vibrate in one place.

If energy is supplied to a solid:
- its particles vibrate more violently
- they may separate from each other
- and become free to move.
- This is *melting*.

soluble: will dissolve, like the sugar you put in your coffee (see *solution*, *solute*, *solvent*).
- Most ionic compounds are soluble in water.
- Most covalent compounds are insoluble in water.

solubility: how much *solute* will dissolve, usually measured in g per 100 g of solvent (percentage by weight).

solubility curve: shows how temperature affects the *solubility* of a substance.
- For most solids, increasing the temperature increases the solubility.
- For most gases increasing the temperature decreases the solubility.

solute: the substance present in the smaller amount in a *solution* (e.g. the sodium chloride in a solution containing sodium chloride and water). It can be a gas, a liquid or a solid.

solution: a homogenous (same throughout) mixture of two substances (see *solute* and *solvent*).

solvent: the substance present in the larger amount in a *solution* (e.g. the water in a solution containing sodium chloride and water). It can be a solid or a liquid.

sound, frequency: the number of wave crests that pass a given point in one second.
- The unit of frequency is the hertz (Hz).
- This wave has a frequency of 3 Hz.
- The higher the frequency the shorter the *wavelength*.
- The higher the frequency the higher the *pitch* (note).

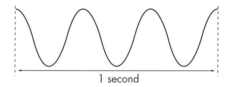
1 second

sound, loudness: the height of the crest of a *sound wave* (the maximum displacement from the mean or rest position; see *amplitude*).
- The louder the sound, the more energy the wave contains.
- The louder the sound the larger the amplitude of a sound wave.

sound, pitch: see *sound, frequency*.

sound waves: are 'push-pull' waves – the vibration is along the length of the wave. You must know the difference between *longitudinal waves* (e.g. sound waves) and *transverse waves* (e.g. light waves).
- Sound waves consist of *compressions* and *rarefactions*; the vibrations are parallel to the direction of the wave.
- We can hear sound waves with *frequencies* between about 15 Hz and 20 000 Hz.

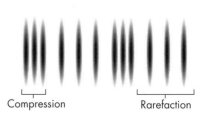
Compression   Rarefaction

- Because we cannot hear them, sound waves with frequencies above 20 000 Hz are called *ultrasound* waves.

---

spectrum (electromagnetic): this is the different types of *electromagnetic radiation* (e.g. light, X-rays) arranged in order of their wavelengths and frequencies.

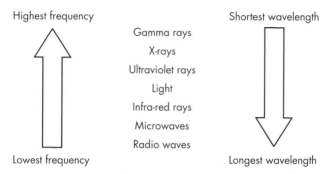

- You need to know the order of forms of radiation.
- Remember – the <u>higher</u> the frequency the <u>shorter</u> the wavelength.

---

spectrum (light): what we see when we split light into its different colours.
- White light is a mixture of seven visible colours (red, orange, yellow, green, blue, indigo and violet in that order).
- These can be split up by passing white light through a *prism*.
- Red light is bent (*refracted*) the least, violet the most.
- This is because violet light is slowed down much more than red light as it passes from air into the prism.

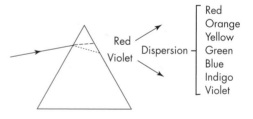

---

speed: how fast an object is moving; its unit is metre/second.
- For an object moving at a steady speed in a straight line:

$$\text{speed (metres/second, m/s)} = \frac{\text{distance travelled (metres, m)}}{\text{time taken (seconds, s)}}$$

- You may be asked to calculate speed from a *distance–time graph*.
- Speed is <u>not</u> the same as *velocity* – velocity is the rate of movement <u>in a particular direction</u>.

---

sperm: the male reproductive cell – your life began when a sperm from your father fused with an *egg* from your mother.

In humans:

- sperm are produced in the *testes*
- they are microscopic
- they are passed into the vagina of the female during sexual intercourse
- they have a head containing the nucleus which contains genetic information as *DNA*

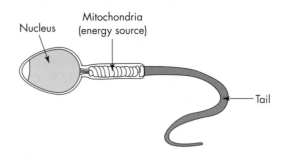

- they have a tail which enables them to swim towards the egg inside the female
- they have a streamlined shape which helps swimming.

Sperm are produced by *meiosis* which means that:

- they have half the number of chromosomes as body cells
- no two sperm have exactly the same genetic information.

sperm duct: a tube that carries *sperm* from the *testes*, where they are made, to the urethra which carries them out of the body (see *sexual reproduction*).

spinal cord: part of the *nervous system* that is surrounded and protected by the bones that make up the spine.

The spinal chord:

- is an extension of the *brain*
- is part of the central nervous system
- acts as the coordinator in many *reflex actions*.

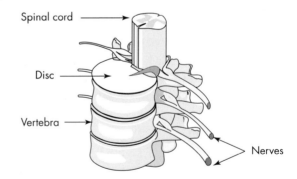

spiracles are tiny holes on the sides of an insect which allow air to enter and leave the insect's body – insects do <u>not</u> breath through their mouths.
Spiracles:

- lead to a system of air tubes that carry air to all parts of the insect's body
- can be closed to reduce water loss from the insect's body.

spongy mesophyll is part of a plant leaf.

- The cells of the spongy mesophyll have large air spaces in between them.

- These allow carbon dioxide to *diffuse* rapidly from the *stomata* to the cells of the *palisade mesophyll* where most *photosynthesis* takes place.

star: an astronomical body like our own Sun – there are countless millions of stars in the universe, arranged in groups called *galaxies.*
- Most stars emit light in, contrast to *planets* which only reflect light.
- Stars form when dust and gases in space are pulled together by gravitational attraction.
- Nuclear reactions inside the star produce very high temperatures which cause the gases to emit *electromagnetic radiation,* including light.
- This radiation from our own Sun provides us, directly or indirectly, with most of our energy.
- Stars do not stay the same forever, they have a life history consisting of several possible stages (see *red giant*).

starch is a material found in foods such as bread, potatoes and corn flakes. It is:
- a *carbohydrate* – a food that provides us with energy
- made in plants from the sugars produced during *photosynthesis*
- an insoluble storage material in plant cells
- digested into sugars in the human digestive system (*see digestion*).

state symbols: symbols in a chemical equation which tell us whether a substance is a gas, liquid, solid or in solution.

State symbol	Means that the substance is
(g)	a gas
(l)	a liquid
(s)	a solid
(aq)	dissolved in water

You will see state symbols in equations such as this:

zinc (s) + hydrochloric acid (aq) $\longrightarrow$ zinc chloride (aq) + hydrogen (g)

They mean that:
- the zinc is solid
- the hydrochloric acid and zinc chloride are dissolved in water
- the hydrogen comes off as a gas.

states of matter: matter can exist in three states – solid, liquid and gas. You have to know the differences between them.

Solids	Liquids	Gases
definite shape	take the shape of the container	spread into all the space available to them
definite volume	definite volume	
cannot be easily compressed	cannot be easily compressed	easily compressed
particles very close together	particles close together	particles well spread out
particles cannot move, only vibrate	particles can move around each other	particles can move around each other

The diagram below shows how these states of matter can be changed into each other. (See also *change of state, melting* and *evaporation*.)

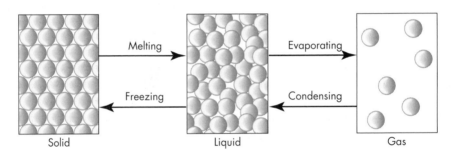

Solid — Melting → Liquid — Evaporating → Gas
Solid ← Freezing — Liquid ← Condensing — Gas

static electricity: stationary electric *charge* on an object as opposed to the moving electric charges in an electric current (see *electrostatics*).

steel is a form of iron which is used to make a wide variety of objects (e.g. motor cars and bridges).
- Steel is made by burning off most of the carbon (3–4%) which is present in iron from a *blast furnace*.
- Steel contains about 0.8% carbon.
- Removing most of the carbon makes the steel less brittle than iron.
- Other metals are sometimes added to give the steel special properties (e.g. adding chromium produces stainless steel).

stem: the part of a plant that supports the leaves above ground.
Stems:
- carry water and mineral salts from the roots to the leaves

- carry food materials (e.g. sugars) from the leaves to both the roots and the developing shoots (see *xylem* and *phloem*).

sterile means 'without life' – we use the word in two different ways:
- In *reproduction* it means 'unable to produce offspring'. *Hormones* can be used to help some women who cannot become pregnant (see *fertility*).

In relation to *microbes* it means 'free of microbes':
- Medical instruments should be sterile – this can be achieved by using *gamma radiation* to kill any microbes.
- Food treated with gamma rays will remain sterile for a long time because there are no microbes in it to make it go bad.

stigma: one of the female reproductive organs of a flower – important in *pollination*. The stigma:
- is supported by a structure called the style
- is usually sticky to capture *pollen* from an insect's body or from air currents
- produces a sugary liquid which stimulates the pollen grains to produce a pollen tube that grows down the style.

stimulus: a change in the environment which usually brings about a response; if, for example, we touch something hot with a finger the arm is automatically pulled away – the hot object is called a stimulus (see *reflex action, nervous system*). We have different *receptors* for different stimuli, e.g. light receptors in the eye and sound receptors in the ear.

stoma (pl. stomata): tiny holes on the surface of leaves and green stems that allow the plant to 'breathe'.
Stomata:
- allow carbon dioxide to *diffuse* into the leaf for *photosynthesis*
- also allow water vapour to diffuse out of the leaf (*transpiration*).
- Each is surrounded by two *guard cells*.

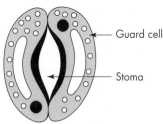

Changes in the shape of the guard cells cause the stomata,
- to open during the day, to allow carbon dioxide in
- to close at night, reducing the amount of water vapour lost.
- Changes in the shape of the guard cells are caused by water entering or leaving via *osmosis*.

stomach: the part of the body where the food goes when you have swallowed it (see *digestion*).

The walls of the stomach contain layers of muscle that contract to churn the food (see *peristalsis*). *Glands* in the walls of the stomach produce gastric juice which contains:

- an *enzyme* (*protease*) that breaks down *proteins* into shorter chains of *amino acids* called peptides
- hydrochloric acid which kills microbes present in the food and provides acid conditions for the protease to work.

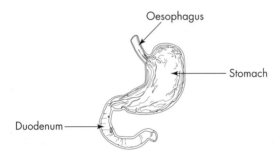

stopping distance: the distance it takes a motor vehicle to stop in an emergency.

Stopping distance depends mainly on:

- the distance the vehicle travels during the driver's *reaction time*
- the distance the vehicle travels whilst the brakes are applied (the braking distance).

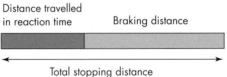

The overall stopping distance also depends on:

- how fast the vehicle is travelling
- how fast the driver's reactions are (e.g. alcohol makes the reactions slower)
- weather conditions (whether the roads are wet or icy, which affects the *friction* between the tyres and the road)
- the condition of the brakes and the tyres (these also affect friction, within the brakes and between the tyres and the road).

subduction occurs where two of the plates that make up the Earth's *crust* collide – the *oceanic plate* is forced under the *continental plate* (see *destructive boundary*).

sublimation is when a solid changes directly into a gas without first becoming a liquid.
- If iodine is warmed gently in a flask, solid iodine soon appears near the top of the flask.
- This is because solid iodine turned into a gas when warmed then iodine gas turned into solid iodine when it cooled.

substrate: what an *enzyme* acts on, or what a *microbe* feeds on. Lactose in milk is a substrate for bacteria that turn milk into yoghurt.

sugar: the group name for small, soluble *carbohydrates*.
- During *digestion* large, insoluble carbohydrates such as *starch* are broken down into smaller soluble carbohydrates, such as *glucose*, called sugars.
- Almost all living organisms use *respiration* to transfer energy from sugars.

sulphate test: a chemical test for sulphate. A few drops of nitric acid then a few drops of barium nitrate solution are added to the substance under test.
- A white precipitate (barium sulphate) is formed if sulphate ions (SO_4^{2-}) are present.

sulphur (S) is a light-yellow, non-metallic element. Sulphur:
- is used to make *sulphuric acid*, an important industrial chemical.
- forms sulphur dioxide when burned in air (see *acid rain*).

sulphur dioxide (SO_2) is a colourless gas with a sharp smell.
- Sulphur dioxide is formed when sulphur burns in air (see *acid rain*).

  sulphur + oxygen $\longrightarrow$ sulphur dioxide

  $S(s)$ + $O_2(g)$ $\longrightarrow$ $SO_2(g)$
- It dissolves in water to form sulphurous acid:

  sulphur dioxide + water $\longrightarrow$ sulphurous acid

  $SO_2(g)$ + $H_2O(l)$ $\longrightarrow$ $H_2SO_3(aq)$
- Its main use is the manufacture of sulphuric acid.

sulphur trioxide is a gas made during the manufacture of *sulphuric acid*. Sulphur dioxide is oxidised to sulphur trioxide:

  $2SO_2(g) + O_2(g) \longrightarrow 2SO_3(g)$

sulphuric acid manufacture: the diagram shown on the next page is an outline of the Contact process.

Sulphur is burned in oxygen:
$$S(s) + O_2(g) \longrightarrow SO_2(g)$$
sulphur + oxygen $\longrightarrow$ sulphur dioxide

Sulphur dioxide is mixed with oxygen then passed over a vanadium catalyst at 500°C to form sulphur trioxide:
$$2SO_2(g) + O_2(g) \rightleftharpoons 2SO_3(g)$$
sulphur dioxide + oxygen $\rightleftharpoons$ sulphur trioxide

The sulphur trioxide is passed through 98% sulphuric acid – the sulphur trioxide reacts with the water in the acid to produce sulphuric acid:
$$SO_3(g) + H_2O \longrightarrow H_2SO_4$$
sulphur trioxide + water $\longrightarrow$ sulphuric acid

---

sulphuric acid, reactions: sulphuric acid is a strong *acid* (see *acids and alkalis*).

● In water it splits up almost completely into hydrogen ions and sulphate ions:

$$H_2SO_4(aq) \longrightarrow 2H^+(aq) + SO_4{}^{2-}(aq)$$

● It neutralises alkalis to form *salts* (see *neutralisation*):

| acid | + | alkali | $\longrightarrow$ | salt | + | water |

sulphuric acid + sodium hydroxide $\longrightarrow$ sodium sulphate + water
$$H_2SO_4(aq) + 2NaOH(aq) \longrightarrow Na_2SO_4(aq) + 2H_2O(l)$$

● It reacts with many metals to form hydrogen (see *metals, reactivity series*):

zinc + sulphuric acid $\longrightarrow$ zinc sulphate + hydrogen
$$Zn(s) + H_2SO_4(aq) \longrightarrow ZnSO_4(aq) + H_2(g)$$

---

sulphuric acid, uses: its main use is in making *fertilisers* such as ammonium sulphate.

It is also used to make:

● rayon (a textile fibre)
● paint

- dyes
- detergents.

Sun: the star in our *solar system*. Our Sun:
- is one *star* in the *galaxy* called the Milky Way
- consists of about 70% hydrogen gas, 28% helium and 2% other elements
- is very hot due to the nuclear reactions taking place at its core
- is a star in the main stable stage of its life history (see *red giant*)
- provides us with light
- provides us with most of our energy needs, either directly or indirectly.

supernova: what happens when a *red giant* star explodes.

surface area is the area of all the surfaces of an object or a living thing.
- Surface area is important in chemical reactions (see *rate of reaction, effect of surface area on*).
- It is important in living organisms in the exchange of materials – the larger the surface area the greater the rate at which materials can be exchanged.

In humans:
- the surface area of the lungs is increased by *alveoli* for the exchange of oxygen and carbon dioxide
- the surface area of the *small intestine* is increased by folding and by *villi* for the absorption of soluble food.

In plants:
- the surface area of the roots is increased by the *root hairs* for the absorption of water and mineral salts from the soil
- the surface area of the leaves is increased by their flattened shape for the absorption of light and the internal air spaces of the *spongy mesophyll* for the absorption of carbon dioxide.

survival of the fittest: one of the main features of the theory of *evolution* by *natural selection*. In broad terms:
- organisms show *variation*
- some variations make organisms better adapted to the environment
- these organisms are more likely to survive to breed (i.e. survival of the fittest)
- their offspring will inherit these variations.

suspensory ligaments: strands in the *eye* that hold the lens in place.

sweating is a mechanism for cooling the body if we are overheated.
- A square centimetre of your skin contains over 100 sweat glands.
- These produce sweat, consisting mainly of water and mineral ions.
- When the core body temperature rises the *thermoregulatory centre* in the brain sends impulses to the sweat glands to increase the rate of sweating.
- It is the evaporation of sweat that cools the body.
- If it is very humid, sweat cannot evaporate quickly and the body temperature may still rise.

switch: part of an electric circuit that controls the flow of an electric current. When you switch a light on at home, pressing the switch completes an electric circuit so the current can flow through the light bulb.

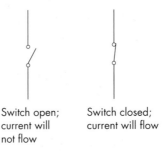

Switch open;   Switch closed;
current will   current will flow
not flow

symbols: see *state symbols, hazard symbols, circuit symbols.*

synapse: the junction of two *neurones* (see *nervous system*). When a nerve impulse in a neurone (nerve cell) arrives at a synapse, a chemical is released which causes impulses to be sent along to the next neurone.

synovial fluid: a lubricating fluid that enables your *joints* to move freely.
- It is produced by the synovial membrane.
- It lubricates the cartilage that covers the ends of the bones.
- In arthritis, insufficient synovial fluid is produced and the ends of the bones become inflamed.

synthesis: the building up of large chemicals from smaller units (e.g. *polymers*).

taste: one of our senses – carried out mainly by the tongue and the nose.
- The nose has *receptors* sensitive to chemicals in the air.
- the tongue has receptors sensitive to chemicals in solids and liquids.

---

teeth, structure of: the diagram shows a section of a tooth.

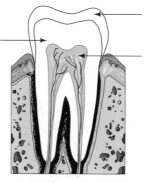

Dentine – softer than enamel, makes up the bulk of the tooth

Enamel – the hard outer part of the tooth

Pulp cavity containing receptor cells and blood capillaries

---

teeth, types of: teeth are specialised for different jobs by their different shapes.

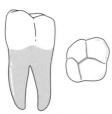
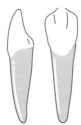
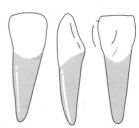

Molar teeth and pre-molar teeth have a flat shape for crushing and grinding food

Canine teeth are pointed for tearing food

Incisor teeth have a chisel-like edge for cutting

---

temperature: is <u>not</u> the same as *heat*. Temperature is a measure of the *kinetic energy* (movement energy) of the particles which make up a substance; the higher the temperature the more kinetic energy the particles have.
- When parts of a substance are at different temperatures, heat (thermal energy) will be transferred from the hotter region to the colder.

---

temperature regulation: the bodies of warm-blooded animals, including humans, have mechanisms to conserve *heat* when they are cold, and to get rid of excess heat, so that the body stays at a constant temperature of about 37°C.

When the core body temperature rises:

- blood vessels supplying the surface capillaries in the skin *dilate* (get wider) – more blood flows through the skin capillaries and more heat is lost by radiation (see *vasodilation*)
- in humans, the rate of sweating increases – evaporation of sweat cools down the body (see *sweating*)

When the core body temperature falls:

- blood vessels supplying the surface capillaries in the skin *constrict* (get narrower) – less blood flows through the skin capillaries and less heat is lost by radiation (see *vasoconstriction*)
- tiny muscles attached to the hairs contract, pulling the hairs upright – the hairs trap a layer of air which acts as an *insulator*; this does not have much effect in humans but is important in animals that have fur
- the animal may shiver – this is caused by muscles contracting, which requires energy from *respiration*, some of which is transferred as heat.

temporary hardness: a type of water hardness that can be removed by boiling (see *hard water*).

tendon: material that attaches a muscle to a bone.

- Muscles work by contracting and pulling on bones.
- Tendons attach muscles to bones; for this they must be tough, flexible and inelastic (must not stretch).

terminal velocity is the maximum *velocity* that an object falling through the atmosphere reaches. It is also the maximum velocity a motor car can reach.

- The crucial point to remember is that the faster an object moves through air or water the greater are the *frictional* forces on it.
- So when the frictional forces on, for example, a skydiver equal the force of gravity, there is no net force acting on the diver and she falls with a constant velocity – the terminal velocity.
- Similarly for a car, when the frictional forces equal the maximum forward force developed by the engine, there is no net force on the car and it travels at its terminal velocity.

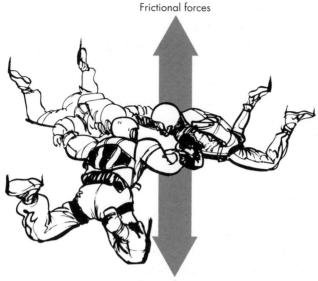

Frictional forces

Force of gravity

Terminal velocity – the forces acting on skydivers

Forward force
from engine

Frictional forces

Terminal velocity – the forces acting on a racing car

test cross: mating two organisms to see whether a particular pair of *alleles* in the organism being tested are the same (e.g. AA, aa) or different (Aa).

- The organism to be tested is crossed with an organism with a known pair of alleles.

- We know for certain that organisms with a *recessive phenotype* have two recessive alleles (aa).

- So we cross this with the organism to be tested, which could be Aa or AA if it has the *dominant* phenotype.

- If the organism tested is Aa, then there is a 50% chance of the offspring having the recessive phenotype (aa):

	a
A	Aa
a	aa

- If the organism tested is AA, then there is no chance of the offspring having the recessive phenotype (aa):

	a
A	Aa

test-tube babies: see *in vitro fertilisation*.

testis: organ where *sperm* are made in male animals (see *sexual reproduction*).
- Testes also produce a male *hormone* called *testosterone*.
- Sperm are produced by a type of cell division called *meiosis*.

testosterone: a *hormone* (chemical controller) produced by male mammals. Produced in the *testes*, it is responsible for the changes that occur in male bodies during *adolescence*, for example:
- growth of hair on face
- deepening of voice
- muscular development
- development of more aggressive behaviour.

thermal decomposition: see *decomposition, thermal*.

thermal energy: the form in which energy is transferred from a hotter to a cooler region; more commonly referred to as *heat*. Thermal energy is <u>not</u> the same as *temperature* – temperature is a measure of the *kinetic energy* (movement energy) of the particles which make up a substance.

thermit reaction: a chemical reaction used to weld iron.
- A mixture of iron oxide and aluminium is heated.
- The reaction is *exothermic* – it transfers a lot of thermal energy.
- This can be used to weld iron.
- Aluminium is more reactive than iron, so it displaces iron from its oxide (see *displacement reaction of metals*):

$$\text{iron oxide + aluminium} \longrightarrow \text{aluminium oxide + iron}$$
$$Fe_2O_3(s) \quad + \quad 2Al(s) \quad \longrightarrow \quad Al_2O_3(s) \quad + 2Fe(s)$$

thermoplastic polymers: see *plastics, thermosoftening*.

thermoregulatory centre: the part of the *brain* that helps warm-blooded animals to keep their body temperature constant at about 37°C. It monitors the temperature of blood flowing through it.
If the blood is too cool it sends impulses:
- to the blood vessels supplying the skin capillaries, causing them to constrict (see *vasoconstriction*)
- to some of the muscles, causing shivering
- to muscles attached to hairs, causing the muscles to contract.

If the blood is too warm it sends impulses:
- to the blood vessels supplying the skin capillaries, causing them to dilate (see *vasodilation*)
- to the sweat glands causing them to increase the rate of sweating.

(See also *temperature regulation*.)

Thermos flask: an appliance designed to keep liquids (e.g. coffee) warm (or cold). The following features of the Thermos flask help to reduce temperature changes in the contents. Remember that:
- particles are needed for energy transfer by *conduction* and *convection*
- silver surfaces are poor radiators of *infrared radiation* and good reflectors of infra-red radiation
- the stopper reduces heat loss by convection
- the vacuum reduces heat loss by conduction and convection (because there are very few gas particles there)
- the silvering on the outside, at X, reduces the rate of heat loss by radiation
- The silvering on the inside of Y reflects the small amount of infra-red radiation radiated from X.

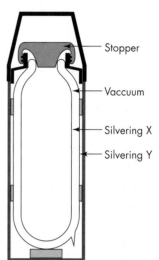

thinking... Image shows labels: Stopper, Vaccuum, Silvering X, Silvering Y

thermosetting polymers: see *plastics, thermosetting*.

thermostat: a device that regulates the temperature of, for example, a room in your house or a car engine. There are two basic kinds of thermostats:
1 Thermostats based on the principle that metals expand when heated – in a central-heating thermostat, a metal expands as it gets warmer and breaks an electric circuit, cutting off the heat supply. In a car engine, the expansion of metal bellows allows water to run from the engine to the radiator to be cooled.
2 Thermostats based on electronic devices, such as *thermistors*.

thinking distance: see *reaction time*.

thorax: the upper of the two body cavities. It is separated from the lower body cavity (*abdomen*) by the *diaphragm*.
The main contents of the thorax are:

- the *breathing* organs
- *the heart* and great blood vessels.

thrombosis: a blood clot that blocks a blood vessel and stops the supply of blood to part of an organ.
- A coronary thrombosis (heart attack) is caused by a clot blocking a *coronary artery* supplying the heart muscle.
- A stroke is caused by a clot blocking the blood supply to parts of the brain.
- The risk of thrombosis is increased by a diet containing too much fat, and by taking too little exercise.

thyroid gland: a *gland* situated in the neck which produces a *hormone* (chemical controller) called *thyroxin*.

thyroxin: a *hormone* (chemical controller) produced by the *thyroid gland*.
- Thyroxin plays a major part in our growth and development.
- A child who does not produce enough thyroxin will show mental and physical retardation unless given thyroxin by the doctor.
- *Iodine* is needed in the diet for thyroxin production.

tin (Sn): a silver-white metal.
- Tin is fairly unreactive; it is low down in the *reactivity series*.
- This is why it is used to coat other metals to protect them from *corrosion*, for example, it is used to coat steel in the cans we use for food.
- It is also used in *alloys* with other metals to produce, for instance, coins and *solder*.

tissue: a group of similar cells organised to carry out a particular job. Examples are:
- *muscular tissue*, which consists of cells that can contract and bring about movement
- *glandular tissue*, which contains cells that produce substances such as *enzymes* and *hormones*
- *xylem* tissue in plants, which transports water.

tissue culture: a technique used to produce *clones* (groups of identical plants) by *asexual reproduction*.
- Small groups of cells are taken from a young plant.
- Each of these groups of cells has the genetic information needed to produce a complete plant.
- Each of the groups of cells has the same genetic information – so all the

new plants will be identical.
- This technique is used to produce large numbers of identical plants from one that has, for example, been bred to resist a new strain of a disease.

tissue fluid is the fluid that surrounds our body cells, bringing them food and nutrients and taking away waste materials.
- Tissue fluid is formed when part of the *blood plasma* is forced out of the *capillaries*.
- When formed it consists of water, nutrients such as glucose, dissolved oxygen and mineral ions such as sodium (Na^+).
- Nutrients and oxygen *diffuse* from the tissue fluid into body cells.
- Waste materials such as carbon dioxide diffuse from the body cells into the tissue fluid.
- Tissue fluid containing waste materials diffuses back into the capillaries.

titration: a method used to find the concentration of an acid or alkaline solution.
- A measured volume of a known concentration of one of the reactants (either acid or alkali) is taken.
- A suitable indicator is added.
- The second reactant is then added slowly until the indicator shows that the mixture is neutral.
- The concentration of the second reactant can then be calculated from the volume of the second reactant used.

EXAMPLE

If it takes 20 cm³ of acid (the second reactant) to neutralise 25 cm³ of 0.1 M solution of alkali, the concentration of the acid is:

$$\frac{25}{20} \times 0.1 \text{ M}$$

$$= 0.125 \text{ M}$$

tongue: the main organ of taste.
- The tongue contains *receptors* sensitive to chemicals.
- It is also muscular and helps the teeth to break down food so that it can be swallowed.
- It also helps us to form sounds during speech.

total internal reflection occurs if the *angle of incidence* of a beam of light passing, for example, from air into glass is greater than a certain angle (the *critical angle*); all the light inside the glass is reflected.

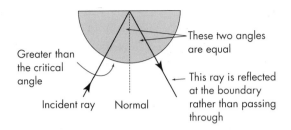

Greater than the critical angle

Incident ray   Normal

These two angles are equal

This ray is reflected at the boundary rather than passing through

- Total internal reflection is the principle used in optical fibres – light travels down the fibre, and stays within it, by total internal reflection.
- Optical fibres are used to transmit signals, e.g. in cable TV.
- They are also used in instruments that allow doctors to carry out internal examinations without the need for surgery.

toxin: a poisonous substance.
- Bacterial infections often make us feel ill because the bacteria multiply rapidly and produce toxins.
- Some kinds of *white blood cells* produce *antitoxins* which neutralise the effects of toxins – we then begin to feel better (see *bacteria, disease*).

trachea: the biological name for the windpipe.
- It carries air from the throat to the *lungs*.
- It branches into *bronchi* which carry air into the lungs.
- It is strengthened by rings of *cartilage* which prevent it collapsing.

transformer: used to change the voltage of an *a.c.* electrical supply, both in the *national grid* and in applications such as model train sets and telephone answering machines.
A transformer consists of:
- two coils – an output coil and an input coil
- a soft iron core.
If an alternating current is supplied to the input, every time the current changes direction (50 times per second) a voltage is induced in the output coil (see *electromagnetic induction*).
- The voltages across the primary and secondary coils are related:

$$\frac{\text{voltage across primary coil}}{\text{voltage across secondary coil}} = \frac{\text{number of turns on primary coil}}{\text{number of turns on secondary coil}}$$

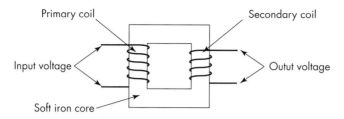

Primary coil

Secondary coil

Input voltage

Outut voltage

Soft iron core

- In calculations you will be given three of the values for this equation and asked to calculate the fourth.

EXAMPLE

A transformer has 200 turns on the primary coil and 10 turns on the secondary coil; if the mains input voltage is 240 V what will be the output voltage?
First transform the equation:

$$\text{output voltage} = \frac{\text{input voltage} \times \text{turns on secondary coil}}{\text{turns on primary coil}}$$

Then insert values:

$$= \frac{240 \text{ V} \times 10 \text{ turns}}{200 \text{ turns}}$$

$$= 12 \text{ V}$$

---

transition metals: metals such as iron and copper which are used widely in industry.
- They occupy a block in the middle of the *periodic table*.

Sc	Ti	V	Cr	Mn	Fe	Co	Ni	Cu	Zn
21	22	23	24	25	26	27	28	29	30
Y	Zr	Nb	Mo	Te	Ru	Rh	Pd	Ag	Cd
39	40	41	42	43	44	45	46	47	48

- They have high melting points.
- Some of them are used as *catalysts*.
- Many of their compounds are coloured.
- They are much less reactive than the *alkali metals*.

---

translocation: this is how materials such as sugars are moved around plants.
- Sugars are made in the *leaves* then moved through a *tissue* called *phloem* to the roots for storage or to the young parts of the plant for growth.
- Movement of sugars into the phloem is usually by *active transport*.
- Do not confuse phloem with *xylem* – xylem carries mainly water from the roots upwards, to the stem and leaves.
- Do not confuse translocation with *transpiration*.

---

transpiration: the loss of water vapour from a plant; it is why plants wilt if they are not watered.

- Thermal energy from the Sun causes water to evaporate from the surfaces of cells inside the leaves.
- This water then diffuses along a concentration gradient, out through the *stomata* into the atmosphere.
- The rate of transpiration can be measured (indirectly) by using a *potometer*.
- When water evaporates from the leaves, water is pulled up the *xylem* vessels from the roots to replace it.
- If the rate of transpiration is greater than the rate of water uptake the plant may wilt.

The following factors increase the rate of transpiration:

- increase in temperature
- increase in wind speed
- decrease in humidity
- light (because the stomata open in light).

---

transverse waves are waves that move up and down, rather than lengthways (see *longitudinal waves*), e.g. waves that travel along ropes or along the surface of water.

- Moving a 'slinky' like this produces a transverse wave:

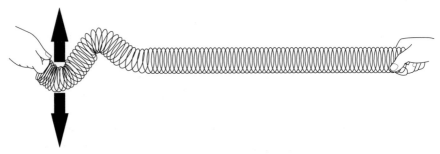

- Whereas moving it like this produces a longitudinal wave:

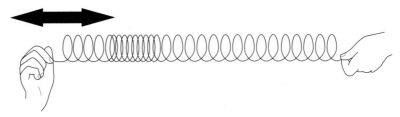

- Light waves are transverse waves – they do not need a medium to travel through (they can travel through a vacuum).

trophic level describes the position of an organism in a *food chain* or *food web*.

Type of feeding	Trophic level
producer – *plants*	first
primary consumer – *herbivore*	second
secondary consumer – *carnivore*	third

In the food chain grass $\longrightarrow$ antelope $\longrightarrow$ lion:
- the grass is in the first trophic level
- the antelope is in the second trophic level
- the lion is in the third trophic level.
- The higher the trophic level, the less of the energy originally trapped by plants remains. This is mainly because some energy is transferred from organisms to the environment, mainly as a result of heat loss from *respiration*.

---

tumour: the result of abnormal, uncontrolled division of cells in the body (see *cancer*).

---

tungsten (W): a silver-white metal.
- Tungsten is a *transition metal*.
- It is the metal with the highest melting point.
- Because of this it is used as the filament in filament lamps, in spark plugs and as the target in X-ray tubes.

---

turbine: a device used to drive a generator in a *power station*.
A turbine is driven by:
- moving water in a hydroelectric or tidal barrage power station
- high-pressure steam in a coal-fired power station or nuclear power station
- hot exhaust gases in a gas-fired power station.

---

turgor helps to keep plants rigid (compare with *wilting*).
- Water enters plant cells via *osmosis*.
- This increases the pressure inside the cells.
- The cells walls become stretched and the cells are firm to the touch.
- The cell is now said to be turgid.
- If a cell loses water it may become *plasmolysed*.

---

ultrasound: waves similar to sound waves, but too high for us to hear. The *frequency* of ultrasound waves is greater than 20 000 Hz – the upper limit of hearing for most people.

Ultrasound is used:
- in industry, both for cleaning and for quality control
- in cleaning it can be use, to 'shake-off' the dirt from delicate instruments without taking them to pieces
- in medicine it is used for pre-natal scanning – looking at an embryo in the mother's womb.

Ultrasound is partly reflected when it meets a boundary. This is why ultrasound is useful in scanners.
- The time taken for a reflection to reach the detector is a measure of how far away the boundary is.
- The times for reflections to reach the detector are converted into a visual display on a screen.

ultraviolet: *electromagnetic radiation* which is used in sunbeds.
- Its wavelength is shorter than that of visible light, but longer than X-rays.
- It can pass through pale skin but is absorbed by dark skin.
- It is responsible for producing a sun tan.
- Too much ultraviolet light can cause mutations in the skin cells, which may result in skin cancer.
- That is why you should not sunbathe for too long and you should use barrier creams which absorb ultraviolet light.

umbilical cord: connects the *placenta* to the *embryo* in the womb.
- The embryo pumps blood through an artery in the cord to the placenta, where oxygen and nutrients pass into the embryo's blood and waste materials pass out.
- The blood then returns to the embryo.
- The cord is cut and clamped when the baby is born.
- After a few days it withers and falls off at the navel.

umbra: the dark shadow formed during an *eclipse* (see also *penumbra*).

unicellular: consisting of only one cell.
- Many microscopic organisms consist of one cell.
- One-celled, plant-like organisms (*phytoplankton*) form the basis for all *food chains* in the open sea – without them there would be no deep-sea fish.

universal indicator: an indicator that tells us how acid or alkaline something is (see *acids and alkalis*).

Colour	Red	orange	yellow	green	blue	navy blue	purple
pH	0–2	3–4	5–6	7	8–9	10–12	13–14
		ACID		NEUTRAL		ALKALINE	

universe: everything that exists.
- It consists of at least a billion *galaxies* each of which may contain millions of *stars*.
- Most scientists believe that the universe began with the *big bang*.

unsaturated hydrocarbon: see *hydrocarbon, unsaturated*.

urea: a waste product that passes out of the body in the *urine*.
Urea is:
- made in the *liver* (<u>not</u> the *kidneys*)
- made by *deamination* (breakdown of excess *amino acids*)
- filtered out of the blood in the kidneys
- passes out of the body in the urine
- a waste product containing nitrogen; it is often referred to as a nitrogenous waste product.

ureter: the tube that carries *urine* from the *kidney* to the *bladder*.

urethra: the tube that carries urine from the *bladder* to the outside.
- In females, it carries only urine.
- In adult males, it carries both urine and *sperm*.

urine is the liquid waste product produced by the body (see *kidney* for details of urine formation).

Urine consists of:
- mainly excess water
- with excess mineral ions
- and *urea*.

Urine is produced in the kidneys. It passes down the *ureters* into the *bladder* then out of the body via the *urethra*.

uterus: the womb – where embryos develop before they are born (see *sexual reproduction, placenta, umbilical cord*).

vaccination: making someone immune to a disease by introducing a form of the *microbe* that does not cause serious disease (see *immunisation; disease, immunity*).

- If dead or mild forms of disease microbes are introduced into the body, the *white blood cells* respond by producing *antibodies* that kill the infective microbe, or *antitoxins* that neutralise the *toxins* produced by the infective microbe. This is called *active immunity*.
- If the disease microbes enter the body for a second time, the white cells produce antibodies and antitoxins more quickly than before – the person is then said to be immune to the disease.
- An example of active immunity is vaccination against poliomyelitis.
- If a person has been exposed to a dangerous infective organism, antibodies and/or antitoxins may be injected in a serum taken from somebody who is already immune, to give them immediate protection; this is called *passive immunity*.
- An example of passive immunity is the tetanus inoculation.

vacuole: a fluid-filled sac within a plant cell (see *cell, plant*).

vacuum: a space from which nearly all matter has been removed (it is impossible to remove every last molecule from a space). Vacuums are used in:
- *Thermos flasks* – because there are very few particles to transfer energy by *conduction* or *convection*.
- light bulbs – so that there is practically no oxygen with which the hot filament could react

Remember that *electromagnetic* radiation can pass through a vacuum but sound waves cannot.

vagina: the part of the female reproductive system which receives the *penis* during sexual intercourse; it also acts as the birth canal (see *sexual reproduction*).

valve: a device or structure which allows fluids to flow in one direction only (see *heart, structure*).

Valves are essential in the blood system to keep blood flowing in the correct direction by preventing backflow (see *blood, circulation*):

- valves between the *atria* and the *ventricles* in the heart allow blood to pass from atria to ventricles
- valves at the entry to the aorta and the pulmonary artery allow blood to enter these arteries from the heart
- valves in the veins let blood flow towards the heart.

vanadium (V): a silver-white metal. Vanadium:

- is a *transition element*
- has a high melting point
- is relatively unreactive
- is one of the hardest metals
- is used to make parts of engines which need to be hard and able to withstand high temperatures.

variable resistor: a resistor whose *resistance* can be varied (e.g. the volume control in your Walkman).

- Its symbol is:

- It is used to vary the *current* in a circuit since the higher the resistance, the lower the current.
- It is usually wired in *series*.

variation is the differences between individuals – you share similarities with each of your parents but are not identical to either (see *continuous variation*, *discontinuous variation*).

- Differences between individuals are due to differences in the *genes* they inherit (genetic causes) and differences in the conditions in which they develop (environmental causes).
- Genetic variation can result from *mutations*.
- *Meiosis* brings about genetic variation during *sexual reproduction*.
- Organisms produced by *sexual reproduction* show far more variation than organisms produced by *asexual reproduction*.

vasoconstriction: what happens to blood vessels in your skin to make you go pale (or even blue).

- The blood vessels supplying the skin capillaries get narrower (the capillaries themselves stay the same width).

- This means that less blood flows through the skin capillaries and therefore less heat is lost by radiation.
- This helps the body to conserve heat when it is cold (see *temperature regulation*).

vasodilation: what happens to blood vessels in your skin to make you go red.
- The blood vessels supplying the skin capillaries get wider (the capillaries themselves stay the same width).
- This means that more blood flows through the skin capillaries and therefore more heat is lost by radiation.
- This cools the body down when you are too hot (see *temperature regulation*).

vein: a blood vessel that returns blood to the heart; you need to know the differences between *arteries*, veins and *capillaries*.
- Veins have thinner walls than arteries.
- Their walls contain less elastic and muscular tissue than those of arteries.
- All veins (except the pulmonary vein) carry deoxygenated blood (blood with a low concentration of oxygen and high concentration of carbon dioxide).
- Veins, unlike arteries, have *valves* to prevent blood flowing backwards (away from the heart).

velocity: how fast an object is moving in a given direction.
You need to know the difference between velocity and speed:
- velocity has both magnitude and direction
- speed has only magnitude.

$$\text{velocity (metres/second, m/s)} = \frac{\text{distance travelled in a given direction (metres, m)}}{\text{time taken (seconds, s)}}$$

velocity–time graph: velocity plotted against time; useful because we can use it to calculate both acceleration of an object and the total distance an object travels (see *acceleration*).

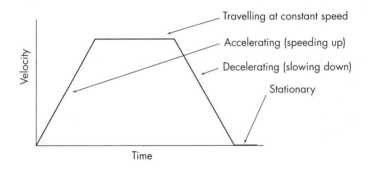

- You may be asked what an object (e.g. car) is doing at various points on a velocity/time graph.

---

vena cava: the main vein of the body (see *blood system, circulation*).
The vena cava:
- collects blood from most of the other veins in the body
- returns blood to the right *atrium* of the *heart*.

---

ventricles: the parts of the *heart* that pump blood out of the heart – you can feel a *pulse* in your *arteries* (e.g. at the wrist) every time the left ventricle contracts.
- Ventricles receive blood from the *atria* of the heart.
- The right ventricle pumps blood to the lungs.
- The left ventricle pumps blood to all the other organs of the body.
- This is why the left ventricle has a much thicker muscular wall than the right ventricle.

---

vertebrae are the bones that make up your spine (backbone).
- The spine is the main supporting structure of our body.
- It also protects the *spinal cord*.

---

vertebrates are animals which have a backbone (spine); this includes humans.
There are five major groups of vertebrates (see the individual entries for the features of each group):
- *fish*
- *amphibians*
- *reptiles*
- *birds*
- *mammals*.

---

vibration: a repeated side-to-side or backwards and forwards movement.
- Light waves are *transverse waves*: they vibrate from side to side.
- Sound waves are *longitudinal waves*: backwards and forwards vibrations.

---

villus (pl. villi): microscopic finger-like projections from the wall of the *small intestine*, where most of the food that you eat enters the blood after being digested.
- Villi increase the *surface area* of the small intestine for the absorption of soluble food.

- They are well supplied with blood capillaries to increase the rate of absorption.

virtual image: an image that cannot be formed on a screen. An example is the image of your face you see in a mirror which appears to be behind the mirror – but the image cannot be focused on a screen held behind the mirror (see *image, virtual*).

virus: a tiny disease *microbe*, too small to be seen with a light microscope. An example is the microbe that produces poliomyelitis.
- Viruses have a very simple structure; a protein coat surrounding a strand of *DNA*.
- They can only reproduce inside other living cells.
- They damage the cells inside which they reproduce.
- It is the substances released when these cells burst to release the virus that make us feel ill.
- *Antibiotics* <u>cannot</u> be used against viruses because the viruses are inside our cells.
- *White blood cells* produce *antibodies* to kill viruses.

vitamin: a substance needed in tiny amounts in our food to keep us healthy (e.g. *vitamin C* in fresh fruit). If we do not have enough of a vitamin we suffer from deficiency symptoms. For example we may get scurvy if we do not eat enough vitamin C.

vitamin A: a food substance needed in tiny amounts to keep our skin and eyes healthy.
- Vitamin A is found in carrots, liver and dairy produce.
- Without sufficient in the diet the skin may become scaly and the eyes sore.

vitamin C: a food substance needed in tiny amounts to keep membranes and blood vessels healthy.
- Vitamin C is found in fresh fruits and vegetables.
- Without sufficient in the diet scurvy might develop – one symptom of which is bleeding gums.

vitamin D: a food substance needed for healthy bones and teeth.
- Vitamin D is found in dairy products.
- Without sufficient in the diet rickets may develop – the bones and teeth may become soft and leg bones grow deformed.

viscosity describes how easy a liquid is to pour (e.g. water has low viscosity and pours easily, but treacle has high viscosity and pours very slowly). Viscosity is important in lubricating oils – they must have a suitable viscosity at the temperature at which they work.

volcano: a place where *magma* (molten rock) is forced through weak points in the Earth's *crust* and erupts as *lava*. Volcanoes are often produced where *oceanic plates* in the Earth's crust collide (see *destructive boundary*).

volt: symbol V, the unit of *voltage* (*potential difference*).
- One volt is the voltage between two terminals when one *joule* of energy is transferred as one *coulomb* of charge moves from one terminal to the other.
- The potential difference needed to cause a *current* of one ampere to flow through a *resistor* with a value of one *ohm* is one volt.

voltage: what causes a current to flow in a circuit (see *potential difference*).
- Voltage is what causes electrons to flow in a circuit.
- It is the result of a potential difference.
- A torch battery has a voltage of about 1.5 V – this means that there is a difference in potential of 1.5 V between the terminals.
- Voltage can only be measured <u>across</u> a component because a *voltmeter* measures the <u>difference</u> in potential.

voltmeter: an instrument for measuring *voltage* (*potential difference*).
- A voltmeter is always connected across a component (in parallel with it) because it measures the difference in potential between the two ends of the component.
- Compare with the *ammeter* in this circuit – the ammeter is connected in series with the resistor, the voltmeter in parallel.

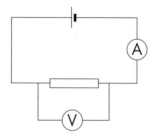

washing soda: a substance used to make *hard water* softer so that it lathers easier.
- It is the presence of calcium ions that makes water hard.
- Washing soda is a form of sodium carbonate (Na_2CO_3).
- The carbonate ions (CO_3^{2-}) from the washing soda react with the calcium ions (Ca^{2+}) in water, forming insoluble calcium carbonate ($CaCO_3$):

$$Ca^{2+}(aq) + CO_3^{2-} \longrightarrow CaCO_3(s)$$

Watson, James: an American scientist born in 1928 who was a member of the team who discovered the structure of *DNA* (see *Crick, Francis*).

watt (W): the unit of *power*; named after the Scottish engineer James Watt.

$$power\ (watts,\ W)\ =\ \frac{work\ done\ (joules,\ J)}{time\ taken\ (seconds,\ s)}$$

In electricity:

$$\begin{array}{ccc} power & = & potential\ difference & \times & current \\ (watts,\ W) & & (volts,\ V) & & (amperes,\ A) \end{array}$$

(See *power* especially for how to do calculations.)

wave: a way in which energy is transferred from place to place without matter being transferred. It is how energy from the Sun is transferred to Earth – without this energy there would be no life on Earth (see *transverse waves* and *longitudinal waves*).
- Light waves are transverse waves and can travel through a vacuum.
- Sound waves are longitudinal waves – they can pass through solids, liquids and gases but <u>not</u> through a vacuum.

wavelength is the distance between the crests of two waves that are next to each other.
- The pitch of a sound depends on wavelength – the shorter the wavelength, the higher the pitch (note).
- The colour of light depends on wavelength – for visible colours of the spectrum, red rays have the longest and violet rays the shortest wavelength.

- Wavelength, wave speed and *frequency* are related as shown by the equation:

$$\text{wavelength (metre, m)} = \frac{\text{wave speed (metres/second, m/s)}}{\text{frequency (hertz, Hz)}}$$

- Since all sound waves travel at the same speed in air, the higher the frequency, the shorter the wavelength.
- Since all *electromagnetic waves* travel at the same speed in air, the higher the frequency, the shorter the wavelength.

wax (plant): a solid, fatty material which forms a layer on the outside of plant leaves and young plant stems.
- Its job is to reduce the rate at which water evaporates from the plant.
- Plants which live in hot, dry places (e.g. *cacti*) often have a much thicker layer of wax.
- The reason that holly is able to keep its leaves in winter is that holly leaves have a thick layer of wax that helps to reduce the rate of water loss. This means the plant can conserve as much moisture as possible when water becomes temporarily unavailable, for example when it is frozen in winter.

weathering is the action of rain, snow and changes in temperature on rocks; it usually makes their surfaces crumble.
- Most rocks consist of a mixture of minerals, each of which expands at a different rate when heated. This causes stresses which crack the rock.
- Water expands as it freezes, so if water gets into the cracks then freezes, this can cause the rock to crack.
- Carbon dioxide in the air dissolves in water to form a weak acid (carbonic acid). Although weak, this acid slowly dissolves calcium carbonate in *limestone*:

$$\text{calcium carbonate} + \text{carbonic acid} \longrightarrow \text{calcium hydrogencarbonate}$$
$$\text{(insoluble)} \qquad\qquad\qquad\qquad\qquad\qquad \text{(soluble)}$$

- It is this reaction that has caused the formation of many caverns and potholes in limestone regions.

weedkiller: a *hormone* (chemical controller) that kills plants we do not want (weeds), leaving the crops or garden plants we do want unharmed.
- Weedkillers work by disrupting the normal growth patterns of the weed plants, e.g. the growth of clover plants in a lawn.

weight is the gravitational force acting on an object. It is <u>not</u> the same as *mass*. You may have a mass of 70 kg but that is not your weight. Your weight is the force of gravity that acts on your mass. That is why you would have the same mass if a rocket took you to the Moon, but your weight on the Moon would only be about one sixth of your weight on Earth.

- Since weight is a force its unit is the *newton*, N (the unit of mass is kg).

$$\begin{array}{cccc} \text{weight} & = & \text{mass} & \times & \text{gravitational field strength} \\ \text{(newtons, N)} & & \text{(kilograms, kg)} & & \text{(newtons/kilogram, N/kg)} \end{array}$$

- The gravitational field strength on Earth is about 10 N/kg – so to roughly convert mass in kilograms to weight, multiply by 10 and change the unit to newtons (N).

---

white blood cells: the cells in our blood that help to protect us from disease microbes (see *disease, immunity*).

- Some white blood cells engulf microbes.
- Some produce *antibodies* to kill microbes.
- Others produce *antitoxins* to neutralise the toxins (poisons) made by disease microbes.

---

white dwarf: the final stage in the life of some types of stars (for details of the life history of a star see *red giant.*)

---

wilting is what happens when a plant droops because it does not have enough water.

- Plants are kept rigid and firm by the pressure of water inside their cells (see *turgor*).
- Plants continually lose water vapour through their *stomata*.
- This is called *transpiration*.
- If the rate of transpiration is greater than the rate of water uptake from the roots, the plant wilts because there is a net loss of water from its cells.

---

wine is an alcoholic drink produced when yeast ferments grape juice.

- Yeast cells use the sugars in the grape juice as food.
- They break down the sugars into *alcohol* (ethanol) and *carbon dioxide* by *anaerobic respiration* (respiration without oxygen):

    glucose $\longrightarrow$ alcohol + carbon dioxide

- The reactions which break down sugar are catalysed by *enzymes*.

---

work: when a force moves an object (e.g. if you kick a football) energy is transferred (to the football) and work is said to be done (on the football)

- Work done = energy transferred, therefore:

  work done = force applied × distance moved in direction of force
  (joules, J)   (newtons, N)   (metres, m)

- Don't forget – if the work done is lifting something, then the force applied is equal to the *weight* of the object (weight = *mass* × gravitational field strength).

(See also *joule, power, gravitational potential energy.*)

X chromosome: one of the pair of chromosomes that determines *gender* (whether you are male of female).

- Human *eggs* contain one X chromosome.
- Human *sperm* contain either an X chromosome or a *Y chromosome*.
- Human female body cells contain two X chromosomes.
- Human male body cells contain one X chromosome and one Y chromosome.

X-rays: rays used to produce shadow pictures of structures inside the body (e.g. bones).

- They are *electromagnetic waves*.
- They have *wavelengths* shorter than light waves but longer than *gamma rays*.
- They pass through soft tissues like muscle easier than hard tissues like bone, which is how an X-ray image is produced.
- Some X-radiation is absorbed by body tissues – this can cause the cells to produce *cancers*.
- High doses of X-radiation kill cells – such doses are sometimes used to kill cancer cells.

---

xylem: the cells in plants that carry water and mineral ions up the stem.

- Most mature xylem cells are dead.
- Their end walls break down so they form long tubes.
- When water evaporates from the leaves, water is pulled up from the roots through these tubes by suction.

Y chromosome: one of the pair of chromosomes that determines *gender* (whether you are male of female).

- Human *sperm* contain either an *X chromosome* or a Y chromosome.
- Human *eggs* contain one X chromosome.
- Human male body cells therefore contain one X chromosome and one Y chromosome.
- Human female body cells contain two X chromosomes.

yeast: microscopic, one-celled organisms used to make *wine*, beer and bread.

- Yeast are *fungi*.
- They occur in nature on the surfaces of fruits such as grapes.
- They feed on sugars.
- In *baking*, yeasts break down sugar in *respiration* to release carbon dioxide gas – it is this gas that makes bread rise.
- In *brewing* and wine making, the yeast breaks down the sugars by *anaerobic respiration*, producing *alcohol* (ethanol) and carbon dioxide.

yoghurt manufacture: yoghurt is made by the action of 'yoghurt bacteria' on milk.

- A culture of yoghurt bacteria (or 'live' yoghurt) is added to warm milk.
- The bacteria ferment the sugar in the milk (lactose) to produce *lactic acid* (see *fermentation*).
- The lactic acid causes the proteins in the milk to solidify and produce yoghurt.

zinc (Zn): a bluish-white metal.

Zinc:

- is a *transition metal*
- has a high melting point
- is fairly unreactive
- is more reactive than iron or steel – so it is used to *galvanise* iron and steel to prevent them from *rusting*.

zinc extraction:

- Ore containing zinc is heated in air or oxygen to convert zinc compounds into zinc oxide.
- The zinc is then extracted from the zinc oxide by heating the oxide with carbon.
- The carbon is more reactive than the zinc, so it *reduces* the zinc oxide to zinc (the carbon is oxidised to carbon monoxide):

  zinc oxide + carbon $\longrightarrow$ zinc + carbon monoxide

  $ZnO(s)$ + $C(s)$ $\longrightarrow$ $Zn(g)$ + $CO(g)$

- As you can see from the symbol equation, the zinc comes off as a gas which is *condensed* to form zinc metal.

zinc, reactions of: zinc is just about in the middle of the *reactivity series*.

- It burns when heated in air to form zinc oxide.
- It reacts with steam (but not with cold water) to form hydrogen gas and zinc oxide.
- It reacts with dilute acids, giving off hydrogen.

zooplankton: microscopic animals that live near the surface of lakes and seas.

- A litre of lake water often contains hundreds of millions of these tiny organisms.
- Most of them eat *phytoplankton*, which are the main producers in lakes and seas.
- The zooplankton are in turn eaten by larger organisms such as fish.

zygote: the cell formed when a *sperm* fuses (joins with) an *egg* – this is how a new life begins.

- The fusing of an egg and a sperm to form a zygote is called *fertilisation*.
- The sperm cell and the egg cell each have half the number of *chromosomes* of a body cell.
- A zygote has the same number of chromosomes as a body cell.
- The zygote divides repeatedly by *mitosis* to form body cells.

zymase: a name sometimes given to the *enzymes* in *yeast* that break down sugars to form alcohol in wine and beer (see *anaerobic respiration*).

EXAMINERS' TERMS

Every year examiners report that large numbers of candidates do not do themselves credit by failing to follow instructions.

You should realise right from the start of your course that instructions such as 'Describe...' and 'Explain...' do not mean the same thing.

You should also realise that you will never see 'Write all you know about...' in an examination paper; you therefore have to be selective in your answers.

You never receive marks for repeating the question, so don't waste your time doing it.

Above all, remember that the examiners are on your side, and all the following terms are used to help you show them what you know and what you understand.

Calculate/work out means that you must produce a numerical answer and make it clear what this answer is – don't leave it to the examiner to search through the working to find the answer.

Always show all your working. You will usually be given some marks for giving the correct method, even if you press the wrong buttons on your calculator.

Compare means that you need to describe the similarities and/or differences in sets of provided data. Don't just describe one feature and leave the examiner to complete your answer – he or she won't!

Complete means that you have to put the answers in spaces left in sentences, a diagram, tables etc. The space will always be big enough for the answer – so if you can't fit your answer into the space you are probably doing something wrong.

Describe: there are two ways in which this term is used:

- you might be asked to describe data in a graph or a table – always look for the main trends in the data and write these down; you will not gain marks for simply repeating the data
- you might be asked to describe a process, e.g. 'Describe what happens to carbon compounds in a compost heap' – here you should give a step-by-step account of what happens. The mark allocation will tell you how many points you are expected to make.

Draw a bar chart means that you need to plot a series of values as bars.

Draw a graph means that you need to:

- plot a series of values as points
- then draw a line of best fit or a curve.

On the higher level paper, you may have to draw a scale – use as much of the graph paper as possible and label the axes.

There may be anomalous points – your line or curve should not pass through these.

Explain means 'Give a reason for'. You will not gain any marks for a description. More candidates lose marks for failing to do this than for any other reason. Always ask yourself 'have I said *why*?'

Give a reason (or How) means that you have to use your scientific knowledge to give the reason.

Give/Name/State/Write down means that you should write a concise answer without attempting to say why.

List means write down concise answers one after the other.

Predict means that you have to make logical links between pieces of information. You will probably not have seen the information before – so you have to work out the answer.

Sketch a graph means that you need to draw a line on a graph to show a trend or pattern – you do not need to plot a series of points.

Suggest means that there is no unique answer, and that you will not have been taught the answer. You have to use the information in the question to give a sensible answer. If you have used sound scientific reasoning, you will be given the marks.

Use the information means that your answer must be based on the information provided in the question – if you do not use this information you may not receive any marks.

Use your understanding means that you will not have been taught the answer but you should be able to work it out using your scientific understanding.

What is meant by means that you should give a definition.

REVISION LISTS

These list have been designed to help you with your revision.

To use the lists, find the topic you are revising then look up the terms listed in that topic. This is your staring point. Then use the cross-references to build on the basic ideas explained under each term.

The syllabus of each examining board is slightly different, but all are based on the National Curriculum. The following topics are common to all Double Science examinations There are two levels of examination papers – Foundation and Higher.

Terms printed in italics will be found on the Higher papers only.

BIOLOGY

1 Structure and function of cells
2 Human nutrition
3 Human circulation
4 Human breathing and respiration
5 Human nervous system
6 Human hormones
7 Human homeostasis
8 Human health
9 Plant nutrition
10 Plant hormones
11 Plant–water relations
12 Variation
13 Inheritance
14 Evolution
15 Adaptation and competition
16 Energy and nutrient transfer

CHEMISTRY AND EARTH SCIENCE

1 Atomic structure
2 Bonding
3 Useful products from oil
4 Useful products from ores and rocks
5 Useful products from air
6 Representing reactions
7 Quantitative chemistry
8 Changes to the atmosphere
9 Geological changes
10 The periodic table
11 Metals and non-metals; acids and alkalis
12 Rates of reactions: reactions involving enzymes
13 Reversible reactions: energy transfer in reactions

PHYSICS

1 Electrical circuits
2 Mains electricity
3 Electric charge
4 Electromagnetic forces: electro-magnetic induction
5 Force and acceleration
6 Force and non-uniform motion
7 Force and pressure
8 Characteristics of waves
9 The electromagnetic spectrum
10 Sound and ultrasound
11 Seismic waves
12 The solar system and the universe
13 Energy transfer
14 Work, power and energy
15 Radioactivity

BIOLOGY

1 Structure and function of cells: top 20 revision terms

active uptake (active transport)

allele

cell membrane

cell wall

chloroplast

chromosome

concentration gradient

cytoplasm

diffusion

fertilisation

gene

meiosis

mitochondria

mitosis

nucleus

organ

organ system

osmosis

tissue

zygote

2 Human nutrition: top 30 revision terms

amino acid

bile

carbohydrase (amylase)

carbohydrate

digestive system

emulsify

enzyme

faeces

fat

fatty acid

gall bladder

glycerol

hydrochloric acid

large intestine

lipase

liver

mineral salts

muscular tissue

oesophagus (gullet)

pancreas

peristalsis

protease

protein

saliva

small intestine

starch

stomach

sugar

villus

vitamin

3 Human circulation: top 15 revision terms

artery

atrium

blood, circulation

blood, transport by

capillary

haemoglobin

heart

lungs

plasma

platelet

red blood cells

valve

vein

ventricle

white blood cells

4 Human breathing and respiration: top 15 revision terms

aerobic respiration
alcohol (ethanol)
alveolus
anaerobic respiration
breathing
bronchiole
bronchus
diaphragm

lactic acid
lung
oxygen debt
rib
rib muscle (intercostal muscle)
thorax
windpipe (trachea)

5 Human nervous system: top 25 revision terms

ciliary muscle
cone (some boards)
coordinator
cornea
effector
eye
iris
lens
motor neurone
nervous system
nerve impulse
optic nerve
pupil

receptor
reflex action
relay neurone (connector neurone)
response
retina
rod (some boards)
sclera
sensory neurone
spinal cord
stimulus
suspensory ligament
synapse

6 Human hormones: top 15 revision terms

contraceptive
diabetes
fertility
FSH (some boards)
gland
glucagon (some boards)
glycogen
hormone

insulin
LH (some boards)
menstrual cycle
oestrogen
pancreas
pituitary gland
testosterone (some boards)

7 Human homeostasis: top 20 revision terms

ADH

bladder

deamination (some boards)

excretion

filtration

homeostasis

nerve impulse

pituitary gland

receptor

selective reabsorption

shivering

sweating

temperature regulation

thermoregulatory centre

urea

ureter

urethra

urine

vasoconstriction

vasodilation

8 Human health: top 10 revision terms

antibody

antitoxin

bacteria

blood, clotting

blood, defence

disease, immunity

disease, transmission

drug abuse

mucus

virus

9 Plant nutrition: top 5 revision terms

chlorophyll

leaf

limiting factor

mineral salts

photosynthesis

10 Plant hormones: top 5 revision terms

cuttings

geotropism

hormone

phototropism

weedkiller

11 Plant–water relations: top 15 revision terms

active transport

diffusion

guard cell

leaf

osmosis

phloem

plasmolysis

potometer

root hair

stoma (stomata)

transpiration

turgor

wax

wilting

xylem

12 Variation: top 10 revision terms

asexual reproduction	gene
cancer	*meiosis*
characteristic	*mitosis*
clone	mutation
gamete (sex cell)	sexual reproduction

13 Inheritance: top 10 revision terms

allele	*heterozygous*
DNA	*homozygous*
dominant	recessive
gender	X chromosome
gene	Y chromosome

See also the inherited diseases specified by your syllabus, e.g:

cystic fibrosis	*sickle cell anaemia*
Huntington's chorea	*haemophilia*

14 Evolution: top 5 revision topics

evolution	*natural selection*
extinction	variation
fossil	

15 Adaptation and competition: top ten revision terms

acid rain	*global warming*
adaptation	*greenhouse effect*
competition	pesticide
eutrophication	predator–prey relationships
fertiliser	sewage

16 Energy and nutrient transfer: top 10 revision topics

carbon cycle	primary consumer (herbivore)
decay	producer
food chain	pyramid of biomass
food web	pyramid of numbers
nitrogen cycle	secondary consumer (carnivore)

CHEMISTRY AND EARTH SCIENCE

1 Atomic structure: top 20 revision topics

atom
boiling point
electron
element
evaporation
gas
hazard symbols
isotope
liquid
mass number

melting
molecule
neutron
nucleus
proton
proton number
solid
solute
solution
solvent

2 Bonding: top 15 revision topics

bonding
compound
covalent bonding
covalent giant structure
giant structure
ion
ionic bonding
ionic compound

ionic giant structure
metal giant structure
molecular compound
molecule
noble gas
thermosetting plastic
thermosoftening plastic

3 Useful products from oil: top 10 revision topics

addition polymer
alkane
alkene
crude oil
crude oil, cracking of distillation
    products

crude oil, extraction
crude oil, fractional distillation
hydrocarbon, saturated
hydrocarbon, unsaturated
polymers

4 Useful products from ores and rocks: top 15 revision topics

aluminium, extraction
anode
blast furnace
cathode
cement
copper, extraction
copper, purification
electrode

electrolysis
glass
limestone
oxidation
quicklime
redox reaction
reduction

5 Useful products from air: top 5 revision topics

air

ammonia, manufacture

fertiliser, manufacture

Haber process

nitric acid

6 Representing reactions: top 5 revision topics

electrolysis

equations, balancing

equations, ionic

equations, word

state symbols

7 Quantitative chemistry: top 5 revision topics

chemistry calculations, formulas

chemistry calculations, percentage
    composition

*chemistry calculations, reacting
    mass*

chemistry calculations, relative
    atomic mass

chemistry calculations, relative
    formula mass

8 Changes to the atmosphere: top 10 revision topics

acid rain

atmosphere

carbon cycle

combustion

fossil fuels

greenhouse effect

nitrogen oxides

oxidation

oxide

sulphur dioxide

9 Geological changes: top 15 revision topics

constructive boundary

core (of the Earth)

crust

destructive boundary

extrusive rocks

faulting

intrusive rocks

mantle

metamorphic rocks

mountain formation

plate boundaries

plate tectonics

rock cycle

sedimentary rock

volcano

10 The periodic table: top 10 revision terms

alkali metals

brine, electrolysis

chlorine

halogens

iodine

noble gases

periodic table

silver halides

sodium hydroxide

transition metals

11 Metals, non-metals; acids and alkalis: top 10 revision terms

acids and alkalis

corrosion

galvanise

metal oxides

metals

metals, reactions with acids

metals, reactions with oxygen

metals, reactions with water

non-metals

reactivity series

12 Rates of reactions; reactions involving enzymes: top 10 revision terms

activation energy

catalyst

enzymes

fermentation

pressure

rate of reaction, effect of catalyst on

rate of reaction, effect of
    concentration on

rate of reaction, effect of pressure on

rate of reaction, effect of surface
    area on

rate of reaction, effect of
    temperature on

13 Reversible reactions; energy changes in reactions: top 10 revision terms

bond breaking

bond energy

bond making

chemistry calculations, bond energies

endothermic reaction

energy level diagram

equilibrium reactions

exothermic reaction

Haber process

reversible reaction

PHYSICS

1 Electrical circuits: top 20 revision terms

ammeter

ampere

charge

circuit, parallel

circuit, series

circuit symbols

coulomb

current

diode

ohm

potential difference

power

resistance

resistor

thermistor

variable resistor

volt

voltage

voltmeter

watt

2 Mains electricity: top 6 revision terms

alternating current

earth, electrical

electric meter

kilowatt-hour

mains electricity

plug, three-pin

3 Electric charge: top 6 revision terms

current

electricity

electrolysis

electroscope

electrostatics, theory of

electrostatics, uses and dangers

4 Electromagnetic forces; electromagnetic induction: top 10 revision terms

electromagnetic induction

generator

grid, national

magnet

magnetic effect of current

magnetic field.

magnetism, Earth's

power station

motor

transformer

5 Force and acceleration: top 6 revision terms

acceleration

distance–time graph

force

speed

velocity

velocity–time graph

6 Force and non-uniform motion: top 5 revision terms

braking distance
friction
reaction time

stopping distance
terminal velocity

7 Force and pressure: top 6 revision terms

Boyle's law
elastic behaviour
elastic limit

Hooke's law
hydraulics
pressure

8 Characteristics of waves: top 10 revision terms

amplitude
critical angle
diffraction
frequency
longitudinal wave

reflection
refraction
total internal reflection
transverse wave
wavelength

9 The electromagnetic spectrum: top 10 revision terms

electromagnetic radiation
gamma radiation
infra-red radiation
light
microwaves

prism
radio waves
spectrum
ultraviolet
X-rays

10 Sound and ultrasound: top 5 revision terms

sound, frequency
sound, loudness
sound, pitch

sound waves
ultrasound

11 Seismic waves: top 5 revision terms

Earth, structure of
P-wave
S-wave

seismic wave
seismometer

12 The solar system and the universe: top 16 revision topics

big bang	satellite communication
comet	satellite, monitoring
galaxy	solar system
Moon	star
orbit	Sun
planet	*supernova*
red giant	universe
satellite	*white dwarf*

13 Energy transfer: top 10 revision terms

absorber	energy, heat
conduction, heat	insulation, heat
convection	radiation
efficiency	temperature
emitter	Thermos flask

14 Work, power and energy: top 10 revision topics

energy, kinetic	mass
energy, potential	newton
force	power
gravitational potential energy	weight
joule	work

15 Radioactivity: top 20 revision topics

alpha radiation	half-life
atom	ionisation
background radiation	isotope
beta radiation	neutron
cancer	nucleon
chain reaction	nucleus of an atom
dating	proton
electron	radioactive
fission, nuclear	radioactive decay
gamma radiation	radionuclide

Why not use our range of *Complete A–Z Handbooks* **to support your A levels and Advanced GNVQs? All the** *A–Zs* **are written by experienced authors and Chief Examiners.**

0 340 65467 8   *The Complete A–Z Business Studies* Second Edition £9.99
0 340 65489 9   *The Complete A–Z Geography Handbook* £9.99
0 340 64789 2   *The Complete A–Z Leisure, Travel and Tourism Handbook* £9.99
0 340 65832 0   *The Complete A–Z Sociology Handbook* £9.99
0 340 65490 2   *The Complete A–Z Psychology Handbook* £9.99
0 340 66985 3   *The Complete A–Z Economics and Business Studies Handbook* £9.99
0 340 66373 1   *The Complete A–Z Biology Handbook* £9.99
0 340 72513 3   *The Complete A–Z Chemistry Handbook* £9.99
0 340 68804 1   *The Complete A–Z Physics Handbook* £9.99
0 340 68803 3   *The Complete A–Z Mathematics Handbook* £9.99
0 340 67378 8   *The Complete A–Z 19th and 20th Century British History Handbook* £9.99
0 340 67996 4   *The Complete A–Z 20th Century European History Handbook* £9.99
0 340 69131 X   *The Complete A–Z Media and Communication Studies Handbook* £9.99
0 340 68847 5   *The Complete A–Z Business Studies CD-ROM* £55.00 + VAT
0 340 69124 7   *The Complete A–Z Accounting Handbook* £9.99
0 340 70557 4   *The Complete A–Z Health and Social Care Handbook* (Spring 1999)
0 340 72120 0   *The Complete A–Z Law Handbook* (Spring 1999)
0 340 72051 4   *The A–Z Business Studies Coursework Handbook* £6.99

All Hodder & Stoughton *Educational* books are available at your local bookshop, or can be ordered direct from the publisher. Just tick the titles you would like and complete the details below. Prices and availability are subject to change without prior notice.

Buy four books from the selection above and get free postage and packaging. Just send a cheque or postal order made payable to *Bookpoint Limited* to the value of the total cover price of four books. This should be sent to: Hodder & Stoughton *Educational,* 39 Milton Park, Abingdon, Oxon OX14 4TD, UK. EMail address: orders@bookpoint.co.uk. Alternatively, if you wish to buy fewer than four books, the following postage and packaging costs apply:

UK & BFPO: £4.30 for one book; £6.30 for two books; £8.30 for three books.
Overseas and Eire: £4.80 for one book; £7.10 for 2 or 3 books (surface mail).

If you would like to pay by credit card, our centre team would be delighted to take your order by telephone. Our direct line (44) 01235 400414 (lines open 9.00am– 6.00pm, Monday to Saturday, with a 24 hour answering service). Alternatively you can send a fax to (44) 01235 400454.

Title _____ First name _____ Surname _____

Address _____

Postcode _____ Daytime telephone no. _____

If you would prefer to pay by credit card, please complete:

Please debit my Master Card / Access / Diner's Card / American Express (delete as applicable)

Card number _____ Expiry date _____ Signature _____

If you would not like to receive further information on our products, please tick the box
☐

The following *GCSE A–Z Handbooks* are available from Hodder & Stoughton. Why not use them to support your other GCSE and Intermediate GNVQs? All the *A–Z*s are written by experienced authors and Chief Examiners.

0 340 68366 X *GCSE A–Z Business Studies* £7.99
0 340 73060 9 *GCSE A–Z Double Science* £7.99
0 340 72447 1 *GCSE A–Z Geography* £7.99 (Spring 1999)

All Hodder & Stoughton *Educational* books are available at your local bookshop, or can be ordered direct from the publisher. Just tick the titles you would like and complete the details below. Prices and availability are subject to change without prior notice.

Send a cheque or postal order made payable to *Bookpoint Limited* to the value of the total cover price of the books including postage and packaging. This should be sent to: Hodder & Stoughton *Educational*, 39 Milton Park, Abingdon, Oxon OX14 4TD, UK. EMail address: orders@bookpoint.co.uk. The following postage and packaging costs apply:

UK & BFPO: £4.30 for one book; £6.30 for two books; £8.30 for three books.
Overseas and Eire: £4.80 for one book; £7.10 for 2 or 3 books (surface mail).

If you would like to pay by credit card, our centre team would be delighted to take your order by telephone. Our direct line (44) 01235 400414 (lines open 9.00am– 6.00pm, Monday to Saturday, with a 24 hour answering service). Alternatively you can send a fax to (44) 01235 400454.

Title _____ First name _____ Surname _____

Address _____

Postcode _____ Daytime telephone no. _____

If you would prefer to pay by credit card, please complete:

Please debit my Master Card / Access / Diner's Card / American Express (delete as applicable)

Card number _____ Expiry date _____ Signature _____

If you would not like to receive further information on our products, please tick the box
☐